Waterstone's Guide to Scottish Books

Edited by Neil Johnstone

D0434270

WATERSTONE'S GUIDES SERIES EDITOR
Nick Rennison

Contents

Introduction by Neil Johnstone

Scotland's literary tradition is a rich and vital one and it is a tradition which has, in recent years, seen a remarkable and vibrant new dawn. Yet no-one has attempted to produce an easily accessible guide to the riches of Scottish writing in all its forms, from Walter Scott to Irvine Welsh, from books on Scottish football to books on the Highland Clearances.

This *Waterstone's Guide to Scottish Books* is one of a wide-ranging series and it aims to be approachable, authoritative and enjoyable. It is a structured in a straightforward A-Z format, starting with Art and ending with Travel. It recommends new and undiscovered writers as well as unjustly neglected old ones. Its overall objective is to encourage people to explore Scotland's literary heritage, to investigate the range of Scottish writing and publishing. The *Waterstone's Guide to Scottish Books* looks at the very best Scottish books around, from whatever field and whatever era, be it art, fiction or drama, or the 13th, 16th or 20th century. In short, the guide hopes to include within its pages all the books that would be found in the ultimate Scottish library.

What have been my criteria for inclusion? What, for example, is a Scottish book? For the purposes of this guide I have decided that it is any book written by a Scottish author or any book primarily interested in some aspect of Scotland. Unsurprisingly it is difficult to decide, in the case of some books, whether or not they meet these criteria. The inclusion of some books in the guide may be open to debate. This is a good thing. The vast majority of titles mentioned in this guide are in print and currently available, although, sadly, some fine Scottish titles have had to be excluded because they are out of print. Readers of the guide will also note that it includes very few Gaelic books. This is not because there are not enough books of sufficient quality written in Gaelic. Quite the reverse. The number is so large that it would require a separate guide to cover Gaelic literature in the depth it deserves. The Gaelic books included are restricted to language learning books or bilingual editions.

The *Waterstone's Guide to Scottish Books*, then, aims to be a key to Scotland's rich literary past and present. I hope that any reader will have as much enjoyment and pleasure in reading it as I did in researching and editing it.

Art & Architecture

General Works

The Concise Catalogue of the Scottish National Gallery of Modern Art
N.G.S. pb 0903598396 £15.95

Since it opened in 1960 the Scottish National Gallery of Modern Art has become one of the most important repositories of modern art in the UK outside London. Compiled by Patrick Elliott, this book lists all 4,500 paintings, sculptures, prints and drawings contained in the collection, nearly one quarter of them accompanied by illustrations. This guide is of vital importance to anyone wishing to understand this major collection.

The Concise Catalogue of the Scottish National Portrait Gallery
N.G.S. pb 0903148935 £19.95

Compiled by Helen Smailes, this is a lavishly illustrated checklist to every work of art in the Gallery. Indispensable for anyone interested in art, portraiture, biography or history.

The National Gallery of Scotland Concise Catalogue of Paintings
N.G.S. pb 0903598655 £15.95

Since it opened in 1859 the National Gallery of Scotland has amassed an outstanding collection which includes magnificent Old Masters, important impressionist works and a superb collection of Scottish art. This handbook containing 1200 illustrations is an invaluable reference work.

Billcliffe, Roger
The Scottish Colourists: Cadell, Fergusson, Hunter and Peploe
John Murray pb 0719554373 £20.00

The story of the Scottish Colourist group of painters is articulately told in Roger Billcliffe's excellent book on the movement. The book contains numerous high quality illustrations.

Billcliffe, Roger
Glasgow Boys: The Glasgow School of Painting 1875-1895
John Murray hb 0719541182 £50.00

Over a century ago a small number of young artists in their mid twenties became renowned throughout Europe and America. They were collectively known as 'The Glasgow Boys'. They were not all trained or born in Glasgow, but at some point all worked in studios there. What linked them most strongly was their enthusiasm for realism in subject, strong use of colours and their willingness to range widely in subject and setting. Among them were James Guthrie, Arthur Melville and E.A Hornel who in later years all found fame and fortune.

National Gallery of Scotland

Burkhauser, Jude
Glasgow Girls: Women in Art and Design 1880-1920
Canongate pb 086241413X
£20.00

Painters and designers such as Bessie MacNicol, Jessie M. King and Frances Macdonald gained considerable international recognition when they developed the Glaswegian Art Nouveau style. This authoritative volume gives a thorough account of the movement and its artists and designers.

Campbell, Mungo
Drawings and Watercolours of Edinburgh in the National Gallery of Scotland
N.G.S. pb 0903598078 £5.95

The rich variety of architecture and landscape in Edinburgh has long provided inspiration for artists. This copiously illustrated catalogue of drawings and watercolours represents some of the finest examples of these works in the National Gallery of Scotland's collection.

Couldrey, Vivienne
Painters of Scotland: A Celebration of Scottish Landscape
House Of Lochar hb 1858770033 £19.99

The long and rich tradition of landscape painting in Scotland is reviewed using largely colour reprints of the works. Couldrey takes the reader on a tour of Scotland by means of the paintings, occasionally including a modern photograph of the view to highlight the ways in which the landscape has changed.

Errington, L. (Ed.)
Scotland's Pictures: The National Collection of Scottish Arts
N.G.S. pb 0903148994 £8.95

The wide range of paintings possessed by the National Galleries of Scotland can prove daunting. This copiously illustrated guide is both a highly readable history of Scottish painting and a guide to some of the key works in the various collections, with enough information to keep the specialist and the general art lover happy. The book is a valuable tool for the understanding of Scottish painting.

Harris, P. & Halsby, J.
Dictionary of Scottish Painters: 1600 to the Present (2nd Edition)
Canongate hb 0862417783 £40.00

The previous edition of this book covered the years up to 1960. This is a completely revised and updated version, with numerous new entries and illustrations, and in its revamped form it is one of the definitive reference books on Scottish art. Heavily illustrated, it features both major and minor figures in Scottish art, not to mention all the significant artistic movements, such as the Glasgow Boys and the Colourists. An essential book for any library on Scottish art.

Hartley, Keith
Scottish Art Since 1900
N.G.S. pb 0853315590 £12.95

This book is an authoritative overview of the major artists and movements in Scotland since 1900, a period that has seen an explosion of different approaches to art and a strong interest in artists and their work.

Holloway, James
Great Scots
N.G.S. pb 0903148536 £4.95

A collection of portraits and drawings from the Scottish National Portrait Gallery of famous Scots down the centuries, complete with short biographical details of the sitters and information about the paintings themselves.

Holloway, James
Patrons and Painters:
Art in Scotland 1650-1760
N.G.S. pb 0903148897 £7.95

The role of patrons and their relationship to artists in Scotland during the Baroque period is assiduously examined in this book. This was a time of dramatic change in Scotland. The book shows that Scottish aristocratic families had aspirations as high as those of their European neighbours.

McEwen, John
Glenkiln
Canongate hb 0862413249 £20.00

This remote estate in south-west Scotland is the site of the world's first sculpture collection set in a natural environment, a place much loved by Henry Moore. The collection was brought together by Sir William Keswick, who owned the estate. *Glenkiln* tells the story of the creation of this artistic vision in words and photographs.

MacMillan, Duncan
Scottish art in the 20th Century
Mainstream hb 185158630X £20.00

This vital reference book tells the story of modern Scottish painting and sculpture, starting with artists such as Charles Rennie Mackintosh and moving on to chart the remarkable achievements of, among others, Ian Hamilton Finlay, Joan Eardley and John Bellany, before taking the story into very modern times with such artists as Steven Campbell and Ken Curry. An essential book for anyone interested in modern Scottish art and its history.

MacMillan, Duncan
Scottish art 1460-1990
Mainstream pb 1851588620 £25.00
Mainstream hb 1851582517 £45.00

One of the most important Scottish art books available, this book is well researched, covering all the major artists and movements, and written in a clear, forthright manner. The book is packed with illustrations and is indispensable for anyone with an interest in Scottish art.

Marshall, Rosalind K.
Costume in Scottish Portraits 1560-1830
N.G.S. pb 090314865X £3.95

An absorbing guide to the clothes and fashions worn by sitters in some of the portraits in the Scottish National Portrait Gallery. In many cases these portraits are the only record of what people were wearing at that period of time. Written in a straightforward and non-specialist way, the book would serve equally well as a supplementary guide to the Gallery or as a general reference work.

Pearson, Fiona (Ed.)
Virtue and Vision: Sculpture and Scotland 1540-1990
N.G.S. pb 0903598140 £12.95

Twelve essays that explore Scotland's native sculptural tradition down the ages, beautifully illustrated with 178 images covering a wide diversity of works.

Smailes, Helen
A Portrait Gallery for Scotland:
The Scottish National Portrait Gallery 1882-1906
N.G.S. pb 0903148633 £6.95

A fascinating book on the foundation, architecture and mural decoration of the Scottish National Portrait Gallery, a major architectural landmark of Edinburgh in its own right, and a fine example of Gothic revivalism.

Smailes, Helen & Thomson, Duncan
The Queen's Image
N.G.S. pb 0903148714 £6.95

This book is a celebration of the many images of Mary, Queen of Scots. The images fall into two broad categories: one of reality, the other of romantic legend. The early works painted during her own lifetime emphasize her beauty, charm and humanity. The later works, while no less interesting, tend to reflect the artists' own interpretation of the story. A captivating book that will hold the interest of many people.

Williams, Julia Lloyd
Dutch Art and Scotland:
A Reflection of Taste
N.G.S. pb 090359823X
£14.95

At one point in time Scotland possessed some of the most important paintings of Dutch Art, including pieces by Rembrandt, Hals, Cuyp and Vermeer. The historical and cultural reasons for this are examined in this fully illustrated book that includes major essays on the subject by leading art historians.

Individual artists

The National Galleries of Scotland's 'Scottish Masters' series, all published in paperback at £2.95, provides short but informative introductions to major Scottish artists. Among those currently available are the following :-

James Tassie 0903148692
Alexander Carse 0903148706
William Carrick 0903148765
Jacob More 0903148757
Robert Herdman 0903148773
John De Medina 0903148781
James Cox 0903148838
William Aikman 0903148846
David Wilkie 0903148854
Henry Raeburn 0903598434

"You can't paint from a vacuum. Whether you're in a state of serenity or absolute anguish . . . if you're being honest it comes through in the work."
John Bellany

John Bellany
(b.1942)

The life and work of one of Scotland's most influential artists is studiously explored in *John Bellany* which examines the roots of his figurative painting and his sources of imagery - mythology and symbols, fisherfolk and the sea. The book is complete with an overview of his entire artistic development and numerous colour and black & white illustrations. John McEwen's *John Bellany* is a major book on the artist, covering most of his career.

Keith Hartley ed.
John Bellany
N.G.S. pb 0903148684 £6.95

John McEwen
John Bellany
Mainstream hb 1851586326 £30.00

Cadell

Francis Campbell Boileau Cadell
(1883–1937)

Containing over 90 full colour plates, Tom Hewlett's work is the first book devoted entirely to the life and work of Francis Campbell Boileau Cadell (1883-1937). The extensive research undertaken in the production of this work pays handsome dividends, with a number of illuminating insights into the artist's interests and character traits.

Hewlett, Tom
Cadell: A Scottish Colourist
Canongate pb 0862415810 £14.99

Sir David Young Cameron

An influential character in both London and Edinburgh art worlds, Sir David Young Cameron is remembered for his archetypal paintings of the Scottish Highlands. However Bill Smith shows he had many other aspects to his work. His sister Katherine was an accomplished artist in her own right, and her life and work are also covered here. Thoroughly researched, the book includes 75 colour plates.

Smith, Bill
David Young Cameron: The Visions of the Hills
Atelier Books pb1873830025 £14.99

Stephen Campbell

Stephen Campbell was one of the new Glasgow painters who became fashionable in the 80s. His work has a very post-modern feel mixed with surrealist touches and has similarities to some of the Scottish painters of the 40s. His works reveal a bold handling of paint and often depict characters who seem to have emerged from Boys' Own Adventure tales of the 30s yet also show Campbell's own peculiarly Scottish outlook.

MacMillan, Duncan
The Paintings of Steven Campbell
Mainstream hb 185158546X£14.99

Joseph Crawhall (1861–1913)

The Glasgow Boys, of which Crawhall was a leading figure, are now renowned worldwide for their distinctive approach to painting. This study of his life and work is illustrated in colour throughout and contains many pictures of privately owned works normally inaccessible to the public.

Hamilton, Vivien
Joseph Crawhall 1861-1913: One of the Glasgow Boys
John Murray pb 0719555655 £20.00

William Crozier (1893–1930)

William Crozier was a key member of the Edinburgh school which included Anne Redpath, William MacTaggart and William Gillies. His work has tended to be neglected due to his tragically short career, which lasted only about ten years. Ann Simpson's brief but highly informative book shows he was a painter who produced some outstanding works and who, had he lived longer, might have gone on to even greater heights.

Simpson, Ann
William Crozier 1893-1930
N.G.S. pb 0903598566 £6.95

Alan Davie

As well as being a renowned artist, Davie is an enthusiastic jazz musician. In the 50s and 60s he brought ideas from jazz improvisation into his art work. He uses colour in a strong and vigorous fashion, often avoiding developing images, preferring instead to use symbols that show the appearance of having ancient religious origins. Davie is interested in expressing things using pure intuition as his guide, and is known for his keen interest in Zen philosophy, an interest that has deeply affected much of his work. In some of his more recent paintings he has become much more controlled in his approach, yet these pieces still defy direct interpretation.

Hall, Douglas (Ed)
Alan Davie
Lund Humphries hb 0853315973 £45.00

David Donaldson

This heavily illustrated book looks at the life and works of David Donaldson, one of Scotland's finest and most daring portrait painters who is also a skilled still life and landscape painter. Donaldson talks frankly about his time as a teacher in the Glasgow School of Art and his early years struggling to rise above the limitations of his background.

Smith, W. Gordon
David Donaldson: Painter and Limner to Her Majesty The Queen in Scotland
Mainstream hb 1851588264 £25.00

Joan Eardley (1921–1963)

Born in Sussex, Joan Eardley studied at the Glasgow School of Art. Her work was initially heavily influenced by Vincent Van Gogh, both in choice of subject matters and technique. However she quickly developed her own talent and vision to such an extent that she has been described as one of the best artists of our century. She is famous for her portraits of poor children from the Glasgow tenements and her inspirational land- and seascapes in and around the tiny fishing village of Catterline.

Oliver, Cordelia
Joan Eardley RSA
Mainstream hb 1851581669 £14.99

William Russell Flint (1880–1969)

A specialist in watercolours in the style of Melville, Flint is unfortunately better known for his paintings of scantily clad Spanish women. His earlier works are notable for the skill and delicate quality of his paintwork. Looking at his later pieces one cannot but help feel that he squandered his talent.

Lewis, Ralph
Sir William Russell Flint
David & Charles hb
0715393065 £40.00

Ian Hamilton Finlay (b.1925)

A shamefully underrated artist in Scotland, Ian Hamilton Finlay has a huge reputation abroad. He constantly questions assumptions on a wide range of issues. He works in a wide variety of media, the artistic pinnacle of his achievement being his neo-classical garden, Little Sparta, in which he weaves all the strands of his art into a harmonious and beautiful whole. Among his many influences are the classical tradition, fishing boats, French Revolutionary figures, the aesthetics of military hardware and the power of the written word, whether printed, carved in stone or wood, or inlaid. Much of his work is done in conjunction with collaborators, both artists and craftsmen. Yves Abrioux's analysis of his work is penetrating and thorough, charting the full extent of his career so far, superbly illustrated with numerous black & white and colour images. As poet and critic Robert Crawford has said: 'Finlay is our avant garde'. *Wood Notes Wild* is the first collection of essays to consider Finlay's work as a whole. It includes pieces by Duncan MacMillan, Edwin Morgan and Charles Jencks.

Abrioux, Yves
Ian Hamilton Finlay: A Visual Primer
Reaktion pb 094846240X £17.95

Finlay, Alec (Ed)
Wood Notes Wild: Essays on the Poetry and Art of Ian Hamilton Finlay
Polygon pb 0748661859 £11.95

Finlay, Ian Hamilton
Prints 1963-1997 (Ed. Pia Simig)
Works In Europe 1972-1995
Cantz hb 389322341X £39.95
Cantz hb 3893227490 £45.00

William Gillies (1898–1973)

William Gillies' watercolours are regarded as among the best and most important produced in Scotland in the 20th century. He was familiar with the cutting-edge of modern painting in Europe, and as he developed his own style he incorporated some modernist elements. His works are astute studies in colour, light and mood and powerfully evoke the landscape. Philip Long's superbly produced book includes not only twenty-four colour plates, but also photographs from family archives of the artist at work and play, and is accompanied by an informative and well-written introduction to his life and works. W. Gordon Smith's book is a far-reaching and heavily illustrated biography of this important figure in Scottish art. Sir William Gillies was known as an *enfant terrible* in the 1930s who went on to become one of Scotland's most popular landscape painters. He was highly regarded as a teacher, eventually becoming Principal at Edinburgh College of Art. *William Gillies: A Monograph* places Gillies firmly in the context of 20th century British painting, using a lot of previously unseen material to illustrate his much loved landscape painting.

Kellar, V. & Soden, J.
William Gillies: A Monograph
Canongate hb 0862417880 £25.00

Long, Philip
William Gillies: Watercolours Of Scotland
N.G.S. pb 0903598485 £7.95

Smith, W. Gordon
WG Gillies: A Very Still Life
Atelier Books hb 1873830009 £20.00

Edward A. Hornel (1864–1933)

Bill Smith's book is a superbly illustrated critical biography of Hornel, commonly viewed as one of the greatest colourists. A member of 'The Glasgow Boys', Hornel's striking use of colour and harmonious compositions have ensured that he is as popular more than sixty years after his death as he was in his lifetime. The book includes seventy colour reproductions, and the author has gleaned much information from the archives of the Hornel Trust.

Smith, Bill
Hornel: The Life and Work of Edward Atkinson Hornel
Atelier Books hb 1873830149 £20.00

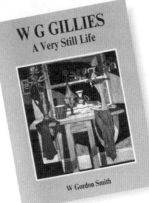

Peter Howson

Peter Howson's early works draw much of their inspiration from Glasgow street life. Although he only really broke through onto the art scene in 1985, his figurative works that evoke the human condition so well have already established him as a major artist. Heller's book is an overview of his work which explores its genesis and significance. Peter Howson went as a war artist to record the effects of the Bosnian War. The atrocities he witnessed there were to have major ramifications on his art and personality. Jackson's heavily illustrated book reveals the work Howson produced at this time and subsequently, work that further enhances his reputation as one of the most powerful figurative painters around.

Heller, Robert
Peter Howson
Mainstream hb 1851585419 £14.99

Jackson, Alan
A Different Man: Peter Howson's Art from Bosnia and Beyond
Mainstream hb 1851589473 £18.00

George Houston

This is the only book available on George Houston. It features many works from private collections which have never before been published. His tranquil landscape paintings of the Lowlands and the West Coast of Scotland are very highly regarded. His choice of scenes to paint was influenced by his passion for fishing. Acclaimed during his lifetime, until relatively recently he had become sadly neglected, but his luminous paintings have now found a new audience.

Robson, Euan
George Houston: Nature's Limner
Atelier Books hb 1873830297 £20.00

Oskar Kokoschka

When Oskar Kokoschka arrived in London in 1938 after fleeing from the Nazis, he had only £5 to his name. During his stay in London he made six trips to Scotland and produced a sizable body of work. This book features much of the work he created during these visits. The paintings contain a spiritual and artistic sense of renewal markedly different from the work he was producing in London at the same time. Richard Calvocoressi recounts these visits and the art Kokoschka produced, including the portrait he painted of the Duke and Duchess of Hamilton on his return visit to Scotland in 1969.

Calvocoressi, Richard
Kokoschka and Scotland
N.G.S. pb 0903589035 £5.95

Charles Rennie Mackintosh (1868–1928)

Born in Glasgow, where his most famous work was later done, Mackintosh is the one Scottish architect and designer who had an indisputable influence on the mainstream European tradition. There are a number of excellent books about him in print. Wendy Kaplan's book is a far-reaching study of Mackintosh's work that examines his architectural and design work, and also some of the myths that have grown up around him. The *Charles Rennie Mackintosh Pocket Guide* is an illustrated guide that critically assesses the work of Mackintosh and shows visitors where to find, particularly in Glasgow and the West of Scotland. The guide includes a brief biographical sketch of the man himself. *Remembering Charles Rennie Mackintosh* is a sympathetic and intimate biography that includes many recollections from people who knew him personally. Mackintosh regarded himself as much a painter as a designer or architect. His watercolours had an important connection with his architectural and design work. Roger Billcliffe's *catalogue raisonné* is complete with a thorough introduction that places these works in their true context. Timothy Neat, in *Part Seen, Part Imagined*, takes an in-depth look at the symbolic meaning of Mackintosh's work, that gives the viewer a new insight into his achievements.

William MacTaggart

This informative and stylishly produced journey through the work of William MacTaggart shows an artist using strong colour and strong handling, revelling in his prodigious talent. His subject matters were mainly land- or seascapes, and his unique, richly coloured expressionist style has earned him a prominent place in the modern Scottish school.

Gale, Iain
William MacTaggart 1903-1981
N.G.S. pb 0903598752 £9.95

Billcliffe, Roger
Mackintosh Watercolours
John Murray pb 0719536782
£15.99

Kaplan, Wendy (Ed.)
Charles Rennie Mackintosh
Abbeville Press hb 1558597913
£45.00

McKean, John
Charles Rennie Mackintosh Pocket Guide
Colin Baxter flx 190045548X
£6.00

Moffat, Alistair
Remembering Charles Rennie Mackintosh
Colin Baxter pb 1900455455
£12.00

Neat, Timothy
Part Seen, Part Imagined: Meaning and Symbolism in the Work of Charles Rennie Mackintosh
Canongate hb 0862413664
£14.99

"... if Architecture has national peculiarities impressed upon it, then it must be history - the world's history written in stone." Charles Rennie Mackintosh

Alberto Morrocco

Born in Aberdeen in 1917 of Italian parents, Alberto Morrocco is renowned for his superb draughtsmanship and his still-lifes. A much sought-after portrait painter, his themes have a strong Italian influence and include peasant women and melon sellers in an imagined Mediterranean world. He died in Dundee in March 1998.

Keller, Victoria & Young, Clara
Alberto Morrocco
Mainstream hb 1851585907
£14.99

Sir Robin Philipson

Brilliantly illustrated with over seventy colour reproductions, this book includes contributions from some of Scotland's leading art figures. Sir Robin Philipson is known as a significant and innovative artist, who though born in Cumbria made a significant impact on Scottish art, not least during his many years of teaching at the Edinburgh College of Art.

Smith, W. Gordon
Philipson
Atelier Books pb 1873830041
£15.00

Arthur Melville

Regarded as the Scottish Impressionist, Arthur Melville was an enigma. Born a grocer's son, he became the most important and influential Scottish water-colourist of his time who died just as his star was beginning to ascend. Iain Gale's copiously illustrated book reappraises his work and gives a new angle on this much misunderstood artist.

Gale, Iain
Arthur Melville
Atelier Books pb 1873830092
£15.00

Sir Henry Raeburn
(1756–1823)

Sir Henry Raeburn is recognised as one of the greatest portrait painters of all time. He started his working life as a goldsmith and it was as a miniaturist that he began his artistic life. He is best known for his large portraits of Scottish society figures. However, unlike many other portrait painters of the time, his frank approach and directness of style bring out the sitters' humanity rather than stereotyping them and their position. It is this aspect of his work that causes his portraits to transcend notions of time and place. The National Gallery of Scotland publication is a superb overview of his life and work, published for the 1997 Raeburn exhibition in Edinburgh. It includes x-rays and detailed close-ups of the paintings as well as numerous colour and black & white plates and is a suitably major work for such an important artist.

Thomson, Duncan et al
Raeburn
N.G.S. pb 0903598698 £19.95

Anne Redpath (1895–1965)

Anne Redpath was one of the most celebrated Scottish artists of the 20th century and her style constantly evolved throughout her life. Her deep understanding of the decorative possibilities of many of her subjects made her highly popular. She used several main subject matters including landscapes and common domestic scenes which she painted in her rich, complex decorative style. Philip Long's illustrated book is a celebration of her achievements as an artist. Patrick Bourne's volume from Atelier Books reveals the complex and intellectual character behind her sensual paintings. With eighty seven colour illustrations included, the full extent of her prodigious talent is shown here in glorious detail.

Bourne, Patrick
Anne Redpath
Atelier Books hb 0951475304 £20.00

Bourne, Patrick
Anne Redpath
Canongate pb 0862416523 £14.99

Long, Philip
Anne Redpath 1895-1965
N.G.S. pb 0903598639 £9.95

John Slezer

A volume of engravings by John Slezer who was licensed by Queen Mary in 1693 to produce a collection of famous views of Scottish towns, castles, cathedrals and abbeys - his Theatrum Scotiae - presented here in their entirety, along with a review of his career and achievements.

Cavers, Keith
A Vision of Scotland: The Nation Observed by John Slezer 1671-1717
HMSO hb 0114942455 £14.95

Allan Ramsay

Allan Ramsay
(1713-1784)

Allan Ramsay, son of the poet of the same name, was one of the most important portrait painters of the 18th century. He was born in Edinburgh and became court painter to King George III. Regarded as one of the key figures in the Scottish Enlightenment, he had interests in many fields outwith art, including languages and philosophy. Smart's heavily illustrated biography explores this erudite artist, covering both his development as a painter and his philosophical ideas.

Smart, Alastair
Allan Ramsay: Painter, Essayist and Man of the Enlightenment
Yale U.P. hb 0300056907 £55.00

Tim Stead

Using pieces of timber many people might disregard, Tim Stead creates functional pieces which defy categorisation. They emerge from his environmentally aware relationship with nature and his work has a universal appeal.

Sutherland, Giles
Explorations In Wood: The Furniture and Sculpture of Tim Stead
No Butts Pub pb 0952820307 £14.99

Phoebe Anna Traquair (1852–1936)

Irish born and Dublin trained, Phoebe Anna Traquair was a talented and versatile craftswoman who excelled in many media. These included book illumination, embroidery, enamels and murals. She moved to Edinburgh in 1874 and quickly became a key figure in the Scottish cultural renaissance of the time. A major and sadly underrated artist, nearly all of her significant works were created in Edinburgh and many of her best murals can be seen there. Unfortunately, her outstanding murals in Edinburgh's Mansfield Place Church are now in a sorry condition. The work of this extraordinary luminary of the Arts and Crafts movement is rightfully being re-assessed in its importance. Cumming's exquisitely produced book surveys her work as a craftsworker, designer and artist. Her characteristic style uses brilliant colour, finely tuned technical skills and romantic imagery. This well laid out and highly illustrated volume gives an excellent insight into her life and work.

Cumming, Elizabeth
Phoebe Anna Traquair 1852-1936
N.G.S. pb 0903598361 £12.95

Turner

Since Henry Vaughan bequeathed thirty eight Turner watercolours to Edinburgh at the end of the 19th century, the National Gallery of Scotland's Turner collection has continued to grow and the January showing of these works has become a highlight of the Scottish artistic calendar. This attractively produced catalogue of the Turner works is authoritatively written and fully illustrated.

Campbell, Mungo
Turner in the National Gallery
N.G.S. pb 0903598310 £8.95

"Perfect harmony, is that not what we all strive after . . ."?
Phoebe Anna Traquair

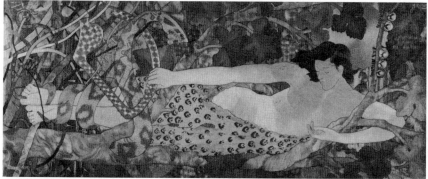
Phoebe Anna Traquair

Architecture

The Royal Institute Of Architecture In Scotland's *Illustrated Architectural Guides To Scotland* give clear, concise and illuminating information on the buildings of many areas of Scotland. They aim to cover the entire architectural history of Scotland, featuring both ancient and modern architecture. All the guides are paperbacks, published by the Rutland Press:

Close, Rob
Ayrshire and Arran
1873190069 £9.95

McKean, C.
Banff and Buchan
1851582312 £7.00

Strang, Charles A.
Borders and Berwick
1873190107 £11.95

Beaton, Elizabeth
Caithness
1873190271 £9.95

Swan, Adam
Clackmannan & The Ochils
0707305136 £5.25

Walker, F.A. & Sinclair, F.
The North Clyde Estuary
1873190077 £8.95

Walker, Frank A.
The South Clyde Estuary
0707304768 £5.75

McKean, C. & Walker, D.
Dundee
1873190093 £10.95

McKean, Charles
Edinburgh
0950146242 £11.95

Pride, Glen L.
The Kingdom of Fife
1851582568 £7.00

McKean, C. et al
Central Glasgow
1873190220 £11.95

Shepherd, Ian
Gordon
1873190115 £11.95

Thomas, Jane
Midlothian
1873190263 £9.95

Peden, Allan
The Monklands
1873190050 £7.95

McKean, Charles
The District of Moray
1873190484 £9.95

Burgher, Leslie
Orkney
1873190026 £7.95

Beaton, Elizabeth
Ross and Cromarty
1873190042 £7.95

Finnie, Mike
Shetland
1851583904 £6.00

McKean, Charles
Stirling & The Trossachs
1873190212 £8.95

Beaton, Elizabeth
Sutherland
1873190247 £9.95

Jaques, R. & McKean, C.
West Lothian
1873190255 £8.95

The *Buildings of Scotland* series of books by Penguin provide definitive regional guides to Scottish architecture. Heavily illustrated and extensively researched, they are both scholarly and easily accessible.

Gifford, J.
Dumfries and Galloway
Penguin hb 0140710671 £35.00

Gifford, J.
Edinburgh
Penguin hb 014071068X £35.00

Gifford, J.
Fife
Penguin hb 0140710779 £35.00

Gifford, J.
Highlands and Islands
Penguin hb 014071071X £35.00

Higgs, M. et al
Glasgow
Penguin hb 0140710698 £35.00

McWilliam, C. & Wilson, C.
Lothian, Except Edinburgh
Penguin hb 0140710663 £25.00

Charles Rennie Mackintosh

Charles Rennie Mackintosh's buildings and interiors established him as a major figure in 20th century architecture and design. David Brett argues that his originality is rooted in 'the poetics of workmanship', in which each aspect of a building is unified using a system of forms. Brett sees the origins of these forms in the Victorian tradition of botanical art and traces them as they evolve into Mackintosh's unique visual language. An insightful and well argued study supported by numerous illustrations.

Brett, David
Charles Rennie Mackintosh: The Poetics of Workmanship
Reaktion pb 0948462221 £9.95

Macaulay, James
Glasgow School Of Art: Glasgow 1897-1909 by Charles Rennie Mackintosh.
Phaidon pb 0714827789 £19.99

One of the greatest architectural works of the Arts and Crafts movement, Charles Rennie Mackintosh's building is based around the contrast of opposites. This heavily illustrated guide to the building reveals its many delights in their full glory

Macaulay, James
Hill House, Helenburgh 1903 by Charles Rennie Mackintosh
Phaidon pb 0714827800 £19.99

Mackintosh's domestic masterwork was largely ignored when built, but is now regarded as an outstanding work of genius by a major architect. Mackintosh also designed the interiors, fabrics and furniture. This guide reveals Hill House in all its glory.

Robert & James Adam

Adam Style was a form of domestic Neo-Classicism that rose during the mid-Georgian era and was eventually named after the leading architects of that time - Scottish brothers Robert and James Adam who constructed, among other notable buildings, Home House in London and Edinburgh's Register House. These well illustrated books show the factors which went into the design, decoration and furnishing of these and other magnificent buildings.

Parissien, Steven
Adam Style
Phaidon pb 071483453X £22.00

Tait, A.A.
Robert Adam: Drawings And Imagination
C.U.P. hb 0521433150 £55.00

General Works

Brown, Iain Gordon
Elegance and Entertainment in The New Town of Edinburgh: The Harden Drawings (reprint)
Rutland Press pb 1873190174 £4.95

A unique look at the domestic conditions in late Georgian Edinburgh using Jessy Allan's detailed accounts of wealthy middle-class lifestyle interspersed with her husband John Harden's elegant drawings.

Carruthers, Annette (Ed)
The Scottish Home
N.M.S. pb 0948636858 £14.99

In this book the wide diversity of Scottish houses and the way in which people have lived in them over the centuries is revealed. A mixture of oral history, inventory and detailed study of domestic paintings forms the text, creating a fascinating historical insight into the Scottish home.

Connachan-Holmes, J.R.A.
Country Houses of Scotland
House Of Lochar hb
1899863001 £12.99

The author uses one hundred of the finest country houses in Scotland to illustrate the thematic evolution of these magnificent buildings. Richly illustrated to illuminate points made in the text, the work is an ideal companion for people interested in Scotland's architectural heritage.

Fawcett, Richard
Scottish Cathedrals
Batsford pb 0713481889 £15.99
Scottish Abbies and Priories
Batsford pb 071347372X
£15.99

The rich and fascinating history of Scottish cathedrals over the course of 900 years is the theme of Richard Fawcett's book. He studies cathedrals as a building type, examining their architecture, the way they were used by the Church and their social context, standing as they did as a very conspicuous symbol of the Christian faith. The book includes plans of all of Scotland's medieval cathedrals.

Fladmark, J.M et al
Tomorrow's Architectural Heritage: Landscape and Buildings in the Countryside
Mainstream hb 1851583785
£14.99

A challenging and highly readable analysis of design in relation to place, based on a study carried out for the Countryside Commission for Scotland. The book argues that we have a responsibility to create buildings that are in harmony with their surroundings, especially in the countryside, and concludes that the architecture of today should be regarded as a valuable legacy for the future.

Garnham, Trevor
Melsetter House, Orkney 1898
By William Richard Lethaby
Phaidon pb 0714827762 £19.99

Lethaby was an English architect, a close follower of William Morris and an influential member of the Arts and Crafts movement. His fairytale palace by the edge of the North Sea is one of Scotland's most celebrated buildings. This guide to the house is a detailed building study.

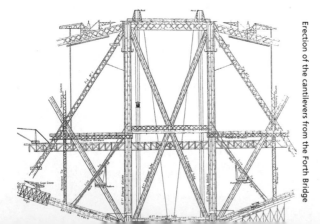

Erection of the cantilevers from the Forth Bridge

Gow, Ian
Scottish Houses and Gardens
Aurum Press hb 1854104888 £35.00

Just over 100 years ago, Country Life magazine started to commission photographs of important Scottish homes for their weekly features. This sumptuously illustrated book is compiled from these photographs. The book includes castles, palaces and family homes, some of which have long since been demolished. Ian Gow's text describes the houses, their histories and their contents in detail, giving the photographs a real sense of context.

Scottish Interior: Georgian and Victorian Decor
EUP hb 0748602208 £25.00

The history and development of Scotland's interiors is traced in Gow's comprehensive work. Using a wide variety of sources he examines interiors as diverse as Edinburgh's Old Town slums, Robert Burns' cottage and the personal vision behind Mackintosh's Hill House. The book provides an elegant record of this fascinating subject.

Glendinning, Miles (Ed.)
Rebuilding Scotland: The Postwar Vision 1945-1975
Tuckwell Press pb
189841033X £20.00

A fully illustrated architectural guide to the buildings erected after the Second World War that now dominate many Scottish skylines. The scale of this building work was at levels previously unheard of, and in the housing sector it was often likened to a crusade.

Glendinning, Miles al (Ed)
A History of Scottish Architecture from the Renaissance to the Present Day
EUP pb 0748608494 £25.00

A compact yet comprehensive account of the development of architectural styles throughout Scotland, listing key designers, architects and major movements and their connections with architectural developments in Europe. A vital text for anyone wishing to understand the history of Scottish architecture.

Gow, Ian & Clifford, Timothy
The National Gallery of Scotland: An Architectural & Decorative History
N.G.S. pb 090314882X £6.95

A historical look at the design and decoration of the National Gallery of Scotland, that celebrates the achievement of its original architect, W.H. Playfair, complete with original architectural sketches and stunning photographs of the Gallery from its construction to the present day.

MacGibbon & Ross (Eds)
Castellated and Domestic Architecture of Scotland (5 vols.)
Mercat Press hb 0901824186 £125.00

A major and hugely important reference work on Scottish architecture.

Mays, Deborah (Ed.)
The Architecture of Scottish Cities
Tuckwell Press pb 1862320284 £20.00

An impressive series of articles on the architecture that gives many Scottish cities their distinctive character. An excellent introduction to the subject that covers many of the leading architects and architectural movements, giving a rounded view of the subject in both words and pictures.

Naismith, Robert J.
The Story of Scotland's Towns
John Donald hb 0859762572 £14.95

Architect Robert Naismith uses numerous maps, illustrations and photographs to chart the development of Scotland's towns and cities. A book that should interest both the general reader and the specialist.

Pride, Glen L.
Dictionary of Scottish Building
Rutland Press pb 187319045X £13.95

A comprehensive and substantial reference guide vital for anyone interested or involved in the building profession in Scotland.

Stamp, G. & McKinstry, S. (Eds)
'Greek' Thomson: Neo-Classical Architectural Theory, Buildings & Interiors
EUP hb 0748604804 £35.00

Prolific Victorian architect Alexander 'Greek' Thomson is now recognised as one of architecture's most important historical figures in Scotland. His ventures into urban planning were notable due to his experimentation with new techniques and materials, as well as his moves away from the restrictions of orthodox classicism. The full range of his talents and his towering intellect are examined in this work by several leading architectural historians and commentators.

Youngson, A.J.
The Making of Classical Edinburgh
EUP hb 0748604464 £25.00

An illustrated study of the planning, financing and building of the New Town of Edinburgh which has become a classic in Scottish architectural literature. Youngson describes the numerous factors that went into the great experiment which eventually made Edinburgh one of the most beautiful cities in Europe.

Biography

General Books

Bailey, Nancy (Ed)
A Scottish Childhood Vol. II
HarperCollins pb 0004721764
£5.99

This anthology published in association with the Scottish Council of Save The Children is a collection of childhood memories from over seventy well-known Scots. The tone of the pieces is wide-ranging in this charming and often hilarious collection.

Bryan, Tom
Rich Man, Beggar Man, Indian Chief: Fascinating Scots in Canada and America
Thistle Press hb 0952095041 £14.95

The fact that Scotland has endured many waves of emigration has meant that people of Scottish descent are scattered all over the globe, and particularly in North America. Tom Bryan's book looks at the life histories of some of these first generation emigrés, finding them to be an intriguing collection of individuals who made major contributions in many fields to their new countries.

Costello, S. & Johnstone, T. (Eds)
Famous Last Words: Obituaries from The Scotsman 1817-1996
Mercat Press pb 1873644639 £9.99

This collection of obituaries from *The Scotsman* provides us with very immediate views of notable Scots written by their peers, and in so doing gives us a social chronicle of their times. We gain a fresh perspective on these famous figures, a perspective often quite different from the image we have of them today. The collection includes obituaries of Sir Walter Scott, John Logie Baird, Harry Lauder, and among more recent subjects are Bill Shankly and Nicholas Fairbairn. In all the entries the Scottish background of the national or world figure is given its deserved attention.

Kydd, R. & N. (Ed)
Growing Up In Scotland: An Anthology
Polygon pb 0748662332 £11.99

This anthology explores the Scottish experience of growing up, seeing the process from various viewpoints within different social classes, communities and times. It uses excerpts from biographies and autobiographies as well as short stories and poems. The book forms a rich tapestry that covers the many aspects and events of childhood.

Lawrence, W. G. (Ed)
Roots in a Northern Landscape
S.C.P. pb 189821879X £7.95

A collection of memories of family life in North East Scotland during World War II, as seen from a child's perspective.

O'Hagan, Andrew
The Missing
Picador pb 0330341375 £5.99

This book is an uncomfortable overview of modern Britain that seeks to bring to light the missing people in our society, be they victims of serial killers or broken homes, alive or dead. O'Hagan uses a mixture of reportage, childhood memoir and social history to create a poignant and painful book that looks at the invisible people of Britain caught up in the dark, frightening world of its underbelly.

ADAIR, ELIZABETH

Flowers and Folk of the North-East
S.C.P. pb 1840170018 £7.95

A series of wide-ranging reminiscences from one of the North-East's best known characters, that cover her life from her London stage career through her years as a BBC Radio Aberdeen producer, right up to her present day life in Aberdeen and its surrounding countryside.

AITKEN, MARGARET

In My Small Corner: Memories of an Orcadian Childhood
S.C.P. pb 1840170026 £7.95

The author's personal reminiscences of life in Orkney over sixty years ago.

Swein Asleifson: A Northern Pirate

Gunn, Robert P.
Whittles pb 1870325109 £2.50

The story of Swein, the son of a Norse governor, has been told in several sagas. His piratical life made him one of the most respected and feared men in Scotland eight centuries ago. This book reveals his exploits in an action-packed account.

BAIN, ALY & CLARK, ALASTAIR

Aly Bain: Fiddler On The Loose
Mainstream hb 1851584315 £14.99

A legend in the world of fiddle music, Aly Bain is known throughout the world for his performances and albums. This revealing biography brings to light many little known facts about his life and work.

Sounds Out Of Silence: A Life Of Alexander Graham Bell

Mackay, James
Mainstream hb 1851588337 £20.00

James Mackay's biography of the Edinburgh-born inventor of the telephone is a thorough piece of research on this remarkable man.

The Ingenious Mr. Bell

Osborne, Brian D.
Argyll hb 1874640319 £15.99

This is the first major biography of Henry Bell (1767-1830), the pioneer of steam navigation. Born in Linlithgow, Bell was the first man to introduce steamships into commercial service when he launched the thirty ton Comet on the Clyde in 1812. The biography is both erudite and accessible.

James Boswell and family

BOSWELL, JAMES (1740–1795)

Author of what many regard as the greatest English language biography, *The Life of Samuel Johnson,* Boswell was born in Edinburgh in 1740 into a well-to-do family. He had a difficult relationship with his father, which heavily influenced his relationship with Samuel Johnson, whom Boswell may subconsciously have regarded as a father figure. He travelled widely, meeting Voltaire and Rousseau during this time. He was also known for his fondness for drink and women. He met Johnson in a bookshop in 1763, and as well as his biography of Johnson, the centrepoint of his literary work, his book on their travels together to the Hebrides did much to create his reputation as one of the great biographers and diarists. His writing is well considered, frank, objective, and incisive, illuminating the complex nature of Johnson and by extension of Boswell himself.

The Life of Samuel Johnson (Ed RW Chapman)
OUP pb 0192815377 £10.99
The Life of Samuel Johnson (Ed Christopher Hibbert)
Penguin pb 0140431160 £7.99
Boswell's Life of Johnson Vol.1 (Ed M. Waingrow)
EUP hb 0748604715 £75.00
Journals of James Boswell (Ed. John Wain)
Mandarin pb 0749312556 £7.99

The Correspondence of James Boswell with James Bruce & Andrew Gibb, Overseers of The Auchinleck Estate
EUP hb 0748606246 £50.00
The Correspondence of James Boswell and William Johnson Temple
EUP hb 0748607587 £50.00

BOYLE, JIMMY
A Sense of Freedom
Pan pb 0330253034 £5.99

The autobiography of the notorious Glasgow hardman who became one of the Barlinnie Prison's Special Unit inmates is powerfully and sharply written. His rehabilitation and artistic achievements (most notably in the fields of sculpture and writing) have made him Scotland's most famous reformed criminal.

Braxfield: The Hanging Judge
Osborne, Brian D.
Argyll hb 1874640033 £15.99

In his searching biography of Lord Robert MacQueen Braxfield (1722-1799), Brian Osborne looks behind the myths surrounding the notorious figure who was the judge at Deacon Brodie's trial. Infamous for his harsh judgements, especially towards political prisoners, Braxfield was a model for Stevenson's Lord Weir in *Weir Of Hermiston*. Osborne finds Braxfield a heavy drinker, hard-headed and cruel, with a gift for black humour, a man who was very much a product of his age.

"Come awa, Maister Homer, come awa' and help us to hang ane o' thae daamned scoondrels."
Lord Braxfield

Dr Mavor And Mr Bridie: Memories Of James Bridie

Mavor, Ronald
N.L.S. with Canongate pb 086241198X £7.95

James Bridie, one of the major 20th century dramatists, wrote more than thirty plays and played a key role in the creation of the Edinburgh Festival and Glasgow Citizens' Theatre. Yet at the same time he had a successful career as a doctor in Glasgow under his true name, Dr. O.H. Mavor. In this biography his son writes about his father's unusual life in two disparate professional worlds.

BROWN, GEORGE MACKAY

Posthumously published at his own request, George Mackay Brown's autobiography, *For the Islands I Sing*, is a haunting and evocative work that gives a unique insight into this major poet and author and his inseparable link to his island home of Orkney. His work is universal and complex and yet deceptively simple, and is in many ways a direct reflection of this remarkable man. *Rockpools and Daffodils* is a selection of works from George Mackay Brown's weekly column in The Orcadian newspaper, which can be viewed as source notes for much of his poetry and fiction.

For the Islands I Sing: An Autobiography
John Murray pb 0719558891 £9.99
Rockpools and Daffodils
Gordon Wright hb 0903065762 £14.95

Gordon Brown: The Biography

Routledge, Paul
Simon & Schuster hb 0684819546 £17.99

The first biography of Labour Chancellor Gordon Brown proved to be a compelling and controversial affair that caused tension between himself and Tony Blair. The book traces the rise of the brilliant son of a Church of Scotland minister who was elected Rector of Edinburgh University while still a student, through his years ascending through the Labour Party ranks and his time as Shadow Chancellor, to his eventual appointment as Chancellor in the new Labour Government. Written 'with his full co-operation', the biography purports to tell the true story behind the struggle for the Labour Party leadership in 1994, as well as providing insights into Brown's political beliefs and private life.

John Buchan: The Presbyterian Cavalier

Lownie, Andrew
Canongate pb 0862416671 £9.99

On the surface John Buchan seemed very much a product of place and society: a famous socialite who moved in the highest circles and expressed many of the prejudices of his class. In Andrew Lownie's major biography, many of the perceived notions of Buchan are exploded. What he finds beyond the commonly held view of Buchan is a complex figure who is not only one of Scotland's but one of Britain's finest writers.

Lord Robert Braxfield

ROBERT BURNS

Catherine Carswell's biography of Burns was first released in 1930 to howls of protest. Written in a vigorous and modern style, it exposed Burns as a drunken, sexually promiscuous individual, a view highly controversial at the time but regarded as accurate now. The book also recreated Burns as a believable person full of passion, generosity and sadness, rather than the romantic Scottish icon previous books had portrayed. It has become known as one of the most honest and accurate appraisals of his life, and even after nearly seventy years is regarded by many as the best Burns biography available. Mackay's biography is a good, modern one, available in paperback. *On a Scotch Bard* is a compact and inexpensive illustrated life. Gavin Sprott's *Robert Burns, Farmer* is a biography with a difference that concentrates on Burns' life as a farmer and sheds an unusual light on his poetic achievement. Another volume by the same author, *Robert Burns : Pride and Passion*, is an exploration of Scotland's national poet that looks specifically at his personality in relation to the Scotland of his time. The author goes some way towards putting real flesh on the man, contrasting this with the legend that has built around Burns today.

Carswell, Catherine
The Life of Robert Burns
Canongate pb 0862412927
£5.99

MacKay, James
**Burns: A Biography of
Robert Burns**
Headline pb 0747242348 £8.99

Mitchell, Keith
**On a Scotch Bard: An
Illustrated Life of Robert Burns**
Neil Wilson pb 1897784228
£4.99

Sprott, Gavin
Robert Burns, Farmer
N.M.S. pb 0948636181 £1.99

Sprott, Gavin
**Robert Burns: Pride and
Passion**
N.L.S. pb 0114957444 £11.95

BURT, EDMUND
**Burt's Letters From The North
Of Scotland**
Birlinn pb 18747449041 £2.99

In 1730 an officer in the English army, Captain Edmund Burt, was posted to Scotland, and from Inverness he regularly sent letters to a close friend in London. At the time the north of Scotland was seen almost as a foreign country by the English and Burt's vivid descriptions of all aspects of the Highlands and Highlanders are informative, witty and satirical but also recognise the harsh poverty and hardship that was rife in these communities .

CAMERON, ARCHIE
**Bare Feet & Tackety Boots:
A Boyhood on the Island
of Rhum**
Luath Press pb 0946487170
£7.95

Archie Cameron's memoirs are also an important piece of social history. He was born and raised on the island of Rhum before World War I, and tells of that long lost way of life as well as his adventures further afield in Scotland.

Moral Desperado: A Life Of Thomas Carlyle

Heffer, Simon
Phoenix pb 1857994469 £12.99

Simon Heffer examines the life and times of Carlyle, the hugely influential Victorian man of letters whose historical works and political thinking were to have such an impact during and after his life. An absorbing and well-written biography.

Little Boss: A Life Of Andrew Carnegie

Mackay, James
Mainstream hb 1851588329 £20.00

Andrew Carnegie was a man of contradictions: one of the world's greatest captains of industry who stopped at nothing to gain his wealth, he also donated hundreds of millions of dollars to worthy causes. This insightful and searching biography charts his life from his birth in Dunfermline to his arrival in America and dramatic rise to fame and fortune.

CARSWELL, CATHERINE

Lying Awake
Canongate pb 0862416833 £5.99

Although unfinished, the autobiography of the socialist, novelist and drama and literature critic Catherine Carswell still relates much of her extraordinary life.

COCKBURN, LORD HENRY

Memorials Of His Time
Mercat Press hb 0901824119 £7.99

The posthumously published memoirs of Lord Cockburn (1779-1854) feature heavily his beloved Edinburgh and its districts. They portray a Scotland during the time of the Napoleonic Wars and offer his own vivid observations on contemporaries such as Adam Ferguson and Dugald Stewart as well as the environment he lived in, bringing them all dynamically to life.

The Big Yin: The Life & Times Of Billy Connolly

Margolis, Jonathan
Orion pb 1857977386 £5.99

It was during his formative years that Billy Connolly first started using his comic talent, largely as a means of survival. This well crafted biography examines the life of this controversial yet much loved comic.

Billy Connolly by John Byrne from The People's Palace Book of Glasgow

Sean Connery: A Biography

Freedland, Michael
Orion pb 1857978714 £6.99

The amazing story of how an Edinburgh milkman went from potential Mr. Universe in 1953 to one of the few real superstars in movies. Through meticulous research, Freedland attempts to get behind the public image of this intensely private man.

COUTTS, BEN

Ben Coutts has written several volumes of autobiography. In *Auld Acquaintance* he tells of the many colourful characters he has met during his rich and eventful life. These people have their roots deep in rural Scotland, and they are vividly brought to life in this work. *Bred in the Highlands* distils a lifetime of experience of the Highland pony and Highland cattle breeds in an evocation of the worlds of stud farm, sale ring and showground. Coutts puts to use his unique powers in describing some of the larger-than-life Highland characters he has met. His unique style as a raconteur is brought to the dramatic and often harrowing story of his wartime experiences in *A Scotsman's War.* This memoir tells of the terrible face wound he suffered in the Sudan, and the days and nights he spent at sea struggling for survival after his ambulance ship was sunk in the Atlantic with the loss of 2000 lives. The tale concludes with the agonising operations he underwent to rebuild his face, performed by Sir Archibald McIndoe. This is a very human recollection of experiencing a world war, not without humour, despite its traumatic content.

Auld Acquaintance: Great Scots Characters I Have Known
Mercat Press pb 1873644302 £7.99
Bothy to Big Ben: An Autobiography
Mercat Press pb 0080363962 £7.99
Bred in The Highlands: Ponies, Cattle and Folk
Mercat Press pb 187364468X £9.99
A Scotsman's War
Mercat Press pb 1873644477 £8.99

DAICHES, DAVID

Two Worlds
Canongate pb 086241704X £5.99

This absorbing autobiography of one of the world's leading literary scholars tells of his childhood and student years and examines Scottish Jewish culture in the years between the wars. The book also contains a moving depiction of Daiches' father.

DICK, ROBERT

I Was Not Alone
S.C.P. pb 1840170069 £9.99

The memoirs of a Scottish boy soldier during World War II, including his involvement in campaigns in the Middle East and India as well as Italy and Germany.

"I'm what I always have been - a Scot, a bit introspective. I don't tell lies and I prefer straight dealing."

Sean Connery

Sean Connery

The Doctor, The Detective & Arthur Conan Doyle

Booth, Martin
Coronet Books pb 0340648988 £7.99

This biography of Arthur Conan Doyle has much to say about his early years and his struggle to overcome the constraints of an alcoholic father and poverty. His professional career as a doctor and his rise in the literary world to become the most popular writer of his time are descriptively relayed. The book also examines many lesser known aspects of Conan Doyle such as his interests in spiritualism, sport and hunting, providing a clear and detailed picture of the creator of the master sleuth Sherlock Holmes.

Isabella Elder, The Lady of Claremont House: Pioneer and Philanthropist

McAlpine, Joan
Argyll hb 1874640971 £15.99

Isabella Elder was an inspirational woman who became one of the greatest benefactors Glasgow has ever had. She fought against the Victorican repression of women, establishing a medical school for women at a time when the female brain was thought to be harmed by too much thinking. After her husband died, she took over the running of his huge shipyard in Govan and was responsible for many innovative and forward-looking initiatives in the fields of welfare and education. This biography is deftly handled and illuminates a badly neglected heroine of the Victorian age.

FEARCHAIR A'GHUNNA

Fearchair a'Ghunna, The Ross-shire Wanderer: His Life and Sayings
House Of Lochar pb 1899863028 £4.95

This anecdotal biography of Farquhar, a 19th century packman with a love of guns and gunpowder, was originally released in 1881. This facsimile edition retains its interest today largely through the witty and often sharp remarks he was famous for.

FRASER, EUGENIE

Eugenie Fraser was born in Archangel, the daughter of a Russian father and Scottish mother. *The House by the Dvina* is the first instalment of her remarkable life story. It recounts her Russian childhood years and the times before, during and after the Russian Revolution. These years had a profound effect on her family and by 1920 she had to flee to Scotland. The different cultures, customs and family backgrounds are vividly explored in an atmospheric and evocative memoir with dramatic passages worthy of any work of fiction. Taking place nearly eighty years after events in the first instalment, *The Dvina Remains* is a haunting and memorable account of Eugenie Fraser's return visits to the Dvina and Archangel where she discovers her family home destroyed and many relatives dead or disappeared. She also finds out the eventual fate of her father who was too ill to leave Russia with his family.

The House by the Dvina
Corgi pb 0552128333 £6.99
The Dvina Remains
Corgi pb 0552145394 £6.99

FRASER, GEORGE M.

**Quartered Safe Out Here:
A Recollection of the War in
Burma**
HarperCollins pb 0002726874
£7.99

George MacDonald Fraser's
vivid memoirs of his time in
the Burma campaign read in
places like some of his
fictional work. There is
however an extra emotional
depth and penetrating
analysis rooted in personal
experience that raises this
book into one of the very best
wartime memoirs around.

GILLIES BROWN, MARGARET

Far from the Rowan Tree
Argyll hb1874640238 £9.99

In the 1950s many Scots
em-igrated to Canada looking
for a better life. In this well
written account Margaret
Gillies Brown relates the
ex-periences of migrating
from a woman's viewpoint:
the diffi-cult sea voyage, the
privations of settling into a
remote farm in Alberta, and
the love and support of her
husband, family and fellow
emigrants which made the
relocation easier to cope with.

Alex: The Authorised Biography of Sir Alexander Gibson

Wilson, Conrad
Mainstream hb 1851585745 £14.99

Alexander Gibson founded Scottish Opera and for twenty five
years was musical director of the Scottish National Orchestra.
During his lifetime in music he championed many Scottish
composers. He was a man with an international musical
reputation who still very much regarded Glasgow as his home.
Despite his standing, he was known as a modest and private
figure - this biography reveals his life story in detail.

Scottish Samurai: Thomas Blake Glover

McKay, Alexander
Canongate pb 0862417465 £8.99

Thomas Glover is today regarded as one of the founding
fathers of the Japanese economic miracle. A business
entrepreneur who arrived in Nagasaki in 1859 during the
overthrow of the Tokugawa Shogunate, he helped the rebels by
supplying warships and arms. He went on to have a complex
business and love life (one of his mistresses inspiring Puccini's
Madam Butterfly). This methodically researched biography took
over ten years to write, and tells the fascinating tale of one of
Scotland's lesser known but highly influential sons.

GRAHAM, DUNCAN

Sunset on the Clyde
Neil Wilson pb 1897784449
£7.99

An autobiography by a former student purser during the last great days of pleasure-steaming on the Clyde.

GRANT, ELIZABETH (1797–1886)

Elizabeth Grant was born in Edinburgh, the daughter of a lawyer and Highland landowner. The journals she is famous for were not intended for publication, although she had written stories and articles for various magazines. The journals were written as a personal diary, and it is this fact coupled with their intimate, down-to-earth style that have made them popular long after many other accounts of the time have faded into obscurity. Her memoirs are detailed and lively accounts of the early years of the 19th century, full of vividly portrayed memories on a wide range of subjects. Her style is friendly and welcoming, and readers quickly grow to like her idiosyncrasies. Volumes 1 and II cover the collapse of her father's legal and political ambitions and the family's unexpected salvation when he is offered a judgeship in India. They end when Elizabeth marries an Irish landowner. *Memoirs of a Highland Lady in Ireland* is the follow-up volume that covers her years on the Baltiboys estate. *A Highland Lady In France* looks at the two years she and her family spent there. The life of the British emigré society is vividly described, while wider political concerns are also commented on. Her insights into class and society coupled with her own family's affairs are related in her own distinctive voice.

A Highland Lady In France
Tuckwell Press pb 1898410909 £9.99
Memoirs of a Highland Lady (Vols 1 & 2)
Canongate pb 0862413966 £7.99
Memoirs of a Highland Lady in Ireland
Canongate pb 0862413613 £7.99

GUNN, NEIL M.

The Atom of Delight
Polygon pb 0748661557 £7.95

An expansive philosophical autobiography that shows Gunn's interest in Buddhism later in his life.

HAMILTON, IAN, QC

Ian Hamilton has produced several volumes of autobiography. *The Taking of the Stone of Destiny* tells of the time in 1950 when, along with Alan Stewart, Gavin Vernon and Kay Matheson, he removed the Stone of Destiny from Westminster Abbey and in so doing became a Scottish national hero. His life since 1950 as a lawyer and SNP activist is told in *A Touch of Treason* and *A Touch More Treason* reveals more of his passionate and controversial views on a wide range of important issues facing Scotland.

The Taking of the Stone of Destiny
House Of Lochar hb
0984403241 £10.99
A Touch of Treason
Neil Wilson pb 1897784309
£7.99
A Touch More Treason
Neil Wilson hb 189778435X
£12.99

The Armstrong Nose: Selected Letters Of Hamish Henderson

Finlay, Alec (Ed.)
Polygon pb 0748661913 £7.99

Hamish Henderson is one of the leading figures in present-day Scottish culture. A songwriter, poet and political fighter, his work on the folk tradition and oral tradition in Scotland is vital to any understanding of the subjects. His letters show his diverse interests, a treasure trove of thoughts, literary conflicts, events, people and history. They shed light not only on Hamish Henderson but also on the cultural concerns of Scotland over the past forty years.

HENDERSON, MEG

Finding Peggy
Corgi pb 0552141852 £6.99

This well-respected journalist recounts her childhood years in 50s' and 60s' Glasgow in a funny, emotionally appealing fashion. The poverty she ex-perienced was severe, but the brutality in her life was tem-pered with the anchor of stability and love provided by her mother. The book cele-brates those strong, everyday women of Glasgow who fought to create a better future for their children.

HESKETH, BARRY
Taking Off: The Story of the Mull Little Theatre
New Iona Press pb 0951628380 £8.95

The Mull Little Theatre opened in 1966 and its history is told here by one of its founder members. Creating Britain's smallest professional theatre on a small Scottish island took a huge leap of faith for the husband and wife team of Barry and Marianne Hesketh. Their story and that of the theatre is told with feeling, particularly towards the end Marianne battles with terminal illness.

The Women Of Royaumont: A Scottish Women's Hospital on the Western Front
Crofton, Eileen
Tuckwell Press hb 1898410860 £17.99

This remarkable book recounts the tale of Dr. Elsie Inglis who was instrumental in setting up the Scottish Women's Hospitals of the First World War. With the help of the Scottish Federation of Women's Suffrage Societies, she offered fully staffed medical units to the British War Office, who rejected the offer. These medical units were quickly taken up by the French and Serbian authorities. This led to the Abbey of Royaumont being set up as a hospital by Miss Frances Ivens. The hospital treated huge numbers of casualties and was recognised as one of the most efficient of World War One, operating from 1915 to 1919. The book, constructed from personal recollections and official records, is full of human interest and is also of social and historical importance.

Without Quarter:
A Biography of Tom Johnston
Galbraith, Russell
Mainstream hb 1851587616 £20.00

A biography of journalist and statesman Tom Johnston, who in 1906 at the age of 25 set up the Glasgow-based Forward newspaper. He went into politics and eventually entered the House of Commons in 1922 as one of the Clydeside group of MPs. He is perhaps best known for being Secretary of State for Scotland in the wartime coalition under Churchill.

I Have Not Yet Begun To Fight: A Life Of John Paul Jones
Mackay, James
Mainstream hb 1840180579 £20.00

A major biography charting the extraordinary life of one of the greatest mariners of all time. John Paul Jones was born in Kirkbean, Kirkcudbrightshire in 1747. He apprenticed on a ship and became a well respected sailor. On inheriting land in Virginia he moved to America and at the onset of the American Revolution in 1775 joined what was to become the American Navy, of which, because of his achievements, he is regarded the founder. In 1779 he was the commodore of a small French fleet flying the American flag which threatened Leith. Accused by the British of being a pirate, he was highly regarded by the French, particularly Louis XVI. In 1788 he joined the Russian Navy as Rear Admiral of the Black Sea Fleet. An enthralling biography of this complex figure.

Jennie Lee: A Life

Hollis, Patricia
OUP hb 0198215800 £25.00

Jennie Lee (1904-88) was a Scottish miner's daughter who went on to become a Socialist MP at the age of 24, before she could vote. This biography of her achievements and life details her major contribution to the Labour Party, from her own gifts of political oration to support of her husband, Aneurin Bevan in his efforts to launch the NHS and deal with internal Party feuds. She later became the first Minister for the Arts in Harold Wilson's Government, responsible for founding the Open University.

LEIGH, MARGARET

A Spade Among the Rushes
Birlinn pb 1874744645 £6.99

An autobiographical account of crofting life on Moidart during World War II. The enchanting beauty of this area is carefully recreated by Leigh, who was already a successful author before she moved to the West Highlands.

The Man Who Invented Himself: A Life Of Sir Thomas Lipton

Mackay, James
Mainstream hb 1851588310 £20.00

The life story of Thomas Lipton who was born in Glasgow and emigrated to America at the age of 15. He eventually returned to Scotland and opened a grocery shop which quickly expanded into a chain. James Mackay relays the story of this colourful and highly successful figure with clarity and accuracy.

Journey To Livingstone: The Exploration of an Imperial Myth

Holmes, Timothy
Canongate hb 0862414024 £9.99

Since his death in 1873 many myths have grown up around Livingstone. Timothy Holmes' thoroughly researched biography returns to the primary sources of information and brings Livingstone dramatically to life, warts and all.

LOMAX, ERIC

The Railway Man
Vintage pb 0099582317 £6.99

This is a powerful and moving memoir by a Scottish prisoner-of-war who was forced to work on the Burma-Siam railway by the Japanese and who met with one of his captors fifty years later. The book speaks of man's capacity for both cruelty and survival. It won the 1995 Waterstone's/Esquire Non-Fiction Award and the 1996 NCR Book Award.

McBEY, JAMES

The Early Life of James McBey
Canongate pb 0862414458 £5.99

James McBey was a well respected artist of his time. This autobiography tells of his struggle to rise above the poverty, ignorance and indifference of his humble beginnings, an ascent that was further hampered by his mother's tragic suicide. His early days are relayed to the reader with a quiet emotional clarity.

Norman MacCaig: A Study Of His Life And Work

McNeill, Marjory
Mercat Press pb 1873644515 £9.99

A biography of one of Scotland's greatest 20th century poets, based on numerous personal interviews with MacCaig by the author over a period of years. The book serves as a straightforward introduction to both MacCaig and his poetry.

Hugh MacDiarmid-George Ogilvie Letters

Kerrigan, C.
Mercat Press hb 0080364098 £24.90

A unique insight into the early life of Hugh MacDiarmid as seen in his correspondence with his English teacher at Broughton School.

MACDONALD, FINLAY J.

The Finlay J. MacDonald Omnibus
Warner pb 0751513482 £7.99

This volume contains Finlay J. MacDonald's three autobiographical works *Crowdie and Cream, Crotal and White* and *The Cornflake and the Lysander.* Relayed in his unique nostalgic and humorous style, they tell of life on the island of Harris before and just up to the start of World War II.

MACINNES, ANGUS E.

Eriskay Where I Was Born
Mercat Press pb 1873644760 £12.99

Angus Edward MacInnes is a natural storyteller. This account of his life tells of his days on Eriskay from before World War One to the present day. The book also recounts his adventures as a sea captain, and the events surrounding the sinking and salvaging of the S.S. Politician, later immortalised in *Whisky Galore,* are covered in some detail. A book full of memorable characters and incidents that also captures the spirit of an island.

Hebridean Song-Maker: Iain MacNeacail of the Isle of Skye

McKean, Thomas A.
Polygon pb 0748662146 £18.95

A fascinating biography that explores the life and work of Gaelic songwriter and singer Iain MacNeacail. Known on Skye as 'The Skipper', he has been making songs since 1917 when he was fourteen years old. The biography draws a lively picture of the links between his life and work and the island's vibrant community. Included with the book is a CD of MacNeacail singing his own songs.

The Glamour Chase: The Maverick Life of Billy MacKenzie

Doyle, Tom
Bloomsbury pb 0747536155
£12.99

The colourful figure of Billy MacKenzie, the front man of Scottish band 'The Associates', enjoyed a handful of hit singles with the band in the early eighties, but at the height of their popularity he left to pursue his own musical career. His attempts to break free of the music industry were eventually to prove fruitless, and he committed suicide in 1997. *The Glamour Chase* charts his career and examines this highly talented singer's complex character which is in turn wild, hilariously funny and just plain mischievous.

Sir James Mackintosh
(1765 - 1832)

O'Leary, P.
Mercat Press hb 008034531X
£14.99

A biography of champion of liberal causes James Mackintosh, a renowned raconteur, judge, historian and politician who during his life inspired both great love and loathing among his contemporaries.

MACLEAN, ALASDAIR

Night Falls on Ardnamurchan
Penguin pb 0140108122 £6.99

Alasdair Maclean's unsentimental account of crofting life shows his unerring eye for natural detail. An occasionally humorous account that weaves his own recollections as a crofter with passages from his father's journal. This book gives an accurate and elegant description of a failing community, and also examines children's often difficult relationships with their parents.

MACLEAN, FITZROY

Eastern Approaches
Penguin pb 0140132716 £8.99

Famous as the commander of the British military mission to the Yugoslav Partisans during World War II, Maclean later became a Conservative MP and eventually Under-Secretary for War. He is said to have been part of the inspiration for Ian Fleming's James Bond. *Eastern Approaches* is an account of his experiences in Russia before the war and his attendance at the show trial of Bukharin, as well as his campaigns with Tito's partisans.

McLEAN, JACK

Hopeless But Not Serious: The Autobiography of the Urban Voltaire
Mainstream hb 1851586644 £14.99

The autobiography of journalist, teacher and media personality Jack McLean. Born in Glasgow just after World War II, his controversial and often scathing opinions on a wide range of subjects from art and sport to politics and social observation underlie his unusual and highly characterised personality.

MACLELLAN, ANGUS

The Furrow Behind Me: The Autobiography of a Hebridean Crofter
Birlinn pb 1874744270 £ 6.99

Angus MacLellan was born into the crofting community on South Uist in 1869. This autobiography is translated from the Gaelic by John Lorne Campbell from tapes made by MacLellan during the 1960s, and is written in a unique and captivating style which replicates MacLellan's oral story-telling turn of phrase.

McPHEE, JOHN

The Crofter and The Laird
House Of Lochar pb 1899863249 £ 8.99

The book that New Yorker staff writer John McPhee wrote about his family's stay in a crofthouse on the tiny Hebridean island of his forefathers during the late 1960s is not a dewy-eyed, romanticised work. Instead his book is an accurate and non-judgemental portrait of a living, breathing community which reveals the tensions that both support and threaten such small localities.

The Sublime Savage: James McPherson & the Poems of Ossian

Stafford, Fiona
EUP pb 0852246099 £14.95

A biography of James MacPherson and the controversy that surrounded his 'discovery' of the works of Ossian.

Wise Enough To Play The Fool: A Biography Of Duncan Macrae

Barlow, Priscilla
John Donald hb 0859764184 £14.95

A biography of one of Scotland's most famous stars of radio, TV, cinema and theatre, covering his entire career from the 30s to his death in 1967.

MILLER, CHRISTIAN

A Childhood In Scotland
Canongate pb 0862412307
£4.99

Although raised in a Scottish upper-class background in the 1920s, Christian Miller's childhood was one of peculiar repression, in which reading and playing with toys were discouraged from an early age, in a society where shooting was second only to religion. Told in a delicate style, the strange contrasts of her early days are lucidly brought to life.

Hugh Miller

MILLER, HUGH (1802–1856)

Hugh Miller was a famous Victorian character, noted for his knowledge of and contribution to many fields. He was born in Cromarty, the son of a ship's captain. His father died when he was five and he was raised by his mother. He was a wild child who had a love of nature and a strong belief in the supernatural. At the age of seventeen he became an apprentice stonemason, a job that was to lead directly to his interest in fossils. He published a book of poems in 1829 and wrote articles for the Inverness Courier. Around the same time he wrote a collection of tales rich in history and folklore, *Scenes and Legends of the North of Scotland*. He moved to Edinburgh in 1834 where he became a leading figure in the Church, siding with the Free Church after its split from the Church of Scotland. He wrote numerous articles on subjects as wide-ranging as child labour and the Highland Clearances. He also wrote three geology books, *The Old Red Sandstone, Footprints of the Creator* and *The Testimony of the Rocks*. The first of these in particular was a well-received bestseller at the time, but his refusal to believe the theory of evolution undermined the value of his geological works in later years. His very readable memoir, *My Schools and Schoolmasters,* promoted the idea of self-improvement. Miller committed suicide in 1856. The B & W edition of *My Schools and Schoolmasters* contains his complete autobiography, finished just before his death.

Hugh Miller's Memoir: From Stonemason To Geologist (By Michael Shortland)
EUP pb 0748605215 £12.95
My Schools and Schoolmasters
B & W pb 1873631189 £9.99
Scenes and Legends of the North of Scotland
B & W pb 1873631383 £8.99

The Nine Lives Of Naomi Mitchison

Calder, Jenni
Virago hb 1853817244 £20.00

This is the fascinating life story of one of Scotland's most remarkable writers, highly praised for its detailed research and rounded appraisal of its subject. Naomi Mitchison's various incarnations as novelist, politician and farmer are fully explored.

Dead Glamorous: The Autobiography Of Seduction & Self-Destruction

Morin, Carole
Indigo pb 0575400358 £6.99

Carole Morin's autobiography takes quite a few liberties with the genre: the line between truth and fiction is severely blurred. It does make for a very gripping read with distinctly noirish overtones.

John Muir: From Scotland To The Sierra

Turner, Frederick
Canongate pb 0862417015 £12.99

John Muir's role in setting up the American National Parks turned him into a national hero there. Yet in his native Scotland John Muir is still relatively unknown. Frederick Turner's excellent biography goes some way to redressing this situation. It reveals a man who lived his dreams and dreamed very deeply.

NEIL, ANDREW

Full Disclosure
Pan pb 0330343483 £5.99

In this often controversial book Andrew Neil gives us an intimate portrayal of power during 1997's general election, as well as his insider's opinion on the big news stories of the 80s and early 90s, covering everything from the Battle of Wapping to the Matrix Churchill scandal.

The Eye That Never Slept: A Life of Allan Pinkerton

Mackay, James
Mainstream hb 1851588256 £20.00

This biography of Allan Pinkerton unravels the truth from the legends surrounding this great detective. Born in Glasgow, Pinkerton fled to America with the law hot on his heels. It was there he was destined to rise through the ranks of the American police force and eventually become the principal of the North West Detective Agency now known as Pinkerton's. Nicknamed 'The Eye' by the Chicago underworld (from which the expression 'private eye' comes), he was a detecting legend during the four decades before the American civil war, with his motto 'We Never Sleep'.

Poet And Painter: Allan Ramsay, Father And Son, 1684–1784

Brown, Ian Gordon
N.L.S. pb 0902220632 £2.00

This study of the Ramsays covers not only their lives and works but also the links between poetry and art in eighteenth century Scotland.

ROB ROY MACGREGOR

Rob Roy, one of the biggest folk heroes in Scottish history, is popularly perceived as a romantic and elusive hero. The facts behind the myth are difficult to illuminate: during his lifetime there was no written record of his childhood or even an image of his physical appearance. Murray's careful reconstruction was used as inspiration for the recent Holywood movie. He has created a sympathetic and comprehensive biography of Rob Roy by searching through archives and estate records of the time. Murray finds that Rob Roy won his place in Scottish history by force of character rather than his politics or subsequent portrayal in the works of Sir Walter Scott. 'The Scourge of Montrose' has never been so completely detailed. Nigel Tranter's book is another fine portrayal of this figure and gives a gripping account tha t searches for the real man behind the myth.

Murray, W.H.
Rob Roy MacGregor:
His Life & Times
Canongate pb 0862415381
£5.99

Tranter, Nigel
Rob Roy MacGregor
Neil Wilson pb 1897784317
£7.99

REA, F.G

A School In South Uist:
Reminiscences of a Hebridean
Schoolmaster, 1890-1913
Birlinn pb 1874744874 £6.99

A marvellous and unique evocation of life in the Hebrides at the turn of the century as seen in the memoirs of Frederick Rea, the first Englishman to become headmaster there and the first Catholic to be appointed to the post since the Reformation.

Jeannie Robertson: Emergent Singer, Transformative Voice

Porter, J. & Gower, H
Tuckwell Press hb 1898410844
£25.00

A biography of one of Scotland's most famous travellers and singers, whose influence on the music of Scotland and of the Appalachian areas of America can still be felt today. The book includes a selection of her best-known songs.

ROBERTSON, MARTHA

A Quiet Life
Whittles pb 1870325710 £14.95

Growing up in remote Scottish lighthouses during the 1920s and 30s was a unique experience. In this autobiography Martha Robertson recounts her early years and relates an unusual childhood.

SANDISON, CHRISTOPHER

Christopher Sandison of Eshaness (1780-1871): Diarist in an Age of Social Change
Shetland Times hb 189885226X £24.00

A compilation of the journals kept by a Shetland school-master during the 19th century, illustrating the many changes taking place on the island at that time.

A Life Of Walter Scott: The Laird Of Abbotsford
Wilson, A.N.
Mandarin pb 0749322411 £7.99

Wilson's penetrating and challenging biography of Scott captures him with clarity and insight, presenting a fresh, believable individual to the reader. Wilson is never over-awed by his subject and studiously avoids some of the pitfalls previous biographers have stumbled into. Instead he creates an insightful and entertaining account, written in an enthusiastic and lively style.

The Jimmy Shand Story
Cameron, Ian
S.C.P. hb 1840170190 £14.99

The full-length biography of the incredibly popular king of Scottish dance music.

SMITH, ADAM (1723–1790)

Smith was a major economist, philosopher and one of the leading lights of the Scottish Enlightenment, whose economic theories are still widely followed. Ross's book is a comprehensive academic biography which covers his life, works and significant achievements. Raphael's work is a concise introduction to the man and his ideas.

Raphael, D.D.
Adam Smith
OUP pb 0192875582 £5.99

Ross, I.S.
The Life of Adam Smith
OUP hb 0198288212 £25.00

SOUTAR, WILLIAM (1898–1943)

Scottish poet William Soutar was confined to bed for fourteen years as a result of spondelytis of the spine, the illness that would finally kill him. During this time he kept a private diary, providing an intimate view of his personal approach to poetry, politics and life. A striking work written by a man who faced death with courage. It is only part of the many diaries and journals written by Soutar, whose poetry is sadly currently out of print.
Diaries of a Dying Man
Canongate pb 0862413478 £4.99

SPARK, MURIEL

Curriculum Vitae
Penguin pb 0140123113 £7.99

Muriel Spark sets the tone for her autobiography by starting off with a piece about her childhood memories of bread and butter. The mixture of the everyday and the extra-ordinary in these memoirs continues throughout the book, in which she carefully avoids pretentiousness to concentrate on creating an engaging work relayed in a style that reveals her love of life.

Robert Louis Stevenson

McLynn, Frank
Pimlico pb 0712658939 £12.50

Stevenson, one of Scotland's most important and popular literary figures, was a complex individual around whom many myths grew. Frank McLynn's magnificent and highly accessible biography takes an accurate and uncompromising look at the life and work of this great man.

Dreams Of Exile: Robert Louis Stevenson

Bell, Ian
Mainstream hb 1851584579 £14.99

Ronald Stevenson: A Musical Biography

MacDonald, Malcolm
N.L.S. pb 0902220977 £8.95

Rated by many as Scotland's pre-eminent contemporary composer and a pivotal figure in Scotland's cultural life, Ronald Stevenson's work is of international standing. This accessible biography highlights his passionate involvement in the arts.

STEWART, JEAN CANTLIE

Pine Trees and the Sky
S.C.P. pb 1898218978 £5.95

A memoir that tells the story of a Highland glen around Corgarff, set among some of the finest mountain scenery in Britain. Its inhabitants are vividly brought to life in this sensitive work.

STEWART, KATHARINE

Katharine Stewart's life has provided her with the material for several books. In *A School in the Hills* she tells the story of her involvement with one small Highland school, from the time before her daughter attended it, to its closure and beyond when it became a base for the filming of Peter Watkin's *Culloden*. She goes on to describe its re-emergence as a crofting museum of which she became the first curator. For over thirty-five years Katharine Stewart and her family were involved in the running of a small Post Office in the Highlands. In *The Post in the Hills,* using her own experiences as a starting point, she explores the history of the postal services in the region. *A Garden in the Hills* is a celebration of Katharine Stewart's highland garden that traces the circle of the seasons. As well as skillfully communicating the joys she feels in relation to the garden, she also includes many parctical tips about gardening, cooking, wine-making and bee-keeping.

A Croft in the Hills
Mercat Press pb 0901824976 £6.99
A Garden in the Hills
Mercat Press pb 1873644329 £7.99
The Post in the Hills
Mercat Press pb 1873644744 £8.99
A School in the Hills
Mercat Press pb 187364454X £8.99

STOTT, GORDON

High Court Judge Lord Stott kept a diary that records his courtroom experiences right up to his retirement in 1984. These books are that diary: *A Judge's Diary* is a follow-up to his *Lord Advocate's Diary* and together the two books provide an insight into life in the upper echelons of the Scottish legal establishment. The third instalment, *QC's Diary,* actually covers the earlier years of 1954-60.

A Judge's Diary
Mercat Press hb 1873644434 £15.99
Lord Advocate's Diary
Mercat Press hb 0080413994 £12.99
Q.C.'s Diary
Mercat Press hb 187364471X £15.99

SUTHERLAND, DONALD

A Highland Childhood
Birlinn pb 1874744289 £6.99
Donald Sutherland, in a child's eye view of his beloved Argyll countryside, describes with affection and humour the vanished society of the pre-war Highlands.

TESSIER DU CROS, JANET

Cross Currents: A Childhood In Scotland
Tuckwell Press pb 1862320691
£9.99

This evocative autobiography is a well written period piece about a childhood that experienced all the comfort and securities of the Imperial era. Janet Tessier Du Cros brings back to life a vanished world, and through her meetings with many of Scotland's leading artistic and literary figures she paints a first-hand account of the cultural scene in Scotland during and just after World War I.

THOMSON, DAVID

Nairn in Darkness and Light
Vintage pb 0099599902 £5.99

Winner of the 1988 NCR Book Award, David Thomson's autobiographical study of Nairn in the 1920s is a work of understated eloquence. He knits together his own experiences with the rich and varied life of the community. During these formative years he suffered an eye injury, an injury that shaped the rest of his life, including his career as a writer.

A Life in Pieces: Reflections on Alexander Trocchi
Campbell, Allan & Niel, Tim (Ed)
Rebel Inc. pb 0862416809 £10.99

A collection of writing celebrating the life and work of one of Scotland's most controversial and influential writers. Trocchi was a charismatic figure who helped define 60s counter culture. Among the writers who contribute are William Burroughs, Irvine Welsh, Allan Ginsberg and Leonard Cohen. The book looks at the various aspects of this talented writer with a colourful past and goes some way towards giving him his rightful place in Scottish literature.

Island: Diary of a Year on Easdale
Waite, Garth & Vicky
Mainstream hb 1851587241 £14.99

Island is a country diary in the best amateur tradition. It is the account by a newly married couple who share a passion for Scotland and its nature. They decide to follow their dream and take early retirement to move to the tiny Scottish island of Easdale. This book covers their first year on the island.

One Foot on the Stage: Biography of Richard Wilson
Roose Evans, James
Orion pb 0752811150 £6.99

Richard Wilson, the actor best known for his portrayal of Victor Meldrew, has had a long and distinguished career in theatre and television. This authorised biography traces his life from his childhood years in Greenock to his major successes, including *One Foot In The Grave*.

Childrens

Children's Books in Scotland: An overview

by Tessa MacGregor, Waterstone's, George Street, Edinburgh

The selection of Scottish books for children has never looked better. There is a wealth of talent and imagination in new writing and illustration as well as many adaptations of classics and folk tales. In non-fiction also there is no shortage, as there once was, of chronicles of Scotland's troubled and colourful history. The titles chosen here will appeal to various age-groups individually as well as to everyone, from tourists to natives, toddlers to schoolchildren.

For younger readers and listeners, you need look no further than flame-haired Katie Morag. Not only is she one of the most popular characters in picture books north of the Border, but there must surely be copies of her stories all over the world, as people take a kid's eye view of Scottish island life home with them overseas. The wonderfully intricate and evocative illustrations by author Mairi Hedderwick ensure the best-selling status of this series. Still in the world of picture books, there is crazy Maisie the cat. She gets up to all sorts of things in all sorts of places. The text is denser, and these books are suitable for slightly older children (age 3-7) than Katie Morag. Aileen Paterson has built up a loyal following for this adventurous cat with her extremely vibrant and humorous illustrations . . . of course Maisie rarely goes it alone, there's always her best friend Archie, or even Granny, able and willing to lend a 'paw'!

In fiction, one of our homegrown publishers, Canongate, produce a wide ranging series called Kelpies, mainly for the 9+ age group. This list takes in many genres from fairy tales to adventures, and features several titles by award-winner Theresa Breslin, who won the Kathleen Fidler First Novel Award for *Simon's Challenge*. There is something for all tastes in this exciting series.

Bringing the past alive is a daunting task for any history book, but Wayland, with their Scottish History series do this admirably. This well produced list of ten titles is unrivalled in its coverage of our past, and is growing all the time. Available in both hardback and paperback, these books are a valuable teaching and project resource as well as being interesting and informative for reading at home.

However, if you want to store up facts and be amazed by Scotland's heritage there is an altogether more narrative rendition in the shape of *Horrible Histories: Bloody Scotland* (Hippo Bks pb, 0590543407, £7.99). This irrepressible and hilarious best-selling series by Terry Deary has previously covered subjects such as the *Vile Victorians* (Hippo Bks pb, 0590554662, £3.50) and the *Rotten Romans* (Hippo Bks pb, 0590554670, £3.50).

This guide would not be complete if the legacy of Robert Louis Stevenson were not mentioned. As in the adults' section, there are numerous editions of those firm favourites *Treasure Island* and *A Child's Garden Of Verses*. The mark that this great, imaginative writer has left cannot be overestimated. One hundred years on his books remain undisputed classics.

The life of Robert Burns is skilfully acknowledged and condensed for children in *Robert Burns: Maker Of Rhymes* by Elisabeth McNair. Biographies for children are all too rare but this one about the bard is a riveting and appealing read . . . and to help with the definitions and meanings of the language of Scots as used by Burns and others, you will need to have the *Scots-English, English-Scots School Dictionary* (Chambers pb, 055011856X, £5.99), a dictionary which is both helpful and interesting in its own right.

So go on! get interested, because there is a lot to read, to do and to see.

Pre-School

(pbd = paperboard)

HEDDERWICK, MAIRI

All these books tell the tales of Katie Morag's shenanigans on the West Coast island of Struay. What will happen when mainland Granma and island Grannie get together? And how does Katie Morag manage to get into such a mess by being postman for the day? Then there are the storybooks, which include rhymes and recipes as well as brand new stories! An absolute must-have for the under-fives and for reading alone up to age 7.

Katie Morag and the Big Boy Cousins
Collins pb 0006637515 £4.50
Katie Morag and the Grand Concert
Bodley Head pbd 0370323351 £9.99
Katie Morag and the New Pier
Red Fox pb 0099220822 £4.50
Katie Morag and the Tiresome Ted
Collins pb 0006631614 £4.50
Katie Morag and the Two Grandmothers
Red Fox pb 0099118718 £4.50

Katie Morag and the Wedding
Red Fox pb 0099463415 £4.50
Katie Morag Delivers the Mail
Red Fox pb 0099220725 £4.50
Katie Morag's Island Stories
Bodley Head pbd 0370323114 £9.99
Big Katie Morag Storybook
Bodley Head pbd 0370324420 £9.99
Second Katie Morag Storybook
Bodley Head pbd 0370323270 £9.99

Oh No, Peedie Peebles!
Red Fox pb 0099206218 £4.50

You never know what Peedie and his paint pots might get up to next as each page turns, in this super rainbow coloured picture book for the under-fives.

Illustration by Mairi Hedderwick from Katie Morag and the New Pier

CHARLES, HRH THE PRINCE OF WALES
The Old Man of Lochnagar
Puffin pb0140544143 £5.99

Prince Charles' book for children is a delightful tale about an old man who lives in a cave by the Loch of Lochnagar. His many unusual adventures are sure to please young readers, who will also enjoy the colourful pictures.

Ages 5-8 Fiction

MILLER, MOIRA

Hamish and the Fairy Gifts
Kelpie pb 0862415659 £3.50
Hamish and the Wee Witch
Kelpie pb 0862415667 £3.50

These collections of fairy stories are a delight to behold! You just know that good will triumph over evil, that the wee folk will have to bestow the greatest honour on Hamish's baby boy to make up for their mischief, and that the 'Wee Witch' will get her comeuppance!
Doom of Soulis
Kelpie pb0862415829 £3.50
Sandy MacStovie's Monster
Scottish Children's pb
1899827277 £3.95

PATERSON, AILEEN

Maisie's dad is off exploring the rainforest and she moves to Edinburgh to live with her granny. So start the tales of this mischievous cat, from the suburbs of her new home to being a film star for the day and falling out of a tree before the fireman could save her, as well as many other adventures. Whatever she does, she does the most entertaining way.

Maisie and the Pirates
Amaising pb 1871512557 £3.50
Maisie and the Posties
Amaising pb1871512034 £3.50
Maisie and the Puffer
Amaising pb 1871512336 £3.50
Maisie Comes to Morningside
Amaising pb 1871705002 £2.50
Maisie Digs Up The Past
Amaising pb 1871512417 £3.50
Maisie Goes to a Wedding
Amaising pb 1871512549 £3.50
Maisie Goes to Glasgow
Amaising pb 1871705010 £2.50
Maisie Goes to Hollywood
Amaising pb 1871512409 £3.50
Maisie Goes to Hospital
Amaising pb 1871512069 £3.50
Maisie Goes to School
Amaising pb 1871512018 £3.50
Maisie in London
Amaising pb 1871705045 £2.50
Maisie in the Rainforest
Amaising pb 1871512298 £3.50
Maisie Loves Paris
Amaising pb 1871512050 £3.50
Maisie's Doll and Activity Book
Amaising pb 1871512574 £4.99
What Maisie Did Next
Amaising pb 1871512093 £3.50

Ages 5-8 Non-Fiction

BRASSEY, RICHARD & ROSS, STEWART

The Story of Scotland
Orion pb 1858815495 £3.99

A colourfully illustrated children's history of Scotland, humorously and informatively done.

BRASSEY, RICHARD

Nessie: The Loch Ness Monster
Orion pb1858813093 £2.99

Whether you believe in the myth or not, you will laugh from cover to back with this funny and quirkily illustrated picture book.

HESKETH, NICK

Bodkin and the Big City
Amaising pb 187151245X £3.99
Bodkin, Keeper of the Marsh
Amaising pb 1871512360 £3.99

Many invaluable lessons will be learned in these tales with an environmental theme.

PATERSON, AILEEN (illus.) & PATERSON, JUDY (text)

Spook's Edinburgh: A Child's Guide
Amaising pb 1871512522 £4.75

Let Spook show you round Scotland's capital city. He's an excellent guide and he'll take you around and tell you lots of fascinating facts whether you're new to the city or you've lived there all your life. If you get lost you can always look at the map or go for a highly recommended snack. Fun for all the family!

Edinburgh Castle Sticker Guide (Historic Scotland)
1900989018 £2.95
Bring the castle to life with this fun activity book.

Illustration by Aileen Paterson from
Maisie comes to Morningside

Ages 9+ Fiction

BRESLIN, THERESA

Bullies At School
Kelpie pb 0862415055 £3.50

Siobhan learns a valuable lesson in this story that doubles as a guide to dealing with bullies.

Homecoming for Kezzie
Mammoth pb 0749725923 £3.99

Kezzie may return to Canada, but right now Scotland needs her and she needs it. Set immediately before the Second World War, this is a wonderfully written and moving sequel to Kezzie.

New School Blues
Kelpie pb 0862414083 £2.99

Mary is smart and she is starting secondary school. Parents and teachers show their true colours in this funny story of growing-up.

Simon's Challenge
Kelpie pb 0862412706 £3.50

Can Simon, our hero, save the day in this exciting detective novel? This book won a First Novel Award for the author who is arguably Scotland's best children's fiction writer today.

Whispers in the Graveyard
Mammoth pb 0749723882 £3.50

This dark psychological drama is about a dyslexic boy and the courage he displays to overcome his frustration with the world. The material is skilfully dealt with in this book which deservedly won the Carnegie Medal.
Different Directions
Kelpie pb 0862415578 £2.99
Kezzie
Mammoth pb 0749717718 £3.99

BROWN, GEORGE MACKAY

Pictures in the Cave
Kelpie pb 0862413184 £2.50

Sigurd lives on an island which has a mysterious cave of black enchantment, found in the Bay of Seals. No-one dares enter it because of a terrible spell that was put on it hundreds of years ago. But one day Sigurd plays truant, and decides to go into the cave. There, he finds out the true story of the island from the seal-folk. A collection of stories full of imagination and wonder. (10+)

DERWENT, LAVINIA

Sula
Kelpie pb 0862410681 £3.50

Magnus MacDuff has a talent, but will the new teacher on the remote west coast island of Sula be able to make this wild boy realise it? An enchanting tale which lights up the world of nature.

The Tale of Greyfriars Bobby
Puffin pb 0140311815 £3.99

Another version of the story of the faithful terrier who kept watch by his master's grave.

FIDLER, KATHLEEN

Desperate Journey
Kelpie pb 0862410568 £3.50

This family's story of the Sutherland Clearances will strike a chord with many. A 'rites of passage' story that takes them from their beloved home across the Atlantic to Canada.

The Droving Lad
Kelpie pb 0862412544 £2.99

A thrilling adventure about a young boy and his first cattle drove, which leads him from the Highlands to the Lowlands of Scotland.

Escape In Darkness
Kelpie pb 0862411572 £2.99
Seal Story
Kelpie pb 0862411955 £2.99

HUNTER, MOLLIE

A Stranger Came Ashore
Kelpie pb 0862414652 £3.50

Tragic and gripping to the end, this eerie story set in Shetland tells of a shipwreck which causes one family's lives to change forever. Mollie Hunter has written many other historical novels for this age range.

MCLEAN, ALLAN CAMPBELL

A Sound of Trumpets
Kelpie pb 862410959 £1.80

Allan Campbell McLean's books are about what it was really like to live in the Highlands of the past and they are based on true events. This book set in the 19th century follows on from *'Ribbon Of Fire'* and tells of the severe problems faced by Alasdair Stewart and the other islanders when their new lairds turn out to be tyrants who make impossible demands. The islanders think up a daring plot, but will it work or will they have to leave their homes? Find out in this action-packed adventure. (10+)

Wayland: Scottish History Series (*some of the titles are published in conjunction with BBC Education*).

DARGIE, RICHARD

The Romans In Scotland (paperboards)
075021550X £10.99
The Vikings In Scotland (paperboards)
0750215704 £9.50

These two books show the effects that the Romans and Vikings had on the native Scottish culture as they invaded and/or settled on the harsh terrain.

DARGIE, RICHARD

Scottish Castles Through History (pbd)
0750220562 £10.99
(pb) 0750221488 £4.99

A chronological look at the architectural development of Scottish castles with insights into the people who lived in them and the legends that surrounded them. Well illustrated, with photographs and drawings accompanying the lively text.

SPANKIE, MARI

Bruce's Scotland (pbd)
0750212322 £9.99

Provides a lively account of this crucial time in the history of both Scotland and England.

ROSE, IAIN

The Union Of 1707 (pbd)
0750217480 £10.99

An informative look at the joining of the Scottish and English parliaments.
The Jacobites (pbd)
075021516X £10.99
(pb) 0750221925 £5.99

Provides an interesting insight into the Uprising of 1745 and the life of Bonnie Prince Charlie.

FOLEY, KATHRYN

Victorian Scotland (pbd)
0750219629 £10.99

We all know how much Queen Victoria loved to visit Scotland, and this book uses extracts from her journal to illustrate this fact.

ROSE, IAIN & MACLEAN, DONALD

Children of Coal and Iron (pbd)
0750217898 £11.99

Tells of the shaping of Scotland as an industrial nation.

GUNN, DONALD et al

Life During The Highland Clearances (pbd)
0750215321 £9.99

The retelling of what went on in this tragic time, and where the thousands of families re-located to.

DARGIE, RICHARD

Scotland In World War II (pbd)
0750218746 £10.99

A look at the contributions Scottish people made to the war.

Merlins
(an imprint of Canongate books) have published a series of 'Scottish History' books. The best of these four titles is:

HUNTER, JOHN
Mary Stuart
Canongate pb 0862416566 £4.99

This expertly brings the troubled queen's story to life and tells the true tale of one of history's best loved monarchs.

Scotties Series
(HMSO/National Museums of Scotland):

Jarvie, Gordon
Clans
HMSO pb0114953015 £4.50

Galloway, Fhiona (Ill.)
Discovering Scottish Plants
HMSO pb 0114957606 £4.50

Galloway, Fhiona (Ill.)
Exploring Scottish Seashores
HMSO pb 0114952728 £4.50

Galloway, Fhiona (Ill.)
Festivals In Scotland
HMSO pb011495271X £3.95

Steel, Ewan (Ill.)
The Jacobites
HMSO pb 0114952507 £4.50

Philip, Carrie (Ill.)
Mary, Queen Of Scots
HMSO pb 11494265X £4.50

Philip, Carrie (Ill.)
The Romans In Scotland
HMSO pb 114942773 £4.50
Travelling Scotland:
Story Of Transport
HMSO pb 0114942641 £3.95

Salgado, A. (Ill.)
Saints of Scotland
HMSO pb 0114952515 £4.50

Whelan, Olwyn (Ill.)
Scottish Castles
HMSO pb 0114942765 £4.50

Salgado, A. (Ill.)
Scotland's Kings and Queens
HMSO pb 0114957533 £4.50

Ellery, Craig (Ill.)
Scottish Rocks and Fossils
HMSO pb 0114952736 £4.50

Jarvie, Gordon
Vikings In Scotland
HMSO pb 0114958130 £5.99

These books cover similar areas to the Wayland series but from an activity-based perspective. There are experiments to do, puzzles to solve and games to play, in this altogether interactive selection, with busy and informative illustrations throughout. Children will have great fun learning about Scotland's heritage, natural history and culture.

Classics

CAMERON, A.D.

Discover Scotland's History
S.C.P. pb 1898218765 £9.95

A beginner's guide to Scottish history designed specifically for children, tourists and novice historians.

FLEMING, MAURICE

The Real Macbeth & Other Stories From Scottish History
Mercat Press pb 1873644701 £6.99

Specially written to bring Scottish history to life for the younger reader, these illustrated accounts of the past balance tales of action and adventure with stories about scientific discovery and everyday life.

MCGEOCH, BRIAN & PORCH, STEVEN

Looking At Scottish Art
Wayland 0750217499 £10.99

This is one of a kind - studying the lives and work of Scotland's artists.

ATKINSON, ELEANOR

Greyfriars Bobby
Puffin pb 014036742X £4.50

The tale of the Skye terrier who devotedly made his way to his master's grave every night for fourteen years has become part of Edinburgh folklore. Greyfriars Bobby is a true story, and Eleanor Atkinson's book telling of Bobby's many adventures, as he sets out to reach the graveyard, is now regarded as a children's classic.

BALLANTYNE, ROBERT M. (1825-1894)

R.M. Ballantyne wrote several novels which were the very essence of a Victorian boy's adventures. He was the nephew of John and James Ballantyne, the Scottish printers who first published Walter Scott's work, and his own books were heavily influenced by Scott. Ballantyne joined the Hudson Bay Company in 1841 and worked in Canada. His first book, *The Young Fur Trader*, was highly autobiographical. He went on to produce several other very popular boys' adventure stories, the most famous being *The Coral Island*, and wrote an autobiography, *Personal Reminiscences in Book Making*. His highly stylised, patriotic adventure stories full of tales of chivalric men expanding the glorious British Empire now seem incredibly dated and very much a product of their time.

The Coral Island
OUP pb 0192826441 £4.99

GRAHAME, KENNETH (1859–1932)

Born in Edinburgh to affluent parents, Kenneth Grahame was sent to Berkshire after his mother died when he was aged five. After his education he took up a job in the Bank of England, eventually becoming Secretary. He is best remembered for his children's classic *The Wind In The Willows,* a wonderful mixture of picnics, crazy escapades, river bank life and colourful characters that has spawned stage and film versions not to mention several excellent follow-up books written by other authors. *The Golden Age* and *Dream Days* were very popular when first published. They tell of the adventures and fantasies of five children who live in the countryside, showing the difference between their imaginative play and the real world of the adults around them. Kenneth Grahame died in Pangbourne in 1932.

Dream Days
Wordsworth pb 1853261661
£1.00
The Golden Age
Wordsworth pb 1853261521
£1.00
The Wind In The Willows
Mandarin pb 0749336706
£7.99

STEVENSON, ROBERT L.

Stevenson's most accessible works are available in children's editions. *Treasure Island,* that tale of awesome adventure on the high seas with Long John Silver and Jim Hawkins, still as popular today as it ever was, is complete and unabridged in the Puffin classic edition (8+) The Everyman edition includes the distinctive illustrations of Mervyn Peake. *Kidnapped,* another Puffin Classic, is yet another thrilling historical adventure, describing the adventures of David Balfour in the 18th century. The third Stevenson title in Puffin Classics is the macabre yet brilliant story of *Dr Jekyll and Mr Hyde* which will send shivers down your spine as the double life of Dr. Jekyll unfolds.

Dr Jekyll And Mr Hyde
Puffin Classic pb 0140367640
£3.99
Kidnapped
Puffin Classic pb 0140366903
£3.50
Treasure Island
Puffin Classic pb 0140366725
£2.99
Treasure Island
Everyman cloth 1857159098
£7.99

Poetry

Wee Willie Winkie: And Other Nursery Rhymes For Small Children
Scottish Children's Press
pb 189982717X £4.95

Traditional rhymes and songs that will take ye back, or if you've never been there, will take ye there! A great selection illustrated with lovely line drawings by Aberdeen schoolchildren.

HUGHES, TED

Nessie the Mannerless Monster
Faber pb 0571162134 £2.99

Nessie is fed up with being told she doesn't exist so she heads off to London for an audience with the Queen. The story is told by Ted Hughes in verse.

ROSE, DILYS

When I Wear My Leopard Hat: Poems For Young Children
Scottish Children's Press
pb 1899827706 £3.99

Some of these original poems are silly and some are serious. An accessible collection which many will enjoy.

STEVENSON, ROBERT LOUIS

A Child's Garden of Verses
Mainstream hb 1851583912 £9.99

This elegantly produced facsimile of R.L. Stevenson's marvellous collection of verse is a lasting treasure. It is exquisitely illustrated by Charles Robinson in beautiful 'arts and crafts' style, and appears exactly as it was when published over a century ago.

A Child's Garden of Verses
Gollancz pb 024113918X £6.99

This dreamily inspired watercolour edition is illustrated by one of Britain's foremost artists, Michael Foreman. His prize-winning style cannot help but capture the imagination.

A Child's Garden of Verses
Puffin Classic pb 014036692X £2.99

Robert Louis Stevenson

Travel

If you've got the travelling bug and the enthusiasm to see Scotland's stunning hills and glens, there are a few guides that you just cannot leave home without. *Scotland For Kids* by **Anne Shade** (Mainstream hb, 1851586792, £9.99) will save the day and keep boredom at bay. It is a mine of information on restaurants, places to stay, activities, sites of interest and much, much more. It is indeed *the* family guide. For the kids themselves, they will delight in *Tin-Tin's Travel Diaries* by **Martine Noblet** (Barron pb, 0812092384, £4.50), in which the French hero dons a kilt and shows you the best of Scotland's history and scenery. *I-Spy Scotland* (Michelin pb, 1856711293, £1.25) will not fail to keep you amused. Get your walking shoes on!

Cookery

ASHWORTH, LIZ
Teach the Bairns to Cook
Scottish Children's Press pb 1899827234 £5.95

Ever wanted to know how stovies are made? Or why haggis is eaten on Rabbie Burns' Night? . . . This traditional Scottish recipe book for beginners tells it all and how to make it.

Biography

MCNAIR, ELISABETH
Robert Burns: Maker Of Rhymes
Viking pb 0670868388 £6.99

This book tells of the poet's life, and all the tradition surrounding Burns' Night is explained.

Cookery

Food & Drink - Scottish Writing
by Kerstie Howell, Waterstone's, George Street, Edinburgh

Food writing in the UK is currently enjoying a phenomenal boom with cultural boundaries cast aside in the voracious pursuit of new flavours and styles to tempt the British palate. In Scotland this is especially evident with a tantalising mix of traditional and modern to flambé the imaginative talents of the country's established authors as well as many new writers. The direction of Scottish food writing is based on the relationship between the sturdy anchor of cherished recipes and native ingredients and the strong Eurasian slant of the TV chef generation.

As cookbooks themselves become glossier, more ambitious and more expensive there remains a wholesome earthiness to many Scottish publications, awash with tartan, the strains of pipes and a dollop of fine sea mist, as well as some of the finest international cuisine. In this traditional mould are **Judy Paterson's** three slender volumes of hearty Scottish fare:-

Scottish Home Baking (Lindsay pb, 1898169004, £4.95)

Scottish Home Cooking (Lindsay pb, 1898169039, £4.95)

The Scottish Cook (Birlinn pb, 1874744351, £4.99)

Complete with tartan and thistle page-trim, these endearingly simple, concise and yet surprisingly expansive books cover a wide range of Scottish dishes. Inexpensive, simple food is reflected in the style of these tiny, well written books. In the same vein is *Scottish Country Recipes* (Country Pub. hb, 1874661006, £3.99) - part of a series of regional cookery writing, simply explained in a no-frills hardback format.

More comprehensive guides and useful reference tools are *Scottish Cookery* by **Catherine Brown** (Chambers pb, 0550200061, £5.99) and *Traditional Scottish Cookery* by **Theodora Fitzgibbon** (Souvenir pb, 0285630652, £8.50) - packed with diverse variations of native recipes, these are similar in outlook and format. Scottish produce and techniques are the key factors and both books are classics for the cook with a passion for real food in unshakably Scottish mould.

One of the greatest exponents of Scots cuisine is **Florence Marian McNeill**. A writer who was first published in 1920, her most popular books are *Recipes From Scotland* (Gordon Wright pb, 0903065797, £7.95) and *The Scots Kitchen* (Mercat Press pb, 187364423X, £9.99). Firmly traditional she remains the best selling Scottish cookery writer this century.

A cookbook rooted in the traditional with a North-East twist is the *Grampian Cookbook* by **Gladys Menhinick** (Mercat Press pb, 1873644221, £6.99). Containing over 200 recipes, many with American overtones, this is a concise, simple regional favourite.

A book which takes a different slant is the mainly historical *The Laird's Kitchen: Three Hundred Years of Food in Scotland* by **Olive M. Geddes** (N.L.S./H.M.S.O. hb, 0114952302, £18.95). The stories behind the Scottish relationship with food over three centuries are evocatively brought to life. In a highly illustrated and well researched book, Geddes opens the lid on eating habits across the classes and eras of a nation.

The Haggis: A Little History by **Clarissa Dickson Wright** (Appletree Press hb, 0862816351, £4.99) is a pocket-sized morsel of Scotland's most famous national dish. This slim volume by one half of the 'Two Fat Ladies' pays homage to the haggis. While it includes no actual recipes, the book's amusing style and tongue-in-cheek cartoon-like illustrations make for a popular if undemanding jaunt through the world of a dish which is archetypally Scottish. Another unusual history of Scottish food is **Wallace Lockhart's** *The Scots and their Oats* (Birlinn pb, 1874744807, £6.99), a funny yet very informative look at Scottish history and culture with reference to diet. Including illustrations, poems and anecdotes, this volume tells you everything you need to know about the Scots and their eating habits.

Other titles worth mentioning in the traditional style include:-
A Year In A Scots Kitchen by **Catherine Brown** (Neil Wilson pb, 1897784791, £9.99)
Broths To Bannocks: Cooking In Scotland From 1690 To The Present Day by **Catherine Brown** (John Murray pb, 0719549884, £11.95)
Game For All With A Flavour Of Scotland by **Nichola Fletcher** (Gollancz pb, 0575053054, £8.99)
Feast Of Scotland by **J. Warren** (Lomond pb, 0947782958, £5.00)
Scottish Recipes (HarperCollins hb, 0004721675, £4.99)
Favourite Scottish Recipes by **Johanna Mathie** (Salmon pb, 189843512X, 99p)
Scottish Tea-Time Recipes by **Johanna Mathie** (Salmon pb, 1898435189, 99p)

Vegetarianism is perhaps the most under-represented field of food writing in Scotland, despite a marked swing in popular tastes away from meat-centred cooking. Ironically though, Scotland has produced one of the standards of vegan cookery writing, a field which is the most neglected of all:
Rainbows And Wellies by **J. Redding & T. Weston** (Findhorn Press hb, 1899171303, £14.95). This is a cookery book with a difference, packed with gourmet vegan dishes designed to tie in with various Scottish ceremonial occasions. The dishes are simple, well-presented and studiously avoid the wholemeal pastry and brown rice school of vegetarian cookery, opting instead for taste and luxury.

Glasgow Greens by **Kathryn Hamilton** (Neil Wilson pb, 1897784112, £5.99) is a vegetarian book with a completely fresh international flavour. It is an inventive collection of recipes which would fit well into any kitchen.

While traditionalism remains a strong staple within Scottish food writing, there is an exciting new wave of internationalism which blurs the line between native roots and adventurous world cooking. Probably the pivotal writer is **Claire MacDonald** whose many highly praised and widely respected books are seen as the bridge between old and new. From her family-run hotel and restaurant on Skye, she has produced a collection of themed paperbacks covering a broad spectrum of cooking styles and dishes. Her own style is uncluttered and accessible, encouraging the freedom to experiment with flavours and techniques. Sometimes dubbed 'the

Delia Smith of the North', Lady Claire MacDonald of MacDonald has carved her own formidable niche in Scottish cookery. Titles include:

Celebrations (Corgi pb, 0552994367, £7.99)

Lunches (Corgi pb, 0552144282, £6.99)

Suppers (Corgi pb, 0552142093, £6.99)

Sweet Things (Corgi pb, 0552992178, £6.99)

Seasonal Cooking (Corgi pb, 0552998044, £6.99)

More Seasonal Cooking (Corgi pb, 0552992887, £5.99)

Delicious Fish (HarperCollins pb, 0586206248, £5.99)

The Claire Macdonald Cookbook (Bantam hb, 0593042689, £25.00)

Claire Macdonald's Scotland: The Best of Scottish Food and Drink
(Little, Brown pb, 0316878901, £10.99)

Sue Lawrence, winner of BBC Master Chef 1991, creates a feast of inspired dinner and supper party menus in *Entertaining at Home in Scotland* (Mainstream hb, 1851584099, £12.99), a 1990s' approach to enhancing domestic cookery from all the Scottish regions.

Most high profile of all is TV cook Nick Nairn whose books include:

Wild Harvest (BBC Books pb, 0563383046, £9.99)

Wild Harvest 2 (BBC Books hb, 0563383186, £15.99)

Chicken, Duck and Game (Weidenfeld & Nicolson pb, 0297822845, £1.99)

Nick Nairn Cooks the Main Course (BBC Books pb, 0563384123, £4.99)

Building on the success of his earlier books Nick Nairn has taken to the coastal waters of Scotland's islands in search of the most unusual, freshest ingredients in *Island Harvest* (BBC Books hb, 0563384220, £16.99), a glossy collection of recipes with succulent close-up photography and a dash of Nairn's Euro-Scots flair.
With a growing reputation for extraordinarily tasty food, La Potiniere restaurant has far more than a cult following among residents of Lothian. *La Potiniere and Friends* by owners **David** and **Hillary Brown** (Harmony Pub. hb, 0952369702, £16.99) captures the simple spirit and finely crafted cuisine with a disticly Franco-Scottish flavour for which they are famous throughout Scotland and beyond. Not perhaps for the budget cook or the novice, this is a special occasion book to be savoured - well-balanced and as appetising as the food itself. **Alison Johnson's** *A House By The Shore/Scarista Style* (Warner pb, 0751523364, £8.99) is likewise linked to a particular eating establishment, this time a hotel on Harris. This is an omnibus edition that contains two separate but linked books. The first is the story of Andrew and Alison

Johnson's retreat from urban life, and their efforts to turn a run-down former manse on Harris into an award-winning gourmet delight of a hotel. The second is a collection of Alison's recipes that have made the hotel so famous.

Scottish writing on the subject of drink is confined largely to whisky, from indispensable fact files for the connoisseur to slickly glossy coffee-table books mixing colourful history and the distinctive flavour of the nation's favourite tipple. Scotland has a long thriving tradition of writing on the subject and a clutch of authors boasting international reputations.
Among the best are:-

Scotch And Water: An Illustrated Guide to the Hebridean Malt Whisky Distilleries by **Neil Wilson** (Neil Wilson pb, 1897784589, £9.99). This classic cult book on malt whisky charts the voyage of a group of young Scots who sailed through the Hebrides on a 38ft ketch. Their aim was to meet the locals and visit and partake of the produce of every distillery on Islay, Jura, Mull and Skye, recording their histories as they went. The book contains many photographs as well as maps of the island areas, and is a celebration of the people, land and whisky industry of these rugged and beautiful islands.

The Original Malt Whisky Almanac 7th ed. by **Wallace Milroy** (Neil Wilson hb, 1897784686, £7.99) is a taster's guide to whisky providing a region to region, distillery to distillery, malt by malt guide to Scottish whisky. Details of distillery opening times and facilities are listed, not to mention a list of which malts best suit specific foods. Wallace Milroy won the 1987 Whisky Writer of the Year award and is regarded as one of the world's foremost whisky connoisseurs.

Michael Jackson is also widely recognised as an authority on Scotch whisky. His *World Guide To Whisky* (Dorling Kindersley hb, 0863182372, £19.99) is a commanding guide to the whiskies of the world, with a large Scottish section. Described by the *Glasgow Herald* as 'the Baedeker of Booze', it contains descriptions of every single malt and up-to-date background information on the various distilleries that produce them.

More famous is his small but perfectly formed *Malt Whisky Companion* (Dorling Kindersley hb, 0751301469, £12.99). Broadly regional and sparingly illustrated this guide details virtually all malts in Scotland, with tasting notes, tips, and marks out of 100. A very personal outlook and a modern classic.

A visual feast for any whisky lover is provided by *Scotland: The Land & The Whisky* by **Roddy Martine** (John Murray hb, 0719553512, £29.95), published in association with

The Keepers Of The Quaich. Complete with numerous photographs by Patrick Douglas-Hamilton, this extensive book looks at the many aspects of whisky: its links to the land, its history and today's famous distilleries.

The Whisky Trail by **Gordon Brown** (Prion hb, 1853751219, £14.95) is a geographical guide to the distilleries and flavours of Scottish regions, while **Brian Townsend's** *Scotch Missed: The Lost Distilleries* (Neil Wilson pb, 1897784538, £7.99) takes a historical look at the same subject. During Victorian times there were many major distilleries which sadly no longer exist. Brian Townsend details the remains of these old distilleries, using meticulous research to bring to life a normally unexplored area of Scottish industrial heritage. He includes records from these Victorian wonders and information about where you might locate bottles of their whisky.

In *Still Life With Bottle: Whisky According To Ralph Steadman* (Ebury Press pb, 0091820243, £9.99) the well-known artist illustrates his own whisky trail. He travelled the length and breadth of Scotland to create this book, finally producing an informative and eccentric tour of the malt whiskies of Scotland, heavily illustrated in his own inimitable fashion.

Scotch Whisky: Its Past And Present by **David Daiches** (Birlinn pb, 187474436X, £4.99) is a combination of social and economic history on the water of life that includes a section of personal tasting notes. As much a celebration of Scotch whisky as a guide book, it contains much of interest to drinkers of the beloved Uisge Beatha. *Malt Whisky* by **Charles Maclean** (Mitchell Beazley hb, 1857326830, £25.00), a superior coffee-table book, provides an in-depth and informative guide to the classic malts and their surprisingly far-flung origins. The book balances the chemistry, artistry and cultural and financial importance of Scotland's most famous export. Charles Maclean is a passionate advocate for the fine art of tasting. While *Malt Whisky* is probably his most accessible work, he is also author of a number of other titles, including:

Pocket Guide To Whisky (Mitchell Beazley hb, 1840000228, £8.99). This guide is packed with information on all the aspects necessary for a full appreciation of the 'water of life'. Most useful is the directory of producers and brands which covers the length and breadth of Scotland. A must-have book for beginner and connoisseur alike.

Other books of interest to lovers of whisky include:-

Discovering Scotch Whisky (New Lifestyle pb, 186095006X, £7.99)

Scotch Whisky (Pitkin pb, 085372797X, £2.50)

Scottish Toasts And Graces (Appletree Press hb, 0862813948, £4.99)

The Original Guide To Scotch Whisky by **Michael Brander** (Gleneil Press pb, 0952533006, £4.99)

Cooking With Scotch Whisky by **Rosalie Gow** (Gordon Wright hb, 090306572X, £6.95)

Whisky And Scotland by **Neil Gunn** (Souvenir pb, 028563433X, £8.99)

Scots on Scotch: The Scotch Malt Whisky Society Book of Whisky edited by **Phillip Hills** (Mainstream hb, 1851584161, £14.99)

Scotch: The Whisky of Scotland in Fact and Story. 7th ed. by **Sir R. Bruce Lockhart** (Neil Wilson pb, 1897784376, £7.99)

Tales of Whisky and Smuggling by **Stuart McHardy** (House Of Lochar hb, 0984403861, £9.99)

The Malt Whisky File by **R. Tucek & J. Lamond** (Canongate hb, 0862416507, £9.99)

For those who prefer tipples other than the national drink, **F. Marian McNeill's** *The Scots Cellar* (Mercat Press pb, 0948403683, £6.99) will be of interest. The book portrays a nation's tradition of hospitality and libation, also painting a picture of the social and drinking customs of the 1950s, when it was first written. Recipes for traditional drinks to suit all tastes are included. Wine enthusiasts who would like to know more about this drink's history should try *Knee Deep In Claret* by **B. Kay & C. Maclean** (Birlinn pb, 0952362600, £9.95). In 1692 over a third of Edinburgh's income came from duty on wine. This unusual history looks at the Auld Alliance between France and Scotland, and the particular role played by wine. The Scots' 700 year old love of wine had major social and economic effects on the country and this book reveals them all.

". . . in Scotland, to challenge the position of drink as a consideration to which priority must unfailingly be granted appears, if not unmanly, at least anti-life."
John Herdman

Drama / Film & Screenplays

Film

BRUCE, DAVID

Scotland - The Movie
Polygon pb 074866209X
£14.99

The film industry in Scotland
has been enjoying a
resurgence with films such
as *Rob Roy, Braveheart,
Trainspotting* and *Shallow
Grave* doing big business.
This guide to a century of
cinema in Scotland includes
actors, anecdotes and a full
filmography of films made
or set in Scotland.

PETER, BRUCE

100 Years of Glasgow's Amazing Cinemas
Polygon pb 0748662103 £12.99

From 1897 onwards Glasgow has had a continuing love affair
with cinema, with more attendances per head of population
than any other city in Britain. In this comprehensive volume
Bruce Peter looks at the history of the cinema there: the
entrepreneurs, patrons, and especially the remarkable cinema
buildings that were built to accommodate Glasgow's desire to
watch movies.

Drama & Screenplays

Two general books on Scottish theatre are Donald Campbell's **Playing For Scotland: A History of the Scottish Stage 1715-1965** (Mercat Press pb 1873644574 £9.99) and Bill Findlay's **A History of Scottish Theatre** (Polygon pb 0748662200 £11.99). The first is the history of Scottish drama told through the achievements of pioneering figures such as Allan Ramsay, who founded his theatre in Edinburgh in 1736 in the face of severe opposition; Jessie Ryder, who was instrumental in establishing theatre in Scotland in the early 1800s; and Donald Macrae, who built his formidable reputation on the stage of Glasgow's Citizens' Theatre. The book is full of entertaining anecdotes, providing a lively and colourful history of the Scottish stage. The second is a comprehensive, illustrated guide to the history of Scottish theatre, which includes information on companies, buildings, actors and trends both historical and modern.

BARRIE, J.M. (1860–1937)

Peter Pan And Other Plays
OUP pb 0192825720 £6.99

During his lifetime J.M. Barrie was one of the most popular and successful dramatists around. Apart from Peter Pan his dramatic works have not survived well, due in part to their close connection to the times in which they were written and also to Barrie's sentimentality. However, they are not without value. *The Admirable Crichton* for example is a humorous play about a family being shipwrecked and their butler becoming the island's dictator, while *Mary Rose* tells of a dead mother's love for her son. The Oxford edition includes *The Admirable Crichton, Peter Pan, What Every Woman Knows* and *Mary Rose*.

"You Scots, Mrs Shand, are such a mixture of the practical and the emotional that you escape out of an Englishman's hand like a trout."

J.M. Barrie, What Every Woman Knows

BYRNE, JOHN

Colquhoun & Macbryde
Faber pb 0571169597 £4.99
The Slab Boys (Screenplay)
Faber pb 0571192548 £7.99

This inventive dramatist and gifted artist was born in Paisley. He trained at Glasgow School of Art, and after a period as a highly successful artist went on to design stage sets, which introduced him to the world of theatre. His first play, *Writer's Cramp*, was staged at the Edinburgh Festival Fringe in 1977. His own early work experience in a local carpet factory was to be the inspiration for his next play, *The Slab Boys*, a very funny and meaningful story about a group of young men and their responses to factory life. This was followed by two more plays following the fortunes of the 'Slab Boys', *Cuttin' A Rug* and *Still Life*. Byrne is also known for his highly popular and acclaimed TV series, *Tutti Frutti*, which was followed by the equally successful *Your Cheatin' Heart*. In 1992 he returned to the theatre with the play *Colquhoun and Macbryde*.

CONN, STEWART

The Aquarium
Calder pb 0714535605 £4.95
The Burning
Calder pb 0714508322 £4.95

Poet Stewart Conn is also a playwright, drama producer, and writer of screen and TV plays. *The Aquarium* contains three Glasgow plays: *The Aquarium, The Man In The Green Muffler* and *I Didn't Always Live Here. The Burning* like McLellan's *Jamie The Saxt*, is a historical play about James VI and concerns his relationship with his cousin, Francis Bothwell. It bears favourable comparison with McLellan's work.

FORSYTH, BILL

Gregory's Girl (Screenplay)
C.U.P. pb 0521388384 £4.75

The screenplay of the humorous coming-of-age movie set in Cumbernauld that put Bill Forsyth on the map and established the career of John Gordon Sinclair.

GLOVER, SUE

Bondagers & The Straw Chair
Methuen pb 0413712109 £9.99

Bondagers won the LWT Plays On Stage Award 1990. It is a haunting work that gives a powerful voice to the women who were used as cheap agricultural labour in the Borders during the last century. *The Straw Chair* is set in the first half of the 18th century and follows Isabel and her minister husband as they arrive on St. Kilda. As they encounter the island's inhabitants, particularly the disturbing figure of Rachel of Grange, events are set in motion which will change their lives for ever. Glover's ear for dialogue and eye for character combine to create fully formed worlds in these plays which reveal her dynamic style.

HODGE, JOHN

A Life Less Ordinary (Screenplay)
Faber pb 0571192815 £7.99
Trainspotting & Shallow Grave (Screenplay)
Faber pb 0571179681 £9.99

The screenplays behind two of Britain's most successful films, both set in Scotland.

KELMAN, JAMES

Hardie And Baird and Other Plays
Secker & Warburg pb 0436232898 £7.99

The acclaimed *Hardie And Baird* is set in the turbulent days of the doomed weavers' rebellion in 1820. It explores the tensions between the two very different but equally principled radical leaders as they wait in their prison cells for their eventual execution. The book includes two of Kelman's shorter plays: *The Busker* and *In The Night*. All three works are rich in the hard-edged language of Glasgow.

LINDSAY, SIR DAVID

Ane Satyre of the Thrie Estaitis
Canongate pb 0862411912
£4.99

First performed in the 16th century, this work is the first great Scottish play. It is a telling satirical piece that exposes the vice and corruption present in the spiritual and secular society of Lindsay's time. A potent work that uses comedy to bring serious matters to the fore, its importance in Scottish literature is crucial.

LOCHHEAD, LIZ

Mary Queen of Scots Got Her Head Chopped Off/Dracula
Penguin pb 0140482202 £6.99

As a playwright Liz Lochhead has been interested in several themes, particularly historical figures and their connection and relevance to modern times. This book contains a reworking of the tragic tale of Mary Queen of Scots, exploring the difficulties of combining public duties and freedom. The second play is a stage adaptation of Bram Stoker's famous novel.

MACDONALD, SHARMAN

Sharman MacDonald Plays 1
Faber pb 0571176216 £8.99

This volume contains four of Sharman MacDonald's award-winning plays: *When I Was A Girl, I Used To Scream And Shout; When We Were Women; The Winter Guest; and Borders Of Paradise.*
All Things Nice
Faber pb 0571164293 £4.99
Shades
Faber pb 0571168841 £4.99

MACDONALD, SHARMAN & RICKMAN, ALAN

The Winter Guest (Screenplay)
Faber pb 0571194796 £7.99

This screenplay is set in a small Scottish seaside town. The weather is bitterly cold, the ocean frozen over. The plot follows a day in the life of some of the town's residents. The screenplay is poetic, humorous and carefully crafted.

MCGRATH, JOHN

Six-Pack: Plays For Scotland
Polygon pb 0748662014 £12.99

A collection of works from one of Scotland's favourite playrights. His plays are hugely enjoyable with strong political overtones. Included here are *Joe's Drum, Border Warfare, Blood Red Roses,* and his best known work *The Cheviot, The Stag And The Black, Black Oil.*

The Cheviot, The Stag And The Black, Black Oil
Methuen pb 0413488802 £6.99

A rollicking, radical review of the past 200 years of Highland history focusing on the lack of popular control of resources, especially the land. Told through a highly entertaining blend of facts, songs, stories and jokes, the play was a massive critical and popular success and became a blueprint for left-wing theatre in the 70s and 80s.

MCLELLAN, ROBERT

Collected Plays Volume One
Calder pb 0714538183 £5.99

Robert McLellan is the best-known modern Scottish historical playwright, and his plays are frequently performed and studied in schools. This collection contains the plays *Torwatletie, The Carlin Moth, The Changeling, Jamie The Saxt* and *The Flouers 'o Edinburgh. Jamie The Saxt,* his first major play, is set during the turbulent final decade of the 16th century, when Lord Bothwell was threatening the throne of his cousin, James VI. The king is the main character, and throughout the work McLellan reveals the contradictions within his personality. The play is of note for several reasons, not least its humour and the sharp dialogue, delivered in a robust and lively Scots.

MALLIN, TOM

Curtains
Calder pb 0714507938 £3.95

The work of Scottish-born Tom Mallin has been compared to that of American dramatist Edward Albee. This play examines a three-sided relationship and an unhappy marriage.

MOWAT, DAVID

The Others
Calder pb 0714508462 £4.95

David Mowat first premiered at The Traverse in Edinburgh, and his plays have been widely performed in smaller theatres. In *The Others* a tyrannical father evokes ghostly strangers to establish his authority.

ROSTAND, EDMOND

Cyrano De Bergerac (trans. E. Morgan)
Carcanet pb 185754028X £6.95

Edwin Morgan's translation into devilish Glaswegian of Rostand's masterwork. It relays the bitter-sweet adventures of the swashbuckling French nobleman with a large proboscis, who falls in love with a beauty but can only express this love through another admirer whom he coaches.

ROSIE, GEORGE

Carlucco and The Blasphemer
Chapman pb 0906772435 £8.50

In these two award-winning plays which explore crucial moments in Scottish history, Rosie uses a flair for drama and scholarship to great effect.

SMITH, SYDNEY GOODSIR

Colleckie Meg
Calder pb 0714510416 £5.99
The Wallace
Calder pb 0714540757 £4.95

As well as being a major poet, Sydney Goodsir Smith was a prominent playwright. *The Wallace* is a passionately nationalistic play written in verse, which succeeds largely due to this passion, the structure being weak in places. *Colleckie Meg* is a hilarious and bawdy account of Edinburgh low life in Smith's own pun-laden Scots brogue and is in effect a dramatic version of his comic novel *Carotid Cornucopious*.

VON TRIER, LARS

Breaking the Waves (Screenplay)
Faber pb 0571191150 £9.99

Lars Von Trier's movie is a harrowing and emotionally intense piece of work. The screenplay conveys much of its impact. Set in a devout religious community in the Outer Hebrides, the story of Bess is one of religious dogmatism, erotic obsession, and one person's salvation through another's degradation.

WELSH, IRVINE

The Acid House Trilogy: A Screenplay
Methuen pb 0413724204 £8.99

Welsh's own adaptation of *The Acid House* for television.

Fiction

An Introduction to Scottish Women Writers

by Val Simpson, Waterstone's, Stirling

As we approach the millennium it is useful to look back on Scottish literature and assess the impact of women writers and the role they have played in Scotland's new cultural Renaissance. 1997 belonged to the centenarian Naomi Mitchison while 1998 sees the 80th birthday of Muriel Spark, creator of the sublime Miss Brodie. However these are only two of the bright stars in the galaxy of Scottish women writers which stretches back beyond the present century.

Scotswomen have always been feisty, strong-willed, intelligent, and, when given the opportunity, equal partners with men in all walks of Scottish life. Looking at women writers in the 19th and 20th centuries we can see that the Scots were no gentle domestic biddies but strong and witty observers of the society around them.

One such observer is **Elizabeth Grant of Rothiemurchus** (1797-1885). In her *Highland Lady* journals she creates a fascinating if sometimes self-righteous portrait of her personal and family life through periods of tremendous national change. When this doughty lady was widowed shortly after her husband inherited an estate in Ireland, she raised her family and successfully managed the estate during the potato famine.

Another major Victorian writer who suffered personal tragedy was **Margaret Oliphant** (1828-97), widowed in 1857 after only five years of marriage. Through her writing she made a living, raising her own three children and caring for her widowed brother's family at the same time. She was a prolific writer who by the time of her death had written over a hundred novels including *The Chronicles Of Claringford* which earned her the sobriquet 'The Feminist Trollope'.

With the fine novelist/biographer, **Catherine Carswell** (1879-1946), we move into the 20th century. She made her reputation as a dramatic and literary critic, moving in circles which included Arnold Bennett and D.H. Lawrence as well as major artists and painters of her time, but she was also a fine biographer, portraying Burns (*The Life Of Robert Burns, 1930*), D. H. Lawrence (*The Savage Pilgrim, 1932*), and Boccaccio (*The Tranquil Heart, 1937*). As well as her own autobiography, *Lying Awake,* she wrote an autobiographical novel *Open The Door* which draws heavily on her experiences of growing up in Glasgow at the turn of the century.

Carswell's contemporary, **Willa Muir** (1890-1970), was likewise a brilliant novelist as well as being a translator, the intellectual equal of her husband Edwin Muir. Like him she was widely travelled and had a great aptitude for languages, but her writing was often overlooked and sometimes her work as a translator was unrecognised, although they often translated jointly, particularly great European writers like Kafka. After Muir's death she wrote *Belonging*, a moving tribute to their long and creative partnership. A collection of her work, *Imagined Selves*, has been published in the Canongate Classics series.

Another neglected writer whose work has been brought back to our attention in this series is **Nan Shepherd** (1893-1981). This fine novelist/critic wrote a series of novels, *The Quarry Wood, The Weatherhouse* and *A Pass In The Grampians*, which have been included in a collection of her works known as *Grampian Quartet.* Her portrayal of the narrow lives of the women of the North East, their potential stifled by society, makes an interesting contrast to Lewis Grassic Gibbon's famous Mearns trilogy, *A Scots Quair.*

In the 20th century there are numerous other major women writers including **Dorothy Dunnett, A.L. Kennedy, Janice Galloway, Liz Lochhead** and **Isla Dewar** to name but a few. Many are worthy successors to Oliphant, Grant and Carswell. However, despite this feast of new writing now available, it is still well worth looking back to the roots of female and feminist writing in Scotland and renewing our acquaintance with the feisty women writers of the past.

BANKS, IAIN

Iain Banks was born in Dunfermline, Fife, and now lives under the shadow of the Forth Road Bridge in a landscape surrounded by concrete defence emplacements from the Second World War both potent symbols that he has used in his work. He came to the public's attention with his controversial first novel *The Wasp Factory*. Gothic, often comic and very intense, it is the tale of a murderous young boy and his dysfunctional family. Banks has gone on to become one of Britain's finest modern writers, changing styles and genres from book to book. His science fiction novels are regarded as among the most innovative around, and mainstream works such as *The Bridge, The Crow Road, Complicity* and most recently *Song Of Stone*, have deservedly built him a huge and very loyal following. He is a natural story teller with a very visual style who is comfortable with many different writing techniques, and who has a strong interest in extreme situations. When asked to describe the difference between his fiction and science fiction works, he describes his fiction as being like piano compositions while his science fiction books are like grand organ works with all the stops pulled out. His work manages the difficult task of being hugely popular while also gaining critical acclaim.

The Bridge
Little, Brown pb 0349102155
£6.99
Canal Dreams
Little, Brown pb 034910171X
£6.99
Complicity
Little, Brown pb 0349105715
£6.99
The Crow Road
Little, Brown pb 0349103232
£7.99
Espedair Street
Little, Brown pb 0349102147
£6.99

Song Of Stone
Little, Brown hb 0316640166
£16.99
Walking On Glass
Little, Brown pb 0349101787
£6.99
The Wasp Factory
Little, Brown pb 0349101779
£6.99
Whit
Little, Brown pb 0349107688
£6.99

"It was the day my grandmother exploded"
Iain Banks, The Crow Road

BARKE, JAMES
(1905–1958)

James Barke shows a great affinity for land and people in this classic novel which follows the lives of David and Jean Ramsay and explores the horrifying nature of poverty at the turn of the century.
Land of the Leal
Canongate pb 0862411424
£7.99

BARKER, ELSPETH

Elspeth Barker's stunning debut has been compared to the work of the Brontes or Edgar Allan Poe. It does bear some resemblance to both but is very much written in her own voice. It is a Gothic tale set during the 1940s and 50s in a Scottish castle, and concerns the short life of Janet, a girl with her own unique outlook. The novel culminates in her murder, as the reader has been forewarned at the start. Full of vividly described passages, the novel has a distinctly un-settling and off-beat feel to it.
O Caledonia
Penguin pb 0140154728 £6.99

BARRIE, JAMES MATTHEW (1860–1937)

J.M. Barrie was born the son of a weaver in Kirriemuir, and was educated in Glasgow, Forfar and Dumfries before completing his studies at Edinburgh University. He moved to London in 1885 to work as a freelance journalist. It was while working as a journalist that he published *Auld Licht Idylls,* a series of short stories based on the village of his childhood, Kirriemuir, which he renamed Thrums in his fiction. He wrote numerous other works about the area including *A Window In Thrums, When A Man's Single* and *Sentimental Tommy,* and much of his fiction is as rooted in a particular landscape as the work of Hardy. Of his fiction only the later novel *Farewell Miss Julie Logan,* a love story with a Scottish setting, is in print. After finding huge success with his dramatic version of *The Little Minister* he started to write more for the theatre. He married the actress Mary Ansell in 1894 but they divorced a few years later. It was after this divorce that he befriended and ultimately adopted the five boys of Arthur and Sylvia Llewelyn Davis. His masterpiece of children's literature, *Peter Pan,* was put together from stories he created for the boys. The work is a clever, perceptive and accurate study of childhood, and many films, radio adaptations and stagings were to follow - indeed, it is often voted the most popular play ever written. Barrie gained numerous honours in his time, including being made Kirriemuir's only Freeman. He wrote many other plays and works of fiction which were popular but most of which are unjustly neglected these days. Barrie was a very gifted writer who nevertheless looks likely to be defined by just one work.

Farewell Miss Julie Logan
Scottish Academic Press pb 0707305764 £6.50

BELL, J.J. (1871–1934)

Wee MacGregor
Birlinn pb 1874744890 £5.99
2-for-1 banded set

Originally created by Bell for the columns of the Glasgow Evening Times, Wee MacGregor quickly came to epitomise the Glasgow working class way of life. A classic reprint of Scottish comedy that includes one of Bell's best stories, 'Courtin' Christina'.

BENZIE, ALEX

The Year's Midnight
Penguin pb 0140251308 £7.99

Alex Benzie's novel is set in a Scottish village. It starts near the end of the 18th century when the town's clocktower has been invaded by an angry mob and the clock destroyed after a man is unjustly hanged. A century later a gifted watchmaker is brought in to mend the now accursed clock. In the process he unknowingly releases a wave of hostility and hypocrisy upon the community. Elements of this book are loosely based on historical fact. Full of solid characterisation, the narrative's style is one of heightened realism and gained Benzie much acclaim.

BLAIR, EMMA

Emma Blair is one of the leading lights of British romantic fiction. Her books contain passion and tragedy in abundance, and her characters are carefully constructed and handled. *An Apple From Eden*, her latest hardback, is a reworking of Romeo and Juliet set on a Scottish estate just after World War II. Her most recent work in paperback is *Flower of Scotland* which tells the story of a whisky distilling family from Perthshire whose lives are forever altered by the outbreak of World War I.

An Apple From Eden
Little, Brown hb 0316882399 £16.99
The Blackbird's Tale
Little, Brown pb 0751505188 £5.99
The Daffodil Sea
Corgi pb 0553406140 £4.99
Flower of Scotland
Warner pb 0751516457 £5.99
Half Hidden
Warner pb 0751516007 £5.99
Hester Dark
Little, Brown pb 0751516678 £5.99
Jessie Gray
Warner pb 0751516651 £5.99
Maggie Jordan
Corgi pb 055340072X £4.99
A Most Determined Woman
Little, Brown pb 0751505196 £5.99
Nellie Wildchild
Little, Brown pb 0751516694 £5.99

Passionate Times Corgi pb 0553406159 £5.99
The Princess of Poor Street
Little, Brown pb 0751509353 £5.99
Street Song
Little, Brown pb 0751507849 £5.99
The Sweetest Thing
Corgi pb 0553403737 £4.99
This Side of Heaven
Little, Brown pb 0751516686 £5.99
The Water Meadows
Corgi pb 0553403729 £5.99
When Dreams Come True
Little, Brown pb 0751508713 £5.99
Where No Man Cries
Little, Brown pb 075151666X £5.99

BLAKE, GEORGE
(1893–1961)
The Shipbuilders
B & W pb 1873631251 £6.99

Blake's study of the effects of a Glasgow shipyard closure in the 30s and the shattering effect on the shipworkers is a sincere and authentic tale. His descriptions of the city itself and its occupants are superbly rendered, making this a fine portrait of the problems faced by a community at a time of industrial decline.

BOLTON, JESS
The Love of Highland Mary
Argyll pb 1874640017 £6.99

A fictionalised biography of the young Highland woman, Mary Campbell, who came to live as a servant in Ayrshire and was to fall in love with Burns, with dramatic and tragic consequences for her. She was immortalised in his song 'The Highland Lassie O.'

BROWN, GEORGE DOUGLAS (1869–1902)

Born in Ayrshire, the illegitimate son of a local farmer, he was educated locally and went to University in Glasgow and later Oxford. After his mother died in 1895 he moved to London to make a living as a journalist. His first book, *Love And A Sword*, a boy's own adventure set in the Afridi War, was published in 1899 under the pen-name Kennedy King. However he will be best remembered for *The House with the Green Shutters*, which he wrote as George Douglas. He died one year later, prematurely depriving Scotland of one of its most gifted writers. *The House with the Green Shutters* was hailed as a breakthrough in Scottish writing. Written as an unsentimental, hard-hitting book on the harshness of Scottish life and the petty jealousies of local communities, it contains a realism and psychological intensity not to be found in the couthy Kailyard school of Scottish writing, to which the book was a reaction. The book revolves around the small community of Barbie, a hotbed of spite and jealousy. The focal point of the resentments is the Gourlay family and their green-shuttered house. The local community's efforts together with Gourlay's own human weaknesses eventually bring about the family's downfall. In its portrayal of hubris and its effects the book has similarities to Greek tragedy.

The House with the Green Shutters
Canongate pb 0862415497 £4.99

BROOKMYRE, CHRISTOPHER

Not The End Of The World
Little, Brown hb 0316640654
£12.99

Using his trademark attributes of humour and action-packed adventure, Christopher Brookmyre delivers another highly enjoyable work. This time it is set in pre-millenium California, full of evangelical media stars, porn cinemas and some well-equipped terrorists gearing up for violent incidents. Brookmyre casts a sharp light on modern America's preoccupations at the end of the 20th century.

BROSTER, D.K.

The Jacobite Trilogy
Mandarin pb 0749313951
£12.99

This omnibus edition contains Broster's three classic novels on the 1745 Rising: *The Flight Of The Heron*, *The Gleam In The North* and *The Dark Mile*. Together they form an epic work full of excitement, heroism and romance.

"When the Deacon was not afraid of a man he stabbed him straight ; when he was afraid of him he stabbed him on the sly."

George Douglas Brown, The House of Green Shutters

BROWN, GEORGE MACKAY (1921–1996)

George Mackay Brown was born in Stromness, Orkney, in 1921. His work is strongly rooted in his background, both in terms of its setting and the culture he explores and it has strong mythological and religious elements. He used the folklore of Scotland and Scandinavia for inspiration, and his work is very much part of the Norse storytelling tradition. His best known work is the Booker-shortlisted novel *Beside the Ocean of Time*. This exquisitely constructed book contains many of Mackay Brown's archetypal themes, using various aspects of Orkney life and history as a microcosm from which he examines issues of universal relevance. The main character, Thorfinn Ragnarson, is a crofter's son who becomes a writer. The novel explores the relationship between him and the imaginary Orcadian island of Norday, particularly the marked effects of modern civilization. Among his other novels his retelling of the story of 12th century Earl Magnus has a timeless power. Magnus was ruthlessly murdered by his cousin after attending a peace meeting. He met his cousin under the terms of a truce, unarmed, yet knowing he was walking to a terrible death. He was subsequently venerated as Saint Magnus of Orkney. Mackay Brown punctuates the mediaeval Orkney tale with flashes of oppression and brutality from the 20th century. This powerful novel, of which the central theme is the transforming power of good over chaos and evil, has been adapted into a chamber opera by Peter Maxwell Davies. George Mackay Brown is also a distinguished short story writer and has been described as 'a miniature northern Homer'. The collection of six short stories, *The Island of the Women*, amply shows why he deserves such praise. The rhythms of island life are present in each tale, whether set in the recent past or the distant realms of Orcadian fable. Indeed, as Seamus Heaney has said, George Mackay Brown transforms everything by passing it 'through the eye of the needle of Orkney.'

Beside the Ocean of Time
HarperCollins pb 0006548628 £5.99
Greenvoe
Penguin pb 0140039783 £6.99
The Island of the Women and Other Stories
John Murray hb 0719558697 £16.99
Magnus
Canongate pb 0862418143 £5.99
The Masked Fishermen
John Murray hb 0719547008 £12.95
Sun's Net
Chambers pb 055023005X £5.99
Vinland
HarperCollins pb 0006546188 £5.99
Winter Tales
HarperCollins pb 0006550312 £6.99

BUCHAN, JOHN (1875–1940)

Best known for his fast-paced, perfectly plotted high adventure
tales, particularly his Richard Hannay novels, John Buchan also
wrote several biographies, notably of Sir Walter Scott and
Montrose. His 1915 novel *The Thirty Nine Steps* became his best
known work, thanks in part to Alfred Hitchcock's thrilling 1935
film version. Educated at Glasgow University and Oxford,
Buchan led a colourful life. He worked in many posts, among
them Private Secretary to the High Commissioner of South
Africa, and Governor General to Canada. His best works still
grab the reader with their blend of action, slightly over-the-top
characterisation, and daring heroics. Of his historical novels
Midwinter is often considered the best. It follows the adventures
of Alastair Maclean, an agent sent into England by Prince
Charles to gather support for the Jacobites. Along the way he
befriends two figures, Dr Samuel Johnson and a mysterious man
known only as 'Midwinter', guardian of the twilight world of
'Old England.' Maclean begins to suspect the Prince has a spy in
his inner circle, but as he comes close to unveiling him he finds
Hanoverian agents hot on his trail. Buchan's talent for writing a
fine story is well illustrated in this tale of treachery and intrigue.
A Lost Lady of Old Years is Buchan's novel set in the 1745 Jacobite
Rebellion, a popular time-frame for Scottish historical fiction.
This is a remarkable work: an unromantic and darkly realistic
portrayal of the Rebellion. *Witch Wood* is set in the Borders and
is an atmospheric tale of religious strife and civil war in the 17th
century containing all the trademark elements of Buchan's
finest works: a superb fast-paced plot and vividly realised historic
settings. The chief characteristic of Buchan's other fiction is its
variety. It ranges from *The Courts of the Morning*, a Richard
Hannay novel set in Scotland and South America, where a
ruthless dictator threatens the world, to *The Gap in the Curtain*,
in which a brilliant professor's experiments allow him to show
the guests of a grand country house a glimpse of the future.
This has profound effects on all who take part, but especially on
a young politician who sees the date of his death only one year
away. Buchan was also a prolific short-story writer. One of his
many talents is shown to great effect in *Supernatural Tales*. The
tales concern the world of the mystical and occult and range in
setting from the moors of the Scottish Borders to Edwardian
England. Buchan's ability to write entertaining and enthralling
shorter pieces is amply proved here.

Adventures of Dickson McCunn
Penguin 0140236473 £8.99
The Blanket of The Dark
B & W pb 1873631413 £5.99
Castle Gay
Sutton pb 0750904836 £4.99
The Complete Richard Hannay
Penguin pb 0140170596 £9.99
**The Complete Short Stories
(Ed. A Lownie)**
Vol.1
Birlinn hb 0952675609 £20.00
Vol.2
Birlinn hb 095267565X £20.00
Vol.3
Birlinn hb 0952675617 £20.00
The Courts of the Morning
B & W pb 1873631200 £6.99
The Dancing Floor
OUP pb 0192832875 £4.99
Free Fishers
B & W pb 1873631324 £5.99
The Gap In The Curtain
B & W pb 187363109X £6.99
Greenmantle
OUP pb 019282953X £4.99
House of the Four Winds
Sutton pb 0750904852 £4.99
Huntingtower
OUP pb 0192832298 £4.99
Island of Sheep
OUP pb 0192824333 £4.99

BURKE, RAYMOND

Spoutmouth
Dualchas pb 0952141884 £4.99
The Return of Burke and Hare
Dualchas pb 0952141833 £4.99

An alienated, unemployed young man living a seemingly aimless life is at the heart of Raymond Burke's *Spoutmouth*. Burke gives little away in terms of this man's past, family or friends - he doesn't even reveal his name. Instead, he uses him to study the social factors that will flip an easy-going individual into a psychopathic rage.

BURNETT, MARGARET

Indians Don't Kiss
Polygon pb 074866212X £7.99

Twenty nine year old Hannah goes back to visit her parents in India. She is pregnant and has just given up her job, and her parents don't yet know. This is a tale of culture clash and the perennial problem of living up to your parents' expectations.

John Burnet of Barns
B & W pb 1873631316 £5.99
John McNab
Penguin pb 0140011358 £4.99
A Lost Lady of Old Years
B & W pb 1873631421 £5.99
Mr Standfast
OUP pb 019283116X £4.99
Midwinter
B & W pb 1873631154 £5.99
The Power House
B & W pb 1873631146 £4.99
Prester John
Penguin pb 0140011382 £4.99
A Prince of the Captivity
B & W pb 1873631685 £6.99
Runagates Club
Sutton pb 075091159X £5.99
Sick Heart River
OUP pb 0192829378 £4.99
Supernatural Tales
B & W pb 1873631782 £7.99
The Thirty Nine Steps
Penguin pb 0140621091 £1.00
The Three Hostages
OUP pb 0192824198 £4.99
The Watcher by the Threshold: Shorter Scottish Fiction
Canongate pb 0862416825 £7.99
Witch Wood
Canongate pb 0862412021 £4.99

BURNSIDE, JOHN

The Dumb House
Vintage pb 0099582716 £5.99

John Burnside's first book is a dark and haunting piece of work based roughly on the myth of Akbar the Great, a Persian king who, it is said, locked newborn children into a palace and deprived them of contact with humans who could speak in an attempt to discover if human language is acquired or innate, an experiment allegedly repeated by James IV. An unnamed narrator attempts to recreate this experiment on his children after their mother has died, with chilling and disturbing consequences.

BUTLIN, RON

Night Visits
S.C.P. pb 184017000X £4.95

When a young boy's father dies, he seeks refuge in a fantasy world beyond love and pain. He is sent to live with his aunt in Edinburgh, who has long been trapped in her own private world of fantasy and terror. Together they enter a hell forged from love perverted into pain and desire. A multi-faceted, disturbing and powerful work.

CANNON, MICHAEL

The Borough
Serpent's Tail pb 1852423838 £8.99
A Conspiracy of Hope
Serpent's Tail pb 1852425172 £9.99

The Borough has some resemblances to the work of Alasdair Gray. Set in a re-imagined Glasgow, the book follows the fortunes of the residents of the maze-like streets of 'the Borough'. Written from the viewpoint of a wandering observer, the book has a haunting nature and is reminiscent in feel to the works of Wim Wenders and the French New Wave cinema. Cannon's second novel, *A Conspiracy of Hope*, is a very different work. Humorous and moving, it revolves around the brief meeting of Jamie and Rachel at a Greek holiday resort. Their paths don't actually cross until over halfway through the book, but their meeting precipitates a huge emotional fall-out. A book full of erotic encounters, and youthful hopes and desires. In these novels Cannon has already proved his ability to write convincingly in several styles.

CARLYLE, THOMAS (1795–1881)

Thomas Carlyle was a renowned Scottish historian and essayist, born in Ecclefechan in 1795, who went on to become one of the major intellectual figures of the Victorian Age. His works include a six volume history of Frederick The Great and a highly idealised history of the French Revolution. His most lasting work is undoubtedly *Sartor Resartus*, a strange work, semi-autobiographical in nature. It is a satirical comment on the value of clothes and a philosophical discussion of human values.
The French Revolution
OUP pb 0192818430 £9.99
Reminiscences
OUP pb 0192817485 £7.99
Sartor Resartus
OUP pb 0192817574 £5.99
Selected Writings (Ed Alan Shelston)
Penguin pb 0140430652 £9.99

CARSWELL, CATHERINE (1879–1946)

Born in Glasgow, Catherine Carswell became well known as the literary critic of the *Glasgow Herald*, a job she lost after reviewing D.H. Lawrence's banned novel *The Rainbow*. Lawrence went on to encourage her own work. The autobiographical novel *Open the Door* is a passionate portrayal of a young woman enslaved by her emotional make-up and yet eventually released by these very same emotions. The book skilfully recreates Glasgow at the height of the Empire. Carswell also wrote an initially controversial biography of Burns, now regarded by many as the best portrayal there is of Scotland's national bard. Her unfinished autobiography *Lying Awake* was recently released by Canongate.

Open the Door
Canongate pb 0862416442 £5.99

CHIRNSIDE, DOUGLAS

Vanity Case
Sceptre pb 0340681810 £6.99
Basket Case
Sceptre pb 034068061X £6.99

Chirnside's sharp and funny novel, *Vanity Case* is set in the rough and tumble world of the media. It centres around a high flying executive and his latest show, an Agony Aunt programme hosted by Irish nun Sister Verity. Chirnside's refreshing style is ideally suited to this quirky novel.

CLARKE, GEDDES

Nemesis in the Mearns: Love, Laughter and Heartache in the Land of Lewis Grassic Gibbon
S.C.P. pb 1898218781 £9.99

A novel based around the life of James Leslie Mitchell (Lewis Grassic Gibbon) which includes moving accounts of the Mearns soldiers in France during the First World War.

Thomas Carlyle

CLOSE, AJAY

Forspoken
Secker & Warburg pb
0436204924 £9.99
Official and Doubtful
Minerva pb 0749395095 £6.99

In Ajay Close's second novel, *Forspoken*, a thirty-something woman is living a near perfect life, a cool rationalist who rises above the spiritual chaos present at the end of the twentieth century. Then her sister returns after seventeen years in the States and things start to go wrong. As the accidents and mishaps escalate in severity she begins to wonder if she might be cursed. The book is an articulate work that builds on the strengths of Close's first novel.

COHEN, MARK B.

Brass Monkeys
Hodder & Stoughton hb
0340712961 £16.99

In the same genre as Tom Sharpe, Mark B. Cohen's first novel romps through the fields of politics and the media, using the accident-prone Hugh Driftwood, candidate for Prime Minister, as its focal point. It relays a tale of political and sexual scandal, involving evil arch enemies and a chimpanzee called Zoe. A confident and hilarious debut from this new writer.

CROCKETT, SAMUEL RUTHERFORD
(1860–1914)

Crockett rose to almost instantaneous literary fame with the publication of a collection of his wry congregational anecdotes called *The Stickit Minister*. He was a minister in the Free Church of Scotland at the time and resigned to work exclusively as a writer. He wrote numerous historical romances and even a theological science fiction novel, but only two of his books are in print at the moment.
The Grey Man
Alloway pb 0907526144 £6.50
The Raiders
Alloway pb 0907526535 £6.50

CRONIN, A.J.
(1896–1981)

A.J. Cronin was forced to abandon his career in medicine due to ill health and turned to literature. His first work, *Hatter's Castle*, was a huge success and he went on to write many other novels. The books were heavily based on Cronin's own life and went on to form the basis of the hugely popular television pro-grammes *Dr Finlay's Casebook*.
The Citadel
Longman pb 0582528895 £2.80
Short Stories From Dr Finlay's Casebook
Longman pb 058253786X £2.35
The Stars Look Down
Cassell pb 0575601272 £5.99

CRUMEY, ANDREW

Andrew Crumey's works are characterised by their playful, multi-layered and intellectual approach. He is in the same tradition as writers like Italo Calvino, Borges and Voltaire. His books are unusual in style, being concerned with the nature of what actually constitutes a novel and weaving this concern around the characters and plot, while still retaining a strong sense of fun.

Music In A Foreign Language (Saltire Best First Book Award, 1994)
Dedalus pb 1873982119 £7.99
Pfitz
Dedalus pb 187398281X £7.99
D'Alembert's Principle
Dedalus pb 1873982321 £7.99

DAVIDSON, DORIS
The Girl with the Creel
HarperCollins pb 0006499732 £5.99

Set in the fishing communities of Buckie and Aberdeen during World War II, Davidson's tale features a young girl who has lived a sheltered life. Her world is turned upside down when she falls in love with a married man. Forced to flee her home town, she has to find deeply hidden inner resources to survive in this heartwarming saga.
The Road to Rowanbrae
HarperCollins pb 0006470599 £4.99
The Three Kings
HarperCollins pb 0006496202 £4.99

DAVIE, ELSPETH
(1919–1995)

Elspeth Davie, a novelist and short story writer, first came to prominence when winning an *Observer* short story competition. Her first novel *Providings* was published in 1965. Her work, largely set in Edinburgh, examines the everyday lives of ordinary people, and concerns the relationship between people and things, looking at the ways in which possessions and habits rule our lives. The novels are deceptively gentle, yet very perceptive. The only one currently in print is the quirky and unusual *Providings* in which the main character is a young man who works in a furniture shop where he observes the ways in which people and furniture seem to complement each other. His mother keeps sending him her home-made jam which he dislikes so intensely that he gives it away, which in turn leads to unforeseen complications. Elspeth Davie won the Katherine Mansfield Award for her collection of short stories including 'The Spark'.
Providings
Calder pb 0714505382 £5.99
The Spark and Other Stories
Calder pb 0714506656 £4.95

DAVIS, MARGARET THOMSON

Margaret Thomson Davies' explorations of domestic and personal situations have given her a strong following of readers who enjoy epic sagas. *The Breadmakers Saga*, described by the *Daily Express* as 'a Glaswegian equivalent of Coronation Street', covers the years from the Depression to the end of World War II and examines the trials and tribulations of a close-knit community. *The Tobacco Lords Trilogy* is a wide-ranging story which starts in Glasgow during the 1745 rebellion. Annabella Ramsay, the impetuous daughter of a Tobacco Lord, and Regina Chisholm, a slum child, become tragically entwined in a tale of squalor and wealth which sets them up as life-long rivals. Expansive in scope, it ranges from the Glasgow slums to the grandeur of Williamsburg in the New World and is fast-paced and dynamically told. Her latest novel, *Gallachers*, is the story of Kate Gallacher, a strong free-willed individual born in the slums of Glasgow. She escapes her run-down environment and marries at the age of 16 in an effort to be her own mistress. Unfortunately this marriage doesn't work out and when she eventually breaks free she vows never again to let go of her independence until she meets the perfect man.

The Breadmakers Saga
B & W pb 1873631278 £7.99
Burning Ambition
B & W hb 1873631642 £14.99
The Dark Side of Pleasure
B & W pb 1873631502 £5.99
Daughters and Mothers
Arrow pb 0099660008 £4.99
Gallachers
Century hb 0712678778 £16.99
Hold Me Forever
Arrow pb 0099353415 £4.99
A Kind of Immortality
Arrow pb 009935361X £5.99

Kiss Me No More
Arrow pb 0099353512 £5.99
Light and Dark
B & W pb 187363143X £6.99
Rag Woman, Rich Woman
Arrow pb 0099799103 £4.99
The Tobacco Lords Trilogy
B & W pb 187363133 £7.99
A Woman of Property
Arrow pb 0099743809 £4.99
Wounds of War
Arrow pb 0099686503 £4.99

DEANS, DAVID
The Peatman
Polygon pb 0748661719 £7.95

This entertaining first novel starts with the anti-hero narrator stealing peat from a Highland croft. The narrator goes on to paint a robust and comic vision of the modern Highlands, complete with collie dogs, district nurses and brush salesmen.

DEWAR, ISLA

Giving Up On Ordinary
Headline pb 0747255504 £6.99

A delicious tale of small town life that concerns a cleaner who decides she has had enough and starts to tackle life on her own terms. A gently moving story entertainingly told, with a strong central character, which portrays one woman's unique response to modern life in a Scottish town.
Keeping Up With Magda
Review pb 0747251126 £6.99
Women Talking Dirty
Review pb 0747251134 £5.99
It Could Happen To You
Review pb 074727648X £9.99

DILLON, DES

The Big Empty
Argyll pb 1874640084 £6.99
Me And Ma Gal
Argyll pb 1874640564 £6.99

The Big Empty is a collection of carefully observed short stories based on modern urban living. The characters live empty, repressed lives, losing themselves in sex, drugs, and violence and yet they have a latent capacity for humanity. *Me And Ma Gal* is a warm and intimate first novel about a Scottish childhood, based on the friendship of two 10-year-old boys growing up in the industrial heartland of the nation. The book has a light touch and skilfully evokes the feelings of childhood, community and friendship.

DOLAN, CHRIS

Ascension Day
Polygon pb 0748662340 £8.99

A carefully crafted tale of menace, human frailty and guilt. The text builds a sinister fantasy that runs at a tangent to our own world.
Poor Angels and Other Stories
Polygon pb 0748662065 £7.99

DONALD, STUART

Para Handy At The Helm
Neil Wilson pb 1897784627
£7.99

This is the third in a series of new Para Handy tales in which Stuart Donald carefully recreates Neil Munro's much-loved characters. These new stories replicate the feel of Munro's originals with skill and humour.
Para Handy Sails Again
Neil Wilson pb 1897784473
£7.99
Para Handy All At Sea
Neil Wilson pb 1897784546
£7.99

DOYLE, SIR ARTHUR CONAN (1859–1930)

Born in Edinburgh and a student of medicine in the University there, Conan Doyle almost single-handedly created the modern detective novel and is known throughout the world as the creator of Sherlock Holmes. He worked as a doctor before turning to fiction. An interesting character in many ways, he was a keen and able sportsman, an adventurer and had a fascination for the occult which was to last to the end of his life. He also wrote several historical romances which have been overshadowed by his Holmes novels, although they found a great admirer in Sir Winston Churchill. One of these books, *The Complete Brigadier Gerard*, was recently re-released. This collection of historical romances features one of Doyle's major literary creations. Brigadier Gerard is a Napoleonic soldier whose exploits showed Doyle's interest in chivalry. Doyle used his distinctive, easy-going narrative style and eye for historical accuracy in these tales, which he regarded as superior to his Holmes novels.

The Complete Brigadier Gerard
Canongate pb 0862415349 £5.99

DUNBAR, INGA

The Queen's Bouquet
HarperCollins pb 0006498833
£5.99

An action-packed period saga set in the court of Mary, Queen of Scots, and told with an emphasis on rounded characterisation and detailed historical background.

Figure of Eight
Pocket Books pb 0671853082
£4.99

DUNN, DOUGLAS

Boyfriends and Girlfriends
Faber pb 0571177107 £6.99

A collection of short stories mainly set in Scotland, that shows Dunn to be a fine wordsmith who carefully observes details of place and character. These works are his humane responses to everyday life events, and reveal the psychological depth behind common situations.

Secret Villages
Faber pb 0571138594 £4.99

DUNNETT, DOROTHY (b.1923)

Born in Fife and educated at Gillespie's High School For Girls, Dorothy Dunnett is a prominent member of the Scottish Society of Women Artists. She has written several crime novels, initially under her maiden name, Halliday *(see Crime Fiction)*. She is best known for her historical novels, the first series of which featured Scottish mercenary Francis Crawford of Lymond, centring around his wanderings in Europe in the 16th century. She began a second series in 1986, featuring the house of Charetty and Niccolo, the most recent of which, *Caprice and Rondo* was released in 1997. The seventh volume of the series is set in Danzig, Poland in the harsh winter of 1474. Nicholas de Fleury is in hiding, keeping the outside world at arm's length. However he will soon be forced to take sides. Dorothy Dunnett's detailed historical works have convincing characters to drive the beautifully paced plots along and she is very much part of the Scottish tradition of historical novel writers.

Caprice and Rondo
Penguin pb 0718140826 £11.99
Disorderly Knights
Penguin tpb 0718141261 £12.50
Game of Kings
Penguin tpb 0718141245 £12.99
Niccolo Rising
Penguin pb 0140113916 £6.99
Pawn In Frankincense
Penguin tpb 071814127X £12.50
Queens' Play
Penguin tpb 0718141253 £11.99
Race of Scorpions
Penguin pb 0140112650 £6.99
Scales of Gold
Penguin pb 0140112669 £6.99
Spring of The Ram
Penguin pb 0140113592 £6.99
To Lie With Lions
Penguin pb 0140112685 £6.99
Unicorn Hunt
Penguin pb 0140112677 £6.99

DUTHIE, NIALL

Natterjack
Faber pb 0571179320 £7.99

Duthie's clever and very eloquent novel relays much of its meaning by the way in which the author relates the story rather than through what actually happens. The narrator is R.T. Shearer, who tells the reader of his life from a room overlooking the Mediterranean Sea: a life of pain, unrequited love and dismay. Shearer's adult self is scarred by his introspective adolescence, which has left him unprepared for life's difficulties. A very original work, which contains within the story a memorable redrawing of Macbeth.

ELPHINSTONE, MARGARET

Islanders
Polygon pb 0748661786 £5.99

An impressive fictional recreation of a 12th century Norse settlement, that opens when Astrid, the only survivor of a shipwreck, is taken in by an island family. Rich in period detail, with vividly realised characters.

FELL, ALISON

Alison Fell has written several novels as well as two collections of poetry. The two novels listed here are very different in subject matter. *Mer De Glace* is concerned with the fortunes of the relationship between mountaineering addict Will and his tutor Kathleen who is ten years older. The book is set among the peaks of the Alps, with the icy setting being heavily reflected in the feel of the book. *The Pillow Boy of the Lady Onogoro* is set in the sexually promiscuous court of Kyoto and although events take place in 11th century Japan, the theme of female sexual suppression is a very contemporary one. Both the books, like most of Alison Fell's work, are written in a very modern style and share the same concern for the way in which human relationships function, both sexually and spiritually.

Mer De Glace (Boardman Tasker Award Winner 1991)
Serpent's Tail pb 185242267X £7.99
The Pillow Boy of the Lady of Onogoro
Serpent's Tail pb 1852422637 £7.99

FERRIER, SUSAN
(1782–1854)

Susan Ferrier, a close friend of Sir Walter Scott, was a significant novelist of her time. She wrote three novels, *Marriage, The Inheritance* and *Destiny*. They deal with issues that were common in fiction at that time, such as social customs and manners, courtship, marriage, domestic issues and female education. However, she reveals forward-looking attitudes, covertly including unconventional ideas along with those that were more 'acceptable'. She views her society with a strongly satirical eye, and her work is often extremely funny. Her novels provide a good insight into Scottish society of the time, particularly in her native Edinburgh but also among the Highland gentry. The only one in print is *Marriage*, a study of provincial social manners surrounding marriage in the late 18th century, at a time when it was seen as proof of a favourable social education

Marriage
OUP pb 0192825240 £6.99

FODEN, GILES
The Last King of Scotland
Faber pb 0571179169 £9.99

A young Scottish doctor recently arrived in Kampala finds himself by a twist of fate Idi Amin's personal physician. Amin, the self-proclaimed 'Last King of Scotland' at first makes few demands on his doctor, but slowly and surely the physician finds himself becoming more and more deeply involved in his bloody and macabre regime. The novel is a chilling study based on true historical events and examines the nature of corruption, responsibility and nationhood.

FRAME, RONALD

His first novel, *Winter Journey*, showed Frame's ability to produce realistically rendered characters. The story is written from the viewpoint of a young girl, a powerfully drawn character, who witnesses a marriage breakdown. In later works such as *Penelope's Hat* and *Bluette*, Frame builds on this talent for creating credible characters, centring these particular novels on the careers of two very different women, Penelope Miller and Catherine Hammond. Frame builds up layers of meaning around his main characters to allow them to emerge as eccentric, flawed yet fully-rounded individuals. He has received numerous awards and has successfully adapted his work for radio and TV.

A Long Weekend With Marcel Proust
Hodder & Stoughton pb
0340428910 £5.99
Penelope's Hat
Hodder & Stoughton pb
0340524553 £5.99
Sandmouth People
Hodder & Stoughton pb
034042320X £5.99
Underwood And After
Hodder & Stoughton pb
0340565403 £5.99

FRANCIS, RICHENDA
The Blood Is Strong
House Of Lochar pb
1899863222 £8.99

When a young Canadian girl returns to the remote Hebridean island of her ancestors she finds herself transported back into the past to the Uist of 1851, in this love story full of historical detail.

FRASER, CHRISTINE MARION

Christine Marion Fraser was born in the Govan district of Glasgow and at the age of ten contracted a rare muscular disease which left her in a wheelchair. She is known as one of the best family saga writers in Scotland with several highly popular series to her name, the best known undoubtedly being the Rhanna series. Set on a fictitious small Hebridean island the novels follow the lives, loves and tragedies of the islanders. Her later Noble series is set around a community in a small Argyllshire powdermill town. However her most recent book belongs to neither series. *Kinvara* is set among the colourful characters and unforgiving landscape of the west coast of Scotland. It relates the story of Robert Sutherland (a deputy lighthouse keeper) and his family, as well as the wider community's interactions with them. Like her other works, Kinvara mixes good story lines with believable characters and settings which feel authentic.

Kinvara
Hodder & Stoughton hb
0340707135 £16.99

Noble Beginnings
HarperCollins pb 0006490131
£4.99

Noble Seed
HarperCollins pb 0006498620
£5.99

Rhanna
HarperCollins pb 0006155987
£4.99

Return to Rhanna
HarperCollins pb 0006170331
£3.99

Stranger on Rhanna
HarperCollins pb 0006470033
£4.99

A Rhanna Mystery
HarperCollins pb 0006499120
£5.99

King's Acre
HarperCollins pb 0006174043
£4.99

King's Close
HarperCollins pb 0006470025
£4.99

King's Exile
HarperCollins pb 000617745X
£4.99

King's Farewell
HarperCollins pb 0006470041
£4.99

FRASER, GEORGE MACDONALD

Born in England but largely brought up in Scotland, George MacDonald Fraser is best known for his Flashman series of books in which he relates the later adventures of the bully from *Tom Brown's Schooldays*. The first of these was *Flashman*, written in 1969. The cowardly cad of a soldier who heaps glory and praise on himself, often in spite of circumstances, has gained Fraser a large and loyal following. His beautifully written and moving war memories *Quartered Safe Out Here* show that he has another dimension to his writing. His latest work, *Black Ajax*, features Captain Buck Flashman, father of arch-cad Harry, who, when he watches ex-slave Black Ajax fight sees a champion in the making. Together they aim to take the title from Tom Cribb, the undefeated champion of England. Set mainly in Regency England, this is the story of a flawed hero fighting the limitations of poverty, ignorance and race hatred. Fraser has also written three volumes of the adventures of Private McAuslan, the world's dirtiest soldier. The books take an affectionate and hilarious look at the life of a private who serves in a fictitious Highland regiment.

Black Ajax
HarperCollins pb 0006499813
£6.99

The Candlemass Road
HarperCollins pb 0006477208
£5.99

Flash For Freedom
HarperCollins pb 0006176798
£5.99

Flashman
HarperCollins pb 0006176801
£5.99

Flashman and the Angel of the Lord
Harper Collins pb 0006490239
£5.99

Flashman and the Dragon
HarperCollins pb 0006173403
£5.99

Flashman and the Mountain of Light
HarperCollins pb 0006179800
£5.99

Flashman and the Redskins
HarperCollins pb 0006178014
£5.99

Flashman at the Charge
HarperCollins pb 0006176763
£5.99

Flashman in the Great Game
HarperCollins pb 0006176771
£5.99

Flashman's Lady
HarperCollins pb 0006177735
£5.99

The General Danced at Dawn
HarperCollins pb 000617681X
£4.99

McAuslan In The Rough
HarperCollins pb 0006176550
£4.99

Mr American
HarperCollins pb 0006470181
£7.99

The Pyrates
HarperCollins pb 0006470173
£7.99

Royal Flash
HarperCollins pb 000617678X
£5.99

The Sheikh and the Dustbin and other McAuslan Stories
HarperCollins pb 0006176755
£4.99

FRIEL, GEORGE (1910–1975)

Friel's first novel, *The Bank of Time*, published in 1959, was a confident debut. Simply and freshly written it was an accessible evocation of a childhood in Glasgow during the forties and fifties. However his best-known novel is *Mr Alfred M.A.*, the story of a timorous elderly teacher who finds it difficult to cope with the sordid realities of everyday life, and who is haunted by his obsessive though innocent love for one of his pupils. At the same time his poetic gift makes him aware of the possibility of transcendence. This echoes a recurring theme in all of Friel's work: an awareness of the sharp contrast between the grim and pitiless nature of life and the hope of renewal, both moral and physical. His work suggests that life need not be so demeaning, and his use of poetic language echoes this concern. Much of his work also makes use of his wry sense of humour. Friel also wrote short stories which construct a vivid portrayal of city life, predominantly in Glasgow, in the years before, during and after World War II. His themes, however, are universal: love and marriage, grief and happiness. The stories are told with truthfulness and economy, revealing Friel's precise eye for detail.

The Bank of Time
Polygon pb 0748661530 £8.95
A Friend of Humanity and Other Stories
Polygon pb 0748661263 £7.95
Mr Alfred M.A.
Canongate pb 0862411637 £4.99

GABALDON, DIANA

This American novelist was inspired to write about a time-travelling Scottish Highlander after watching an episode of *Dr. Who*. The first instalment of this unusual love story starts in 1946 when a wartime nurse walks through a stone circle in the Highlands and finds herself transported back to a violent skirmish in Jacobite Scotland in 1743. Armed with the foreknowledge of Culloden and the dangerous world she is trapped in, she tries to deal with her new excitement-filled life. The stories in the series are told with great humour and have won Gabaldon a unique place in romantic fiction writing.

Cross Stitch
Arrow pb 0099911701 £6.99
Dragonfly in Amber
Arrow pb 0099294710 £5.99
Drums of Autumn
Arrow pb 0099664313 £5.99
Voyager
Arrow pb 0099428512 £5.99

"Love/emotion = embarrassment: Scots equation. Exceptions are when roaring drunk or watching football. Men do rather better out of this loophole."
Janice Galloway, The Trick Is to Keep Breathing

GALLOWAY, JANICE

Born in Ardrossan and educated at Glasgow University, Janice Galloway has become one of the key figures in the recent resurgence of writing in the west of Scotland. Her powerful and innovative writing fiercely challenges contemporary gender roles and urges that women's voices should be heeded, not patronised. Her work mixes everyday realism, humour and a keen eye for detail with a rich imagery which can contain elements of the surreal, grotesque or bizarre. Her first novel, *The Trick Is To Keep Breathing*, is a tour de force: a razor-sharp, intimate study of the suffering a woman experiencing a breakdown endures. Her mental disintegration has been precipitated by the death of her lover. Janice Galloway's style reflects the chaos felt by Joy Stone, the central character. In *Foreign Parts*, her most recent novel, she explores female friendship through the tale of two women on a driving holiday to Normandy, focusing on the effect that they have on each other. Described by one critic as 'a road movie for feminists', the novel is well observed, unsentimental and often caustically funny. Janice Galloway has shown herself to be a gifted writer who has experimented with many themes and styles, and the true meaning of her work is often gleaned from fleeting impressions as well as from the story itself. She can elicit great empathy and compassion for her characters, who are frequently trapped within themselves by society and circumstance, and misunderstood by do-gooders. This compassion is reinforced by a biting satire of society's indifference and its often condescending attitudes. All these qualities are also evident in her short story collections *Blood* and *Where You Find It*. Galloway's elegant use of language and experiments with form are full of virtuosity and poetic skill, marking her as a unique and much acclaimed talent.

Blood
Minerva pb 0749391952 £6.99
Foreign Parts
(1994 McVitie's Prize Winner)
Vintage pb 0099453010 £5.99
The Trick Is To Keep Breathing
Minerva pb 0749391731 £6.99
Where You Find It
Vintage pb 0099453118 £5.99

GAITENS, EDWARD

Dance of the Apprentices
Canongate pb 0862412978
£5.99

Gaitens' tale of the Gorbals Apprentices who aimed to reform the world and dignified their own lives with art and learning is a powerful account of a Glasgow family's struggle at the end of the 1920s. The book is full of comic and witty observations, even when the story is at its saddest moments.

GALFORD, ELLEN

The Fires of Bride
Women's Press pb 0704340208
£6.99

A comic novel set on a mysterious Scottish island that only emerges from the mist every hundred years or so. Why does artist Maria stay? Is it her love affair with Catriona or her strange attraction to the Sisters of Bride? An original, enchanting and very funny work.

GALT, JOHN (1779–1839)

Born in Ayrshire, John Galt started his adult life as a merchant, a venture that was destined to fail. During 1809-1811 he travelled widely and was inspired to write accounts of his journeys, which included a meeting with Byron. The book was called *Letters From Levant*. In 1821 he published his master work, *Annals of the Parish*, based around the life of a parish minister. *Annals of the Parish* is a humorous and wonderfully observed novel that paints an intimate and human picture of Scotland under the reign of George III. The book takes the form of a chronicle of events rather than a plotted story. This book made Galt's reputation and shows his keenly honed powers of satire, observation, and characterisation. As well as containing wonderful personalities the book also provides a unique glimpse into the turbulent changes in society during the early nineteenth century. In 1826 Galt went to Canada and helped to organise immigration to the country. He returned in financial ruin to Scotland in 1829 and went on to write several other notable books, among them *The Member* and *The Radical*, his two great political novels, written in 1832. Still highly relevant today, they are studies in two aspects of politics: the harm that political fanaticism can do to social harmony and order, and the dangers of politicians' desire for self-fulfilment. They are both sharply observed books, full of wit and insight. Of his many other works two of the most interesting are *Ringan Gilhaizie* and *The Last of the Lairds*. *Ringan Gilhaizie* has a strongly sympathetic view of the Covenanters, unusual in Scottish novels of this time. It was written in their defence as a response to Scott's 'attack' on them in *Old Mortality*. *The Last of the Lairds* was finished in1826 but at the time the book was thought to be too full of 'vulgarity and uncleanness' and was adapted into a light romance which has regularly been reprinted. The Mercat Press edition reveals the original work, its first time in print after 150 years of censorship. Galt's gift for comic scenes and characters is well used, yet he avoids the danger of turning the book into a bawdy farce, producing instead an entertaining book with serious overtones.

Annals of the Parish & The Ayrshire Legatees
Mercat Press pb 1873644310 £7.99
Collected Short Stories (Ed. EA Gordon)
Mercat Press pb 0707302188 £5.99
The Last of the Lairds
Mercat Press hb 070730170X £6.99
The Member & The Radical
Canongate pb 0862416426 £5.99
Ringan Gilhaizie
Canongate pb 0862415527 £6.99

GEORGE, MARGARET

Mary Queen of Scotland and The Isles
Pan pb 0330327909 £9.99

Margaret George's romantic and passionate recreation of the tragic life of Mary Queen of Scots concentrates on the relationships between the people involved. She creates a Mary who is rounded in character and believable, skilfully telling of the treachery, murder plots and Mary's own personal weaknesses that were eventually to allow her enemies to triumph over her.

GIBBON, LEWIS GRASSIC (1901–1935)

James Leslie Mitchell, aka Lewis Grassic Gibbon, created one of the seminal texts in Scottish literature when he wrote *A Scots Quair*, a trilogy of books comprising *Sunset Song, Cloud Howe* and *Grey Granite*. The books were released under a thinly disguised version of his mother's maiden name and the first novel took only two months to write. This outstanding trilogy tells the story of Chris Guthrie and her deep inner conflicts between love of the natural beauty of the rural landscape of North East Scotland and her desire to escape the monotonous drudgery of working this land, thus perhaps fulfilling her true potential. The clash between Scottish and English culture is at the heart of the trilogy, expressed through Chris's feelings and developed by Gibbon as he moves her story from countryside to town to city. He skillfully weaves in major historical and political events of the time, such as World War I and the Hunger Marches, creating a rich, complex and emotive portrayal of Chris's life. The language frequently shows Gibbon's ear for gossipy, racy Scots dialect. Passionately written, insightful and possessing some of the most eloquent descriptions of the Scottish landscape, the books are justly regarded as classics. Lewis Grassic Gibbon was a newspaper journalist and a committed Communist Party member. He attempted suicide after being caught fiddling expenses, and eventually joined the RAF in 1925. In spite of his all too short life he wrote many books on a wide variety of themes including Left Wing idealism and science fiction, a Golden Age of Innocence and the importance of land and tradition to the Scottish people. *The Thirteenth Disciple* is a clearly autobiographical novel which follows the life of Malcolm Maudslay, and reflects Gibbon's own intellectual and spiritual development. It is an epic tale of self-discovery that starts in Aberdeenshire and moves on to Glagow where Malcolm starts a career as a journalist. The novel then moves on to his horrific experiences in the trenches during World War I, and ends with Maudslay's quest for the Lost City in Yucutan. In *Persian Dawns, Egyptian Nights* Gibbon's fascination for the Far East is given free reign, the tales covering sorcerors, the Garden of Eden and a hunt for the last Neanderthal man. *Spartacus* is a classic tale of the slave revolt in Rome in 73BC. Gibbon's bloody and engaging account of the revolt hinges around the theme of man's inhumanity to man. The main character, Spartacus, is a compelling creation with a rounded and believable psychological make-up. Gibbon's treatment of the decadent inhuman world of Ancient Rome is notable for its detail and credibility. Lewis Grassic Gibbon died after an operation on an ulcer at the age of thirty four.

Gay Hunter
Polygon pb 0748660496 £7.95
Persian Dawns, Egyptian Nights
Polygon pb 0748662316 £9.99
A Scots Quair
Penguin pb 0140180915 £6.99
A Scots Quair
Canongate pb 0862415322 £5.99
Spartacus
B & W pb 1873631545 £6.99
Speak of the Mearns
Polygon pb 0748661670 £8.95
Stained Radiance
Polygon pb 0748661417 £7.95
Sunset Song
Canongate pb 0862411793 £4.99
The Thirteenth Disciple
B & W pb 1873631553 £6.99

"Mr Walkinshaw, I'm nae prophet as ye weel ken; but I can see that the day's no far aff when ministers of the gospel in Glasgow will be seen chambering and wantoning to the sound o' the kist fu' of whistles, wi' the seven-headed beast roouting its choruses at every ouercome of the spring."

John Galt, The Entail

John Galt

GRAHAM, BARRY
The Book of Man
Serpent's Tail pb 1852423900
£8.99

The Book Of Man is Barry Graham's third work, very much rooted in the Irvine Welsh school of powerful, moody and dark Scottish fiction. The book is a very fictionalised biography, loosely based on the life of Alexander Trocchi. A London-based playwright returns to Glasgow after the death of his junkie writer friend Mike Illingworth, and as he struggles to understand his friend's life and death he becomes aware that in many ways he is on a personal search to understand his own past. The book encompasses many hard-hitting themes including childhood brutality, mental breakdown, the effect of state power on the individual and lost love.
Of Darkness and Light
Bloomsbury hb 0747504741
£10.99

GRAY, ALASDAIR JAMES (b.1934)

Alasdair Gray had already built himself a career as an artist when he published his ground-breaking first novel *Lanark* in 1981. *Lanark* marked a watershed in Scottish fiction writing. The book placed the Scottish novel firmly in the 20th century, linking Scotland's literary past with its emerging vibrant future. The novel is written in four 'books', and is a complex, multi-layered mix of fantasy and reality. It uses a wide variety of themes, styles and elements from childhood memory and science fiction to vivid realism and autobiographical touches. This book (and most of Gray's subsequent work) is accompanied by his unique graphic designs. *Lanark* justly gained rave reviews and is regarded by some as Scottish literature's answer to *Ulysses,* a very modern work that showed the possibility of a new direction for Scottish Literature, while retaining a distinctive Scottish character. He followed *Lanark* with a collection of short stories, *Unlikely Stories, Mostly* which has been recently reprinted to include a new unlikely tale 'Inches In A Column', that was lost at the time of the first print run. The stories vary widely in subject and style from parable, fantasy and myth to scenes from everyday life. This collection helped cement Gray's reputation as one of Scotland's most original and important writers. He has since written numerous other novels and plays. These include *The Fall of Kelvin Walker* and *Poor Things*. The former is a tale of a young Scotsman on the make who gets his rightful come-uppance and is a clever example of his skills as a social satirist. Like all his work, *The Fall of Kelvin Walker* shows his unique artistic vision, whether it be in the production of the books or the inventive tricks

and allegories of which his novels are full. *Poor Things* is Gray's pastiche of a Victorian melodrama. He welds elements of Lewis Carroll, Mary Shelley and Arthur Conan Doyle into the plot, but his prodigious talent ensures that the book is very much his own. The story has many threads, not least of which is the idea that sexual humiliation and cruelty is part of most men and women's lives. The book is thoroughly engaging, original and thought-provoking yet also includes much that is touched by Gray's wicked sense of humour, and not just in the plot - the original hardback featured fake reviews provided by Gray himself. As always Gray's unique, very personal style is frequently very funny and slightly disturbing.

1982, Janine
Penguin pb 014017927 £7.99
The Fall of Kelvin Walker
Penguin pb 0140121609 £5.99
A History Maker
Penguin pb 014024803X £6.99
Lanark: A Life In Four Books
Picador pb 0330319655 £8.99
Mavis Belfrage: With Five Shorter Tales
Bloomsbury pb 0747530890 £5.99
McGrotty and Ludmilla
Dog & Bone pb 187253600X £5.00
Poor Things
Penguin pb 0140175547 £6.99
Something Leather
Picador pb 0330319442 £5.99
Ten Tales Tall And True
Penguin pb 0140175792 £5.99
Unlikely Stories, Mostly
Canongate pb 0862417376 £5.99

"Glasgow is a magnificent city", said McAlpin.
"Why do we hardly ever notice that? ""Because
nobody imagines living here", said Thaw.
Alasdair Gray, Lanark

Shades Of Gray: or Listening to the Oracle in Lanark

by Janice Galloway

> 'He said, "That was very unsatisfying...Why did the oracle not make clear which of these things happened?"
> Rima said, "What are you talking about?"
> "The oracle's account of my life before Unthank. He's just finished it."
> Rima said firmly, "In the first place, that oracle was a woman, not a man. In the second place, her story was about me. You were so bored you fell asleep and obviously dreamed something else."
> **Lanark, p357**

I first encountered Alasdair Gray's Big Book at a friend's house.

It was the middle of a seriously not good time for me. Suffering the immediate aftermath of a double bereavement, becoming daily more certain that talking, getting out of bed, everything really, was nothing more than a variation on a theme of wasting time, I was, to put it mildly, Not Lively. Not, I'd have thought, best placed to open myself to experiment or the excitement of discovery. Then again, reading in a way quite new to me, churning through book after book as though I was trying to exact some kind of revenge from doing it, as though the words owed me something, as though they might *save* me, maybe I was. Maybe reading reminded me there had been things I enjoyed previously; maybe I was simply, simplistically, hoping I'd hit on a phrase, a paragraph that would, inexplicably, *explain why*. I wasn't sure how it was going to do this exactly, but logical considerations weren't all that firm a part of the process. All that mattered was getting to the bottom of the page, the chapter, consuming the thing whole, then starting again. Keeping going. What else I did wasn't much. Off and on, without enthusiasm, I visited people and browsed anything that lay between paper covers in their homes. One friend had whole shelves, but the one I took back with me from my next visit wasn't on them. It was on the floor, where I fell over it, literally; a big paper stumbling-block on the way to the fire. LANARK. I'd never heard of the author and the cover was Hobbes' *Leviathan*, but not. One of the curlicued line-drawings on the spine was of a baby, surfacing between spread legs. Female legs. I was mildly shocked. Let me know what you think," she said. "I'd be...er...interested.

Interested or not, she never found out. I didn't mention the book again in case she asked for it back and I had fallen in love, or something, with it. Its clarity, exactness and near-childlike sincerity struck me as a rare mixture, and its high expectations of me as a reader took me by storm. I felt drawn, almost against my will. This man, whoever he was, seemed to write in a way that made me a partner in his telling; a way that suggested he saw me, without knowing me, as someone capable of equal creative insight, with an equal desire and power to create meaning. He was, in other words, an author who was prepared to take the chance of *trusting* the reader. And the reader was me. Whether I liked it or not, I was in for half the work. Bear in mind I hadn't read prose like this before; not Machado de Assis or Marguerite Duras or Jorge Luis Borges, not yet; nor the superbly make-it-up-as-you-go-along disingenuous iconoclasm of *Humphrey Clinker* or...any number of things I subsequently came to and wouldn't, if I hadn't found Alasdair first. The effect upon me was profound. Mind-expanding. All the more so because this author's syntax and references were - I read the same phrases over and over to check it wasn't a ghastly mistake - *like my own*. He was writing, I realised with increasing fascination, something like the language I, too, thought in. Yes I had read Burns (try going to school in Ayrshire and *not* reading Burns). I had read some (very little) Stevenson and the odd bit of Gunn and Lewis Grassic Gibbon was not a total stranger. But for all I'd been to a Scottish University, I had little knowledge of our Literature: little faith we had one, save as add-on pieces, curios, exceptions to rules. What I had read, I couldn't, as yet, own. In short, I'd taken on my education, which told me my country was a toty wee place with no political clout, a joke heritage, dour or dangerous people and writers who were all male, all dead and obsessed with the land, the land or the sea, the sea. Not so, the book said: on a number of levels, not so. Here was someone still alive, and writing about *now* as if it mattered. About my country as if it mattered. Using my tongue as if it mattered. I was so grateful I carried the thing around with me, even when I went out. I forgot meals, went by my stops on buses and had to walk, cried about something else for a change. I didn't care I couldn't sleep, because the book was there on the pillow: dependable, telling me something. Better than the Valium my doctor was so keen for me to get addicted to, it did me more good.

Why was a question I asked only much later. Much later again. And answers shift. They redistribute their weight, sometimes change aspect altogether and it would be foolish to pin them down here as though they don't. The important part, however, the gratitude, stays. It matters to me to say it. By and large (and well after Kristeva, Barthes et al), most literary academics in this country still have difficulty acknowledging or analysing the bravery, compassion or hope that exist in an author's work. How awkwardly, then, they deal with Gray. Through all the self-referring twaddle I've read about Alasdair's 'postmodern postmodernity', the irritable text-book analyses of his techniques and evasions, gracelessly piqued by Alasdair's confounding of easy pigeonholing; through all the twaddle, indeed, I've read about all sorts of contemporary writers' work, I've held that gratitude tight to remind me of something obvious. What matters is not what the Literary Exam-Markers make of a book, what they deem its significance in their Grand Scheme of Things. What matters really is the common reader's share. Me. What it gives *me*.

And what it gave and gives is something freeing. That voice I first heard in *Lanark* wasn't distant or assumptive. It knew its words, syntax and places, things I knew too, only it used them without any tang of apology. It took its own experience and culture as valid and central, not ancient or rural, tourist-trade quaint or rude-mechanical humorous. It spoke to the intellect directly and simply, didn't proscribe what I was meant to see or think and was not afraid of fun or admissions of emotion. It was aware too of the kinds of self-consciousness and repressions I knew, the tangle of guilts that so often inform the Scottish psyche and bedevil its written expression, yet fought them back (by using ingenious technical devices like the asides and list of plagiarisms), containing them enough to let the story not only emerge but be even truer for their inclusion. Even more, however, it was a voice that took for granted it wasn't the only voice. From its own experience of marginalisation (and they are multiple), it knew the truth hinged on questions of sex too. In short, *it was a man's voice that knew that's all it was - a man's*. And what a rare, hopeful shock that gave me. Women in Alasdair's work weren't only present, they were inescapable; a sometimes paranoid, sometimes warm perception of Things Female permeated the narrative and its menfolk even in Her absence. His men seemed intensely aware of a kind of incompleteness; they longed for (or obsessed about) women, wished to be valued by women, to understand and by doing so, heal (a wish that in *1982, Janine* becomes almost unendurable). While Tom Leonard seemed to wish women would make more of an effort to understand his dilemma, and James Kelman seemed to draw women as a separate, unknowable other, Alasdair Gray *yearned*. And this yearning, this poignant, blighted need to bond or communicate more fully with the other sex, literally spoke volumes to me.

Simultaneously, of course, men and male roles, the anguish of men forced into the sausage skin of what passes for normal masculine behaviour, and the effects of such restriction on his men's sometimes cruel, sometimes selfish, sometimes simply bewildered attitudes to women are scarifyingly detailed. That depth of generosity is something remarkable, yet by and large, I've found academic criticism unable or unwilling (maybe they think men have more important things to do than examine gender?), to deal with it. I can though.

I do.

Lanark helped me through a bad time, and I am grateful for it. But it did more than that. Reading it helped me be braver. The voice that made it was a voice like mine and made me feel acknowledged, spoken to; sometimes, even, listened for. He reminded me I had an Oracle too. And for that reassurance, that reminder some stories were yet to tell, I am very grateful indeed.

JANICE GALLOWAY *is the author of two novels and two collections of short stories. Her first novel,* The Trick Is To Keep Breathing, *published in 1990, won the MIND/Allen Lane Book of the Year and was shortlisted for the Whitbread First Novel and Scottish First Book. Her second novel,* Foreign Parts, *won the 1994 McVitie's Prize and in the same year she won the E.M. Forster Award presented by the American Academy of Arts and Letters.* Where You Find It, *her latest short story collection, was published in 1997.*

GRAY, MURIEL

The Trickster
HarperCollins pb 0006477186
£5.99
Furnace
HarperCollins pb 0006496407
£5.99

The Trickster, TV presenter
Muriel Gray's first outing as a
horror writer, is set in a small
town in the Canadian Rockies
that has an ancient evil
buried deep below the
nearby mountains, an evil
that is about to be unleashed.
Furnace is a tale set in a
supposedly sleepy small
American town, but as long-
distance driver Josh Spiller
finds out, Furnace is a town
full of surprises. Muriel Gray
shows a great ability to write
convincing horror in these
accomplished novels.

GREIG, ANDREW

Electric Brae
Canongate pb 0862417406
£6.99
The Return of John McNab
Review pb 0747253536 £6.99

Electric Brae is a well
constructed tale of betrayal,
art, politics and ice-climbing
and at heart a sensitive love
story full of convincing and
sympathetic characters
unrestricted by stereotypes.
It is a novel far removed from
the angry young Scotsman
genre. Sadly beautiful and
evocative *Electric Brae* explores
the ground of relationships
between men and women.
Greig has also written a vivid
recreation of John Buchan's
style and manner in *The
Return of John McNab*, in
which three friends try to
bring the legend to life again.
The book is not a pastiche,
but more an attempt to
reinvent Buchan. Andrew
Greig's fast-moving Highland
adventure shows his eye for
detail and ear for dialogue.

GUNN, NEIL MILLER
(1891–1973)

Born the son of a fisherman
in Caithness, Gunn's
background strongly
influenced the flavour of his
work, being set mainly in the
Highlands during key periods
of its history. He joined the
Civil Service in 1907 and
became a Customs and Excise
officer. In the 30s he became
highly involved with the SNP
and served on several
government committees. He
wrote many short stories
before his first novel, *Grey
Coast*, gained him recognition
and critical acclaim. He then
went on to produce an
impressive body of work. *The
Silver Darlings* is regarded by
many as Gunn's best work.
This novel is set among the
herring fishers of the Scottish
coast, at a time when many of
the fishermen were crofters
forced into fishing after
being dispossessed of their
land in the Clearances. These
people have a strong love-
hate relationship with the
sea, and this relationship is at
the heart of the book. Gunn
conveys this through the story
of Finn's life: the novel starts
when Catrine, his mother,
loses her husband to a press
gang while she is pregnant
with Finn. The remainder of
the work is concerned with
Finn's growth from boy to

man. Gunn takes the reader deep into normally hidden areas of his characters. The novel deals with one of his central themes: that of examining the Highlands throughout history in times of crisis or change. Earlier novels included *Sun Circle*, both a historical novel and a product of Gunn's deepest beliefs, as expressed through the violent conflict between the pagan Vikings and the newly Christianised Pictish tribes in 9th century Scotland. *The Key of the Chest* is one of Gunn's later works in which he returns to the Highlands, only now he portrays a much darker place that confines and imprisons its inhabitants. Brothers Dougald and Charlie are feared and despised by the villagers. Charlie, a disgraced divinity student, is having an affair with the Minister's daughter and is suspected of murdering a sailor and stealing his chest. The only person who can intervene is the village doctor who so clearly observes the mounting crisis. *The Other Landscape*, Gunn's final work, was an attempt to weave together the themes of his life's work in fiction. It is a book of physical and emotional turmoil and conspires to ask questions about the mystery of life which are impossible to answer. Gunn uses his distinctive traits of setting the action in the remote Highlands and drawing on Celtic traditions in this intense novel, which is both tragic and ironic. Many of his books have the common theme of the importance of history and tradition, and its impact on the Highland fishing and crofting communities. Another recurring motif in his work was the loss and eventual recovery of spiritual wholeness. He remains one of the most challenging and exciting of Scotland's twentieth century novelists.

Bloodhunt
Souvenir pb 0285626736 £6.99
Butcher's Broom
Souvenir pb 0285622889 £8.99
Drinking Well
Souvenir pb 0285623303 £6.95
The Green Isle of the Great Deep
Souvenir pb 0285622021 £6.99
Grey Coast
Souvenir pb 0285622536 £4.95
Highland River
Canongate pb 0862413583 £5.99
The Key of the Chest
Canongate pb 0862417708 £6.99
The Lost Glen
Chambers pb 0550230033 £5.99
Morning Tide
Souvenir pb 0285622013 £7.99
The Other Landscape
House Of Lochar pb 1899863265 £8.99
The Serpent
Canongate pb 0862417287 £6.99
Second Sight
Chambers pb 0550230041 £5.99
Silver Bough
Chambers pb 0550230025 £5.99
The Silver Darlings
Faber pb 0571090419 £10.99
Sun Circle
Canongate pb 086241587X £5.99
The Well at the World's End
Canongate pb 0862416450 £5.99
Young Art and Old Hector
Souvenir pb 0285622544 £7.99

HAMILTON, THOMAS

The Youth and Manhood of Cyril Thornton (Ed. Maurice Lindsay)
ASLS hb 0948877111 £17.50

A largely autobiographical novel written in 1827 that details the life and times of Glasgow at the begining of the 19th century.

HAY, J. MACDOUGALL

Gillespie
Canongate pb 086241427X £6.99

The main character in this novel is a monstrous creation: a man driven by the dark force of ambition, which is in turn fuelled by his ruthless cunning. It is relentless in its exploration of the effects of Gillespie's weakness on his home town (based on Hay's home town of Tarbert). The book is a study of a man who brings on his whole family's downfall through defiance of community values, and it examines the perennial conflict between the individual and the community.

HAYNES, DOROTHY K.

Thou Shalt Not Suffer A Witch
B & W pb 1873631618 £6.99

A collection of supernatural stories in which the boundaries of reality and fantasy, and good and evil are blurred. Illustrated with a series of drawings by Mervyn Peake, these haunting and disturbing tales are full of plot twists and turns.

HAYTON, SIAN

Hidden Daughters
Polygon pb 0748661360 £4.99
Last Flight
Polygon pb 0748661654 £4.99

Hidden Daughters is an imaginative combination of Dark Age history and Celtic fantasy that tells the story of Uthebhan's daughter, who is set adrift in the world of mortals without the protection of her father's magic. In *The Last Flight* Essult, the eldest of Uthebhan's daughters, enters the mortal world as a skilled midwife. She is soon courted by the King of the south-west and is forced to choose between her desire for the King's champion, Drust, and the mission she has been sent to accomplish before her death. Another rich tale set on the edge of tenth-century Christendom.

HENDERSON, MEG

The Holy City: A Tale of Clydebank
HarperCollins hb 0002254352
£12.99

Told from the viewpoint of the Macleod family, *The Holy City* is a novel about Clydebank during World War II. It is passionately told and concerns ordinary people's ability to cope with the most adverse conditions with dignity and bravery. A telltale trademark of Henderson's work is the value she places on the morality and goodness of working class people, with particular emphasis on the role of the mother.

HERDMAN, JOHN

Ghostwriting
Polygon pb 0748662111 £7.99

John Herdman's modern take on the Dr. Jekyll and Mr. Hyde story is an eerie and strange affair in which a writer hires a young man to ghostwrite his work, and soon a disturbing merge of identities becomes apparent.

HIRD, LAURA

Nail And Other Stories
Rebel Inc. pb 0862416779 £8.99

A collection of dark, sinister and often surreal tales from one of the most original new voices on the Scottish literary scene, which explores the areas of conflict between sexes and generations. The stories are set in an Edinburgh of gothic tenements and bland suburbs, and are relayed with black humour.

HODGE, JOHN

A Life Less Ordinary
Penguin pb 0140272151 £5.99

John Hodge is one of the creative talents behind the films *Trainspotting* and *Shallow Grave*. This book is his novelisation of the movie of the same name, which he helped to script. The complex plot concerns two new lovers, Robert, who has just lost his job, and Celine who has just killed her boyfriend. Hodge throws several off-beat ideas into the story to twist things a bit further, including bad poetry, karaoke and divine intervention.

HOGG, JAMES (1770–1835)

One of the key figures of Scottish literature, Hogg wrote several works of fiction and poetry, but his most enduring book is *The Private Memoirs of a Justified Sinner*. This macabre novel, written in 1824, is about a man whose extreme religious belief is so strong that he kills his brother, believing he is doing God's work. He also believes that as one of the pre-destined Elect this murder will not endanger his entry to heaven. However, later in his confessions he begins to suspect he has been led astray by the devil. The story is told in three parts: an Editor's narrative, the sinner's account, and the Editor's concluding comments. Hogg's Presbyterian background together with his grounding in reading and debate allowed him to write with belief and scepticism at the same time. The novel asks its readers to decide for themselves whether the man was possessed by the devil or not. It is full of hints about magic, mystery and possession and mixes theological satire with local legend. Ultimately the evil at the heart of the novel has as much to do with the twisting of religious ideology as with a physical manifestation of evil itself. Hogg's other works, particularly his verse, are steeped in the oral tradition passed on to him by his mother. Because of his country background and his childhood in farm service he was affectionately known as 'the Ettrick Shepherd' and his poetry occasionally shows the influence of Robert Burns. His other major and unjustly overshadowed work, *The Three Perils of Man*, is a fantastic fusion of folklore and innovation which reads in parts like a modern psychological work of fiction.

James Hogg

The Collected Works of James Hogg:
Anecdotes of Scott (Ed J. Rubenstein)
EUP hb 0748609334 £20.00
Lay Sermons (Ed G. Hughes & DS Mack)
EUP hb 0748607463 £29.50
Queen Hynde (Ed D.S. Mack & S Gilbert)
EUP hb 0748609342 £29.50
A Queer Book (Ed P. Garside)
EUP hb 0748605061 £29.50
The Shepherd's Calendar (Ed D.S. Mack)
EUP hb 074860474X £29.50
Tales of The Wars of Montrose (Ed G. Hughes)
EUP hb 0748606351 £29.50
The Three Perils of Woman (Ed D Groves et al)
EUP hb 0748604774 £32.50
Confessions of a Justified Sinner
Everyman pb 0460874713 £1.99
The Private Memoirs and Confessions of a Justified Sinner
Canongate pb 0862413400 £4.99
The Private Memoirs and Confessions of a Justified Sinner
Penguin pb 0140431985 £4.99
The Private Memoirs and Confessions of a Justified Sinner
OUP pb 0192815563 £4.99
The Three Perils of Man
Canongate pb 0862416469 £8.99

HOOD, EVELYN

Damask Days
Warner pb 0751518913 £5.99

A heart-warming tale of a young Paisley girl who dreams of bettering herself, set in the world of the fledgl-ing textile industry. Rich in events and characters, this book, along with her other works, will appeal to readers of Catherine Cookson and Emma Blair.
Another Day
Warner pb 075150839X £5.99
McAdam's Women
Warner pb 0751508411 £.99
A Matter of Mischief
Warner pb 0751518921 £5.99
Pebbles On The Beach
Warner pb 0751508403 £5.99
The Silken Thread
Warner pb 0751518395 £5.99

HOUSTON, TERRY

The Wounded Stone
Argyll pb 1874640882 £7.99

The tale of a modern-day rebellion funded by a long-lost Jacobite treasure. Along the way the US president's son becomes one of the rebels, a Royal is assassinated and Edinburgh Castle is put under siege. This is a contemporary novel which uses some of the same structures as *Kidnapped* and relays a fast-paced adventure of unrelenting action.

HUTH, ANGELA

Wives of the Fishermen
Little,Brown hb 0316643874 £15.99

The harsh background of a Scottish fishing village is the setting for Angela Huth's novel of love and loss, in which the delicate structure of two women's friendship is explored.

JACOB, VIOLET (1865–1946)

Violet Jacob grew up in Angus in a wealthy aristocratic family. She started writing seriously in 1890, when she accompanied her military husband to India. As a Scottish woman in a colonial society she had the status of both insider and outsider, and her writing strongly reflects this. She liked to explore and challenge to some extent the boundaries of her society and time, while remaining a part of that society. She exposes power structures and many of her main characters are marginalised by society. In particular the unconventional Victorian woman recurs in her work. Regarded by some as a writer in the Kailyard style, her best works, particularly *Flemington*, are much more powerful and complex than the narrow confines of that school. *Flemington* was first published in 1911. Set around the time of the 1745 rebellion, it is the tale of a young painter whose visit to the House of Balnillo leads him into a world of adventure, action and great danger. Jacob is careful with the pacing of the novel, slowly but surely intensifying the emotional power and building to a dramatic conclusion. As well as being a Scots romance, the novel contains sophisticated characters and has a strong sense of internal realism. The Canongate edition of the novel includes a selection of Jacob's shorter fiction. She had a recognised place in the literary scene of her time and was compared to Hardy, although until recently her merit as a novelist and short story writer were eclipsed by her success as a poet.
Flemington and Tales From Angus
Canongate pb 0862417848 £8.99
The Lum Hat And Other Stories
Mercat Press hb 0080284493 £4.99

JENKINS, ROBIN

Born in Lanarkshire Robin Jenkins was educated at Glasgow University and worked as a teacher both in Scotland and in countries such as Afghanistan and Borneo. His varied experiences at home and abroad provided much of the inspiration for many of his novels. Set on a country estate, *The Cone Gatherers* is regarded as one of Jenkins' best early works. It is the story of the conflict between an evil gamekeeper and the Christ-like figure of Calum, a simple-minded hunchback who collects pine cones for their seeds. The novel is written almost as a fable, and together with Jenkins' use of poetic language, this infuses the work with an exceptional quality of timelessness. *Fergus Lamont* is the tale of its eponymous hero, who is born an illegitimate child of the Glasgow slums and goes on to redefine his identity, and it is one of success, self-absorption and betrayal. It has at its heart some of Jenkins' later major concerns: that of the restrictive and damaging nature of Scottish society, and the need for an almost spiritual transcendence. Jenkins' ability to evoke a time and place is well used in *Guests of War* in which he imagines a Scottish city, 'Gowburgh', facing up to the onset of World War Two and realising they are bound to be a prime target for the Luftwaffe. The women and children are evacuated to the Borders and the book looks at the consequences of their impact on a remote, middle-class town: a powerful portrait of Scotland at war. Football is a major Scottish preoccupation and Jenkins is one of the few major novelists to examine this. *A Would-Be Saint* is a deeply intelligent novel about a brilliant young Scottish footballer set just before, during and after World War II. His beliefs on non-violence bring him into conflict with his community and eventually cause him to become a conscientious objector. *The Thistle and the Grail* takes a lighter, more comic view in its story of a small Lanarkshire town team's pursuit of the Scottish Junior Cup. In a totally different vein is Jenkins' historical novel *The Awakening of George Darroch*. This novel is based around the Great Disruption of 1843, a conflict which pulled the Church of Scotland apart. The conflict is

JAMIESON, SANDY

The Great Escape
Ringwood pb 1901514013
£7.99

Derek Duncan is a new Scottish manager brought in to revitalise the fortunes of relegation possibility Griston City in this novel that explores the pressures of the professional football world.

JAMIESON, ROBERT A.

Thin Wealth
Polygon pb 0948275103 £4.95
Jamieson's second novel is set in his native Shetland during the oil boom years. It relays the effect the arrival of this industry had on Shetland life in several distinct and different voices which view these changes in radically different ways. Some of these voices belong to natives of the island, others to in-comers, some are for and some against. A carefully plotted novel describing Shetland at a time of irreversible change.

explored through the main character George Darroch who struggles to decide whether he should act in accordance with his conscience or live up to his obligations to family and church. He is a complex and subtle character full of contradictory ideas and emotions. The novel explores personal and religious conflicts in a compelling fashion.

The Awakening of George Darroch
B & W pb 1873631529 £6.99
The Changeling
Canongate pb 0862412285 £4.99
The Cone Gatherers
Penguin pb 0140109331 £6.99
Fergus Lamont
Canongate pb 0862413109 £6.99
Guests of War
B & W pb 1873631707 £6.99
Just Duffy
Canongate pb 0862415519 £4.99
Leila
Polygon pb 0748662049 £8.99
A Love of Innocence
B & W pb 1873631480 £6.99
Lunderston Tales
Polygon pb 0748662219 £8.99
The Thistle and the Grail
Polygon pb 074866193X £8.99
A Would-Be Saint
B & W pb 1873631472 £6.99
Willie Hogg
Polygon pb 0748661522 £7.95

KAY, NORA

Nora Kay is an adopted Scot who has lived nearly all her life in Scotland. She released her first novel when she was in her sixties, and hasn't stopped writing since. Her family saga books are all set in Scotland, many in the Dundee area. They range in period from the late Victorian era to the 1930s. Her most recent book is *Gift Of Love*.

Best Friends
Hodder & Stoughton pb 034061386 £4.99
Beth
Hodder & Stoughton pb 0340639970 £5.99
Gift of Love
Hodder & Stoughton pb 0340689641 £5.99
Lost Dreams
Hodder & Stoughton pb 0340639997 £5.99
A Woman of Spirit
Hodder & Stoughton pb 034061336X £4.99

KELMAN, JAMES

James Kelman was born in Glasgow and educated at Hyndland Secondary School. His family briefly emigrated to America and he returned to Scotland in 1972. His first stories, *An Old Pub Near The Angel*, were published in America. He met Alasdair Gray, Tom Leonard and Liz Lochhead while attending evening classes. Architect of the intense, hard-edged school of new Scottish fiction, his work often has a strong working-class aesthetic and Kafkaesque elements. His fiction tends to show characters full of frustrated desire and anger. These inner feelings of the central characters are developed and emphasised, Kelman deliberately focusing on the characters rather than involved plots. His first collection of short stories published in Britain, *Not Not While the Giro*, appeared in 1983. The stories are written with a delicate touch, anger and biting sarcasm and are set in the urban environment that forms the background to all of his work: places such as race tracks, job centres and snooker bars. However for Kelman the characters and the way they deal with everyday life in psychological terms is at the heart of all these tales and of prime importance. Kelman's Booker Prize winning novel, *How Late It Was, How Late*, is a hard-edged work of great social depth that is punctuated by his dry humour. Sammy, the narrator, is suffering: his new shoes have been stolen along with his wallet, and he's gone blind after being beaten up by the police. He's now let loose to face up to an uncertain future. The novel is a deep exploration of ordinary lives set in Glasgow, written in Kelman's abrasive prose style. The main character strips his feelings down in front of the reader, constantly revealing ever greater depths within himself. Through this exploration of the character and the way he faces up to his many problems Kelman creates a tough work which ultimately has positive things to say about the human character. His latest book, *The Good Times*, is a collection of short stories featuring twenty first person narratives. All reveal men or boys faced with difficult truths such as coming upon some aspect of their own mortality, struggling to understand work or women, or encountering betrayals. Kelman's most recent work is tender, lyrical and dark and shows that he is undoubtedly a master of the short story form. He has also written plays, the best of which is *Hardie And Baird: The Last Days* set during the 1820's weavers' uprising.

The Burn
Minerva pb 074939949X £6.99
The Busconductor Hines
Phoenix pb 1857990358 £5.99
A Chancer
Minerva pb 0749395958 £6.99
A Disaffection
Picador pb 0330307363 £7.99
The Good Times
Secker & Warburg hb 0436412152 £15.99
Greyhound For Breakfast
Picador pb 033030027X £5.99
How Late It Was, How Late
Minerva pb 0749398833 £6.99
Lean Tales (with Agnes Owens and Alasdair Gray)
Vintage pb 0099585413 £5.99
Not Not While The Giro
Minerva pb 074939028X £6.99

KENNAWAY, JAMES
(1928–1968)
Tunes Of Glory
Canongate pb 0862412234 £3.50

Kennaway's first and most famous novel, *Tunes of Glory*, published in 1956, is the exploration of a tragic conflict between two soldiers with very different natures who are vying for the colonelship of a Highland regiment. The underlying themes of the novel are isolation and mental breakdown. The book was later adapted into a very successful film.

KENNEDY, A.L.

Born in Dundee, A.L. Kennedy is a major figure in new Scottish fiction. Her works have several strands that link them. These include her perceptive analysis of people, satirical views of Scotland, surrealism and an empathy for society's outsiders. Kennedy captures her characters and their stories with striking detail, confronting realism with disconcerting, almost sub-conscious images. Like Janice Galloway she creates her stories with a style that encompasses both gravity and humour, and her work often reveals her love of the bizarre and the supernatural. Her writing is both powerful and subtle, and the reader often has to piece the whole story together from fragments of information and the character's impressions. The range of voices in her short story collections is strikingly varied, moving from first person monologues to narrative storytelling and bizarre surrealism. *Night Geometry and The Garscadden Trains* was A.L. Kennedy's first book, a collection of short stories that shot her into the literary limelight and won the John Llewellyn Rhys Prize and the Saltire Award for Best First Book along the way. It contains fifteen often troubling tales of lonely characters pondering the great mysteries of the twentieth century. *Original Bliss* was a further collection of short stories about love and sex or the pain of their absence. Each story is highly perceptive and individualistic, moving effortlessly from the domains of public to private concerns. In these works Kennedy once again showed she is an author with an outstanding command of language. Her two novels are *So I Am Glad* and *Looking for the Possible Dance*. The erotic and personally revealing memories of radio announcer M. Jennifer Wilson are at the heart of *So I Am Glad*. A.L. Kennedy writes in the first person narrative, speaking to the reader as if they were part of an intimate confession being broadcast by the main character over the radio. Mixing in Cyrano de Bergerac, magical realism, the possibilities of love and the main character's sexual self, the novel has much to say about our present generation. It was the joint winner of the 1995 Saltire Scottish Book of the Year Award. In *Looking for the Possible Dance* Kennedy uses her character's memories of dance to sum up human hope and resilience. The structure, with its fragments of different experiences and thoughts, asks the reader to work out the narrative from these pieces. The central character, Margaret, is unable to move on emotionally after the death of her father, which leads to difficulties in her relationship with her lover, Colin. Her first childhood memories are of dancing with her father, and throughout the story she seeks the ultimate dance. Kennedy's distinctive bizarre elements are in evidence and add to the development of Margaret's relationship with Colin. The novel won a Somerset Maugham award.

Looking For The Possible Dance
Secker & Warburg pb
0749397486 £7.99
Night Geometry And The Garscadden Trains
Phoenix pb 1857990668 £4.99
Now That You're Back
Vintage pb 0099457113 £5.99
Original Bliss
Vintage pb 0099730715 £5.99
So I Am Glad
Vintage pb 0099457210 £5.99

Bicycling in Corduroy - Religious Extremism and Scottish Literature

by A.L. Kennedy

Scottish literature, something which currently has a reputation for foul-mouthed, chemically-altered iconoclasm, is in fact deeply traditional and much influenced by the more extreme manifestations of Scottish religion. I can say this, because this is a literary essay and in a literary essay it's possible to say almost anything and then load your piece with convenient quotes and a bit of spurious anthropology to prove your point. But in this case, I may even be telling the truth.

First, a little history. In 1707 the parliaments of Scotland and England were joined in a shady deal involving a good few back-handers of one kind or another - one of which created an established and influential Protestant Church of Scotland. This gave a joy-hating, woman-hating, sex-hating, body-hating, Scot-hating manifestation of Calvinist Protestantism a considerable degree of power in the land. Already in place was the smaller - and sometimes suppressed - Catholic Church, an institution equally enlightened in its views on sex, women and enjoyment. There were also a variety of other manifestations of Protestantism available to ban bicycling on Sundays and the reckless wearing of corduroy. This may explain why the Scots joke about religion in the way the Eastern Europeans used to joke about Communism.

On the other hand, there are the more Pictish, Celtic, tribal, heathen, call-them-what-you-like influences which remain fairly misty and are recorded in generally critical observations made by Roman invaders, Dark Age Christian missionaries, Hanoverian troops and so forth. They seem to have involved a certain love of the extreme, whether in nude, berserker styles of warfare, or good nights out. They also seem to be recorded in the last hiding places of suppressed cultures - songs, myths, stories, ballads and forbidden or 'unfit' languages and dialects.

This means that Scotland is a country of extreme self-denial, emotional and erotic suppression, besotted with conformity, morality, hard work, hard education and bourgeois values. Not to mention virtuous death. It is also a country of artistic abundance, linguistic ecstasy and self-indulgence, besotted with the extremes of its own imagination and physical capacity, and with general chaos. Not to mention heroic death.

These are, of course, the extremes immortalised in the *Dr. Jekyll And Mr. Hyde* of **R.L. Stevenson**. And Stevenson provides an ideal starting point to examine some of the trends we might choose to see in Scottish literature. Stevenson deals with the energy - destructive and creative - generated between opposing forces. He sees the fascination in darkness and chaos, he sees the hypocrisy in the good that is based on ignorance and luck, rather than virtue, he digs - paticularly in his later short stories - behind the apparent virtues of commerce. The street where Jekyll lives has an apparently prosperous, upwardly mobile facade and yet it also contains the door to Hell. Stevenson, in an age in love with empire, showed shabby, venereal disease-riddled Brits abroad, conning, killing and generally screwing native populations.

We might say then that, like **James Hogg** and **Robert Burns** before him, Stevenson fuelled his own creativity from the charge between opposites while also taking it as an inspiration. The same could be said of **Alasdair Gray, Ronald Frame, Betsy White, Elspeth Davie, Jessie Kesson, Margaret Oliphant, Naomi Mitchison, Muriel Spark, George MacDonald, Duncan McLean** and **Irvine Welsh**. All share a sense of the surreality of reality, an outrage at hypocrisy, a clear sense of moral 'rightness' outwith their current society, a fascination with death and God. **Spark's** short story *The Sunday Class* questions the assumed order of God's creation while *The Black Madonna* questions the comforts and prejudices of faith.

Amongst people with such cosmic concerns, it's unsurprising that the Devil, Death and God all appear amongst their characters. The Devil tends to appear in earlier work as a rather dashing, seductive and utterly cruel influence. **Hogg's** 'justified' sinner - assured of a place in heaven, whatever he does - becomes his own *doppelgänger* and his own Satan. Death appears in **Stevenson's** *Will O' The Mill* as a sympathetic, gentle but irresistible force. More recently, God appears in the role of a disinterested Author-behind-the-Author in **Alasdair Gray's** *Lanark* and is a highly inexplicable, numinous presence in most of Gray's work. In **Welsh's** *The Granton Star Cause* God is the coolly and easily cruel author of the central character's hellish catalogue of woes. More minor mysteries, ghosts, memories and visions of conscience rattle through much of Scottish literature.

Nourished on the power of 'The Word' and the power of myth, it's not surprising that Scottish authors quite often break out of the bounds of strict reality. Female authors like **Margaret Oliphant, Elspeth Davie** and **Jessie Kesson** seem to have particularly gravitated to this area of freedom, perhaps as a reaction to the patriarchal society around them, perhaps because literary culture expected whimsy of them and was often incapable of discerning their subversive intentions. The wonderful **Naomi Mitchison** who began writing in the late 1920s - and was arrested for painting Left-wing slogans on the walls of her own family's home - only seemed to feel secure in addressing sexually and politically explosive areas by transporting her characters to other, earlier cultures. Scots female authors are continuing to experiment with the boundaries of reality and also, like **Janice Galloway**, addressing current, highly realistic social concerns. A small number like Galloway (and possibly myself) are now, finally, beginning to find a place on equal footing with their male counterparts, but - in a marketing-led culture - they will always be harder for publishers to sell when the successful - although largely spurious - male Scots author model (macho, hard-drinking, hard-talking, needle-sharing, sexually-indiscriminate) is difficult to apply successfully to women. Female Scottish authors have historically had a shorter shelf life or have come to be identified as 'English'.

Nevertheless, brought up with the tension between forbidden and permitted forms of language it's not a surprise that all Scottish authors, having chosen to use transgressive forms of language, now deal with transgressive topics, including their own sexuality. Once a soul is damned, after all, why not let it be really damned. **James Kelman** attacks the structure of society in prose larded with 'obscenity', **Tom Leonard** questions linguistic and social orthodoxy in 'street language', just as **Robert Burns** reminded a highly stratified (and revolution-shy) society of the equality of man in Lallans - 'Plough-hand's language' - and **Christopher Whyte** can conjure sex and homosexuality into the Catholic Church.

More and more, modern authors seem genuinely free to use whatever language they like - standard or non-standard - to explore even the most extreme areas of experience. Centuries of linguistic and moral oppression have, unsurprisingly, produced authors who understand the transformative energy of language and who believe in the equality of souls and their freedom to face anything, even God. Threaten a nation with Death and Damnation often enough and it will feel it has nothing left to lose, hence perhaps the outbursts of courage, outrage and energy which have almost become an identifying feature of Scottish writing.

A.L. KENNEDY *has written two novels and three short story collections. In 1993 she was chosen as one of the 20 Best of Young British Novelists. Her short stories have won numerous prizes including the Saltire Award for Best First Book. Her first novel,* Looking For The Possible Dance, *won a Somerset Maugham award, and her second,* So I Am Glad, *was joint winner of the 1995 Saltire Scottish Book of the Year. She wrote the script for the BFI/Channel 4 film* Stella Does Tricks, *and her most recent book,* Original Bliss, *was published in 1997.*

KESSON, JESSIE (1916-1994)

Born Jessie Grant MacDonald in a workhouse in Elgin, she was moved to an orphanage when her mother contracted syphilis. The anguish at being separated from her mother at such an early age had profound effects on her. From a very young age her mother's love of music, literature and magic inspired her to become a writer. She was deprived of a university education and went into service in 1932 where she suffered a breakdown. She married in 1934 and moved around Scotland following her husband's career. She worked for many years as an artist's model, cinema cleaner and social worker before eventually being able to devote her time to writing. She wrote plays, novels, poetry and work for radio. She died in London in 1994. Her writing is of the highest quality, every word being carefully considered and judged. Many of her works are rooted in her own difficult personal past. Her ability to combine regional interests with universal themes makes her books very accessible. Her works are rigorously honest, full of intellect and memory, and despite their often grim subject matter are full of human warmth and humour. *The White Bird Passes*, a highly autobiographical novel, is commonly viewed as Jessie Kesson's finest work. Based on her remarkable and very difficult childhood which was full of harsh deprivations and severe hardship, the story has deeply moving passages, shines with honesty and is written in a perfectly balanced prose style.

Another Time Another Place
B & W pb 1873631715 £5.99
The White Bird Passes
B & W pb 1873631693 £5.99

> "Edinburgh. Glasgow. Aberdeen. Dundee. How small Scotland sounded, summed up by its four main cities, but what a width of world its little villages stravaiged."
> Jessie Kesson,
> Glitter of Mica

KUPPNER, FRANK

Kuppner is a quirky and individual writer. In *Life on a Dead Planet* an unnamed narrator wanders through a city at dusk imagining the events behind closed doors and talking to inanimate objects, meeting women and giving them imagined lives. This philosophical book is a perfect platform for Frank Kuppner's finely honed observations on human behaviour. *Something Very Like A Murder* is a hybrid book, part crime story and part journal. Kuppner follows up *A Very Quiet Street*, which is not currently available, with this book that explores time, memory and synchronicity by researching the crime and motives of wretched murderer Bertie Willox, examining his feelings at losing his parents.

A Concussed History of Scotland
Polygon pb 0748660593 £9.99
Life On A Dead Planet
Polygon pb 0748661514 £7.99
Something Very Like Murder (McVities's Prize Winner)
Polygon pb 0748661816 £8.99

LECKIE, ROSS

Scipio
Canongate hb 0862417252 £16.99

The sequel to Ross Leckie's first novel *Hannibal* is about Publius Cornelius Scipio, the man who defeated Hannibal and set the foundations of the Roman Empire. The novel vividly recreates the power and pageantry of the ancient world.

Hannibal
Little, Brown pb 0349108269 £6.99

LEGGE, GORDON

Legge's short story collection, *In Between Talking About The Football*, was his debut as a writer and won him a Scottish Arts Council Award. Less intense than Welsh and more humorous, yet covering the same territory, his stories of sex, music, dope and, of course, football, chart the main obsessions of many young Scots in a way which shows Legge already has a marvellous ear for dialogue. He continued this theme in his first novel, *The Shoe*, a snapshot of the life of Archie, a fan of all things laddish, told in a hilarious and entertaining fashion. His second collection of short stories, *Near Neighbours*, features a colourful cast of characters who live for football, music and sex, who are also window-fetishists, cross-gender *doppelgängers* and sock-throwers. His journeys into urban life are farce-laden affairs full of paranoid creations, who still have a deep-seated humanity to them.

I Love Me, Who Do You Love?
Polygon pb 0748661840 £8.99
In Between Talking About The Football
Polygon pb 0748661123 £7.99
Near Neighbours
Cape pb 0224051202 £9.99
The Shoe
Polygon pb 0748660801 £8.99

LILLIE, HELEN

Home to Strathblane
Argyll pb 1874640408 £5.99
Strathblane and Away
Argyll pb 1874640475 £6.99

Helen Lillie's Strathbane novels are recreations of 18th century life set primarily in the Scottish Borders. She weaves historical detail and atmosphere into her narrative. The themes of her books show her to be familiar with the work of Scott and his tradition.

LINGARD, ANN

Figure In A Landscape
Review pb 0747252963 £5.99

Ann Lingard's debut novel concerns a guilt-ridden woman who lives a quiet, solitary life in a cottage on a remote Scottish island. Her fragile emotional balance is disturbed when a zoologist sets up camp near her to study seals, and in an attempt to protect her solitude she tries to sabotage his work. Things take a new twist when it is she who is forced to move, as her cottage is destroyed in a storm. These changes are to bring a new sense of purpose into her life. The background details are well described in this novel of personal emotional release and discovery.
Fiddler's Leg
Hodder & Stoughton pb
0747252971 £6.99

LINGARD, JOAN
(b. 1933)

Joan Lingard has written over twenty novels and is noted for her successful evocation of contemporary Scottish society, particularly in Edinburgh. The actions and lives of her female characters are often shown to be limited by prevailing views of class and gender. *Dreams Of Love And Modest Glory* has a more European setting. The main characters are witnesses of the Russian Revolution and Latvia's subsequent struggle for independence. The events are seen from several viewpoints: those of Aberdonian twins Lily and Garnet, their respective husbands (a Latvian and a Russian) and the twins' grandchildren, who later want to find out about their family history. There is a distinctive Scottish perspec-tive of the events, as the stability of Lily and Garnet's Scottish middle class back-ground is contrasted with the chaos encompassing Eastern Europe of that time. The characters are well drawn, the varied settings rich in detail and Lingard thoughtfully probes some deep moral issues.
Dreams of Love and Modest Glory
Random House pb 0749323531 £6.99

LINKLATER, ERIC (1899-1974)

Although born in Wales, Eric Linklater moved to Orkney in his early childhood and regarded himself very much an Orcadian. His medical studies at Aberdeen University were interrupted by World War One. He was a sniper for the Black Watch, a horrific experience which was to later inspire his anti-war comedy *Private Angelo*, and a volume of his autobiography, *Fanfare For A Tin Hat*. After the war he took a degree in English Literature before working as a journalist in various countries. During World War Two he worked with the War Office recovering the hidden art treasures of Florence. His first novel, *White Maa's Saga*, set on Orkney, was soon followed by several others including *Poet's Pub* and *Juan In America*. He quickly established a reputation as a writer of satirically humorous works. He went on to write twenty three novels, many of which are now out of print. He also wrote children's books, military history, biographies, plays, travel books and three volumes of autobiography. One of the few books left in print is *Magnus Merriman*, a satirical novel of Scottish life in which budding lover, writer, politician and crofter Merriman hysterically displays his predisposition for failure. No major aspect of Scottish life is spared Linklater's treatment, which reveals the farcical nature of much of the characters' lives.
Magnus Merriman
Canongate pb 0862413133 £4.95
Private Angelo
Canongate pb 0862413761 £5.95

LOUVISH, SIMON

The Days of Miracles and Wonders
Canongate pb 0862418151

Louvish has been compared to the likes of Heller and Vonnegut. This keenly observed satire is concerned with the West's attitudes to the Middle East. At turns surreal, comic and dark, the novel is multi-layered and weaves together numerous threads, from the resurrection of Richard the Lionheart in 1990 to the appearance of the fallen angel of Beirut. A dazzling, complex piece by a gifted writer.

MCARTHUR, ALEXANDER & KINGSLEY LONG, H.

McArthur and Long wrote a classic novel about Glasgow's slum underworld which has coloured the way many people have viewed the city ever since it was first published in 1935. *No Mean City* paints a vivid portrait of the Gorbals area and its violent razor gangs through the story of Johnnie Stark, 'Razor King' of the Gorbals, son of a violent father and downtrodden mother. The novel is powerfully authentic in feel and is indeed heavily based on fact.
No Mean City
Transworld pb 0552075833
£5.99

MCCABE, BRIAN

The Lipstick Circus And Other Stories
Mainstream pb 0906391881
£5.95

A collection of short stories that reveal Brian McCabe's imaginative, lyrical and often humorous style. From a therapist being mistaken for a patient to futuristic factories, his choice of subject matters underlie his concern for the problems of modern society.

MCCALL SMITH, ALEXANDER

Heavenly Date
Canongate pb 0862415357
£8.99

McCall Smith's eye for the human condition is sharp in this collection of short stories. His weird imagination creates both shocking and sinister tales with middle class settings.

MCCALLION, HARRY

Hunter Killer
Penguin pb 0140270965 £5.99

A modern retelling of Buchan's *Thirty-Nine Steps* in which a wounded man with amnesia is relentlessly chased across the moors of a Scottish estate. A stylised adventure thriller.

MACCOLLA, FIONN
(1906-1975)

Born Thomas Douglas MacDonald in Montrose, he trained as a teacher and lectured at the Scots College in Safed, Palestine. On his return in 1929 he went back to teaching, mainly in the Western Isles, and on his retirement in 1967 he moved to Edinburgh. His first novel, *The Albannach*, is set in the Highlands and explores among other things the constraints of Scottish rural life and how rebirth of local tradition and community spirit can alleviate this. All of MacColla's writing is informed by his own beliefs about Scotland, which he saw as a country with great potential encumbered by negative forces such as Calvinism and lack of political independence. *And The Cock Crew* takes up these same threads in the setting of the Clearances. MacColla wrote relatively few works but is nonetheless a major figure of the Scottish renaissance.

The Albannach
Souvenir pb 0285626744 £4.95
And The Cock Crew
Canongate pb 0862415365
£4.99

MCCRONE, GUY

The Wax Fruit Trilogy
B & W pb 1873631219 £8.99

Guy McCrone's three novels, *Antimacassar City*, *The Philistines*, and *The Puritans* are brought together to form an omnibus edition. The trilogy charts the rise of the Moorhouse family from Ayrshire farmers to prominent and wealthy Glasgow citizens. The books are occasionally clichéd in their observations of Victorian society. However the reconstructions of family life, coupled with the depiction of Glasgow at the height of the Victorian age, make them well worth reading.

Aunt Bel
B & W pb 1873631391 £5.99
The Hayburn Family
B & W pb 1873631588 £6.99

MACDOUGALL, CARL

Stone Over Water
Minerva pb 0749390905 £6.99
The Lights Below
Minerva pb 0749397144 £5.99
The Casanova Papers
Minerva pb 0749395249 £6.99

Stone Over Water is Carl MacDougall's impressive first novel. It is largely concerned with what it means to be Scottish. Angus McPhail ends up having an incestuous relationship with his adoptive sister and looking after number one, his self-absorption having already destroyed several relationships with other women. His adoptive brother is busy robbing banks in the name of Scottish socialism. A novel with a delicate touch that is also funny and compelling. In *The Lights Below* a bright young man returns to Glasgow after a term in prison on drugs charges, a charge of which he was innocent. He finds Glasgow much changed since he was put away and sets about trying to readjust and to find out who framed him and why. A well-constructed story that has much to say about Glasgow and one man's experiences and feelings there, written by one of Glasgow's more sensitive writers. *The Casanova Papers* is a mature and complex work in which a Glasgow journalist finds an account of the life of Giacomo Casanova de Signault. As he works through it, it starts to have an influence on his own life and his attempts to make sense of existence after his wife's death. A stylishly realised work, that resonates with meditative intensity.
Elvis Is Dead
Mariscat Press pb 0946588090 £4.95

MCGINN, MATT

Fry The Little Fishes
Calder hb 0714509922 £8.99

This is the only published novel by the well-known Glasgow folk singer and poet. Based on his own experience it is set in a war-time Catholic reform school in Glasgow (he was sent to one for stealing sweets.) The novel is full of humour and skilfully captures the flavour of local life.

MCILVANNEY, WILLIAM A.

Born in Kilmarnock, William McIlvanney finished his education at Glasgow University, going on to become a teacher. In 1975 he left this career to concentrate on his writing. His first novel, *Remedy Is None*, is an uncompromising story of a young man being forced to confront and reappraise his working class past. *Docherty* visits this territory again, the novel being set in Graithnock, an industrial town, during the first quarter of this century. Related from the viewpoint of a young boy, Conn Docherty, the novel creates a powerful sense of place and time, and Conn's father Tam is a vividly realistic character who dominates the book. McIlvanney has written several detective novels set in Glasgow and featuring tough cop Jack Laidlaw *(see Crime Fiction)*. He has also written journalistic pieces and poetry. All of his works are tied together by his interest in the Scottish working classes whose values and beliefs he celebrates, while also commenting on the erosion of these same values in the late 20th century.

The Big Man
Sceptre pb 0340403136 £6.99
Docherty
Sceptre pb 0340407573 £6.99
A Gift From Nessus
Mainstream pb 1851583262 £5.99
The Kiln
Sceptre pb 0340657367 £6.99
The Remedy Is None
0550230068 £5.99
Walking Wounded
Sceptre pb 034050918X £5.99

MCKAY, RON
The Leper Colony
Gollancz pb 0575064749 £9.99

John Downe is clearing away his dead father's possessions. For years there had been only animosity between them. As he tidies up he comes across three dramatic surprises: a passbook with a huge amount of money, a strange photo of his family, and a bomb exploding outside in his hired car. What he thought was reality slowly slips as he realises he has been living under an assumed name and his real past awaits him in Glasgow. A taut, dynamic novel full of the unexpected.
Mean City
Hodder & Stoughton pb
0340617705 £5.99

"... the heart of any place is the relationships you have there. Geography is people."
William McIlvanney

MACKAY, SHENA

Born in Edinburgh, Shena Mckay was brought up in England and published her first book while still in her teens. This was *Dust Falls on Eugene Schlumberger and Toddler on the Run*, two novellas about the urban dispossessed rebelling against the authority that binds them. Amongst her idiosyncratic, often very funny novels are *A Bowl of Cherries* and *Music Upstairs. A Bowl of Cherries* is the story of Rex and Stanley, twins whose connections are deep and close. When Rex's daughter finds a boy in the woods and decides to keep him, a strange relationship blossoms. Like much of Shena Mackay's work this novel unravels some of the more bizarre mysteries of modern living. In *Music Upstairs* a young woman starts a sexual relationship with the couple who are her neighbours. She vacillates between them, oblivious to the chaos around her and the increasingly obsessive behaviour of the male of the couple. Shena Mackay's latest work, *The Artist's Widow*, examines four apparently unrelated incidents in London, but as the story unwinds in New York and London connections between these events and people are brought to light. This is an absorbing, well-handled novel that is the literary equivalent of an intricate jigsaw being constructed.

An Advent Calendar
Vintage pb 0099270781 £5.99
The Artist's Widow
Cape hb 0224051342 £14.99
A Bowl of Cherries
Vintage pb 009927079X £5.99
Collected Short Stories
Penguin pb 0140179011 £7.99
Dunedin
Penguin pb 0140176357 £6.99
Dust Falls On Eugene Schlumberger and Toddler On The Run
Vintage pb 009927406X £6.99
Music Upstairs
Vintage pb 0099270765 £5.99
Old Crow
Vintage pb 0099270749 £5.99
Orchard On Fire
Minerva pb 0749394064 £5.99
Redhill Rococo
Vintage pb 0099270773 £5.99

MACKENZIE, SIR COMPTON (1883–1972)

The great Scottish comic novel was actually written by an Englishman born in West Hartlepool, although both Compton Mackenzie's parents were Scottish and in his long writing career he made much use of Scottish characters and Scottish settings. *Whisky Galore*, his richly humorous tale of the wrecking of a ship filled with whisky just off the coast of Eriskay and the subsequent salvage of its cargo was heavily based on fact. Along with its sequel, *Rockets Galore*, it was adapted in the fifties into a highly successful film.

Highland Omnibus
Penguin pb 0140065415 £9.99
Whisky Galore
Penguin pb 0140012206 £6.99

Sir Compton Mackenzie

MCKENZIE, JOHN

Are You Boys Cyclists?
Serpent's Tail pb 1852425342
£8.99

This is the second novel by ex-boxer John McKenzie. It is a potent and violent mix of sex and boxing that explores the drives that motivate boxers. Set in Edinburgh in 1977, this is a reflective and occasionally funny book full of graphic descriptions of violent sex and fights interspersed with highly personal observations. Writing in a powerful, no-holds-barred fashion, McKenzie belongs very much to the hard new wave of Scottish writing.

MACLAVERTY, BERNARD

Grace Notes
Vintage pb 0099778017 £5.99

Renowned Irish author Bernard MacLaverty's latest work is set partly in Ireland and partly in Scotland. It revolves around the life of a woman composer who is struggling to maintain her artistic talent and credibility while her personal life crumbles around her. The book builds into a delicate yet powerful vision of her life, revealing its full and intricate nature.

MACLEAN, ALISTAIR
(1922–1987)

Born in Glasgow, he served in the Royal Navy during World War II. After graduating from Glasgow University in 1947 he began a career as a teacher. At the age of 32 he entered a *Glasgow Herald* short story competition, which he won. The short story in question, 'The Dileas', so impressed Ian Chapman, an editor at Collins, that he offered him a contract. The resulting novel, *HMS Ulysses*, took ten weeks to write and became one of the most successful British books of all time. The novel was heavily based around MacLean's wartime experiences and was quickly followed by *The Guns Of Navarone* and *South By Java Head*, which cemented his reputation. His books are characterised by fast-moving adventure. He wrote twenty seven books in all, and produced fourteen screenplays. The books are mainly action-adventure tales, although he also wrote a biography of Captain Cook.

HMS Ulysses
HarperCollins pb 0006135129
£4.99
Ice Station Zebra
HarperCollins pb 0006161413
£4.99
When Eight Bells Toll
HarperCollins pb 0006158110
£4.99

MCLEAN, DUNCAN

Duncan Mclean is one of the most talented of the new crop of Scottish writers. *Bucket of Tongues* is a collection of short stories which won the Somerset Maugham award. His first novel, *Blackden,* is out of print. His second novel, *The Bunker Man,* is a menacing tale set on Scotland's north-east coast. A newly-married janitor becomes concerned when a hooded man who lives in a concrete pillbox on the beach starts lurking around the school. He takes it upon himself to sort the matter out. However the interest he has in this 'Bunker man' changes from apprehension into something more depraved and sinister. A sense of darkness pervades this perverse and tension-laden work, a shocking and disturbing book.

Bucket of Tongues (Somerset Maugham Award winner)
Minerva pb 0749397632 £7.99
The Bunker Man
Vintage pb 0099534819 £5.99

MCLELLAN, ROBERT

Robert McLellan spent his childhood on a farm in the Clyde valley and it was his experiences there that inspired his often humorous *Linmill Stories.* Told from the viewpoint of a boy, they are relayed in a vibrant Scots dialect. Throughout the tales McLellan is careful not to limit his work to being simply an expression of childhood, rather he uses his boy narrator to reveal the wider adult world.

Linmill Stories
Canongate pb 086241282X £4.95

MCMANUS, ANNE
I Was a Mate of Ronnie Laing
Canongate pb 0862418135
£8.99

In this debut work Anne McManus produces a very dark novel, set in the harsher regions of modern British society. Her main character is an ex-alcoholic who is down on her luck - she spends her nights and days just getting out of it on alcohol or whatever else she can get hold of. After an appalling incident she manages to turn things around, but her addiction to outrageous sex still threatens to jeopardise her stability. Written in a stream-of-consciousness style, the work is a very personal look into present day society.

MACNEILL, ALASTAIR
Moonblood
Vista pb 0575601981 £5.99

An action thriller set in the Amazon jungle and New York City. A hard New York cop sets out to discover what happened to his brother, in the company of Kelly McBride, captain and owner of 48ft. tramp 'Shamrock Gal'. Both are led into a tough world of politics, money and deceit.

MCNEILL, ELISABETH

A Bridge In Time
Orion pb 1857974069 £4.99
Wild Heritage
Orion pb 0752802879 £5.99

A Bridge In Time is a rich Victorian family saga set in the Borders in the world of Scottish railway construction. It revolves around the efforts of a young woman to ensure that her father's dream of constructing an exceptional railway bridge link are fulfilled. *Wild Heritage* is the sequel to this tale.

MACPHERSON, IAN

Wild Harbour
Canongate pb 086241234X £3.95

In MacPherson's vision of a world threatened by annihilation from weapons of mass destruction, a young pacifist couple decide to opt out and live as renegades in the wilderness. Although written in 1936, this book has a distinctly contemporary feel to it, yet also brings to mind shades of Buchan and Stevenson.

MACPHERSON, JOHN

Tales From Barra: Told By The Coddy
Birlinn pb 1874744033 £5.99

The Coddy (John MacPherson) was one of the people Compton Mackenzie used as inspiration for his characters in *Whisky Galore*. Famous throughout the Hebrides for his story-telling, this is a collection of some of his best tales, written down in 1951-2 just before his memory started to fail. They retain all the qualities that made them so popular when spoken aloud.

MCWILLIAM, CANDIA
(b.1955)

Candia McWilliam's first novel *A Case of Knives* was a poised and articulate work centring on an eminent heart surgeon's emotionally exploitative experiments on a young girl, driven in part by his deep love for a man called Hal Darbo. These emotional experiments have far reaching consequences for all involved. Candia McWilliam's lyrical and poetic style coupled with her handling of the controversial subject matter gained her glowing critical acclaim. She has subsequently published two further novels and *Wait Till I Tell You*, a first collection of short stories which move between Scotland and England. Although each work is a separate entity they are connected by shared themes of love and nationality.

A Case of Knives
Picador pb 0330368435 £6.99
Debatable Land
Picador pb 0330336622 £5.99
A Little Stranger
Picador pb 0330311158 £5.99
Wait Till I Tell You
Picador pb 0330344099 £6.99

MASSIE, ALLAN (b.1938)

Born in Singapore and raised in Aberdeenshire, Allan Massie went to Trinity College where he read History and went on to become a schoolmaster. He lived in Rome for a short while, returning to Scotland in 1975 to take up a career in journalism. His first novel, *Change And Decay In All Around I See*, was published in 1978 and was followed two years later by *The Last Peacock*, a gentle comedy set among the Scottish landed gentry. Massie has written numerous books since but is best known for his historical novels, particularly those set during Roman times. One of his central themes is the dilemma that rulers face in deciding whether to act or refrain from action, and the problems involved in both these positions. He is also recognised as a gifted political journalist and has written a critical work on Muriel Spark. His most recent work is *Shadows Of Empire*, a panoramic novel in which the great-grandson of a millionaire shipbuilder, now in his old age, looks back over his life. It portrays a ruling class gone astray and encompasses the whole tragedy of European politics in the first half of this century, weaving into this the personal lives of a particular family.

Caesar
Hodder & Stoughton pb
0340599103 £6.99
Tiberius
Hodder & Stoughton pb
0340560053 £5.99
Augustus
Hodder & Stoughton pb
0340412240 £6.99
Antony
Hodder & Stoughton pb
0340693029 £6.99
The Hanging Tree
Heinemann hb 0434453013
£13.99

King David
Sceptre pb 0340659904 £6.99
The Ragged Lion
Hodder & Stoughton pb
0340632712 £5.99
Shadows of Empire
Vintage pb 0099274175 £5.99
Sins of The Father
Hodder & Stoughton pb
0340571195 £5.99
These Enchanted Woods
Hodder & Stoughton pb
0340609648 £5.99

MAY, NAOMI

This Lowland writer, now living in London, writes about the affluent classes with both affection and irony. *The Adventurer* concerns the homely elder sister of a rich family, who realises that the man willing to marry her is only interested in her money. She subsequently finds other opportunities in life, outwith her family circle. In *At Home* three sisters share a house with their brother, one of them playing a particularly dominant role in the household. However this set-up is altered when the brother brings his bride to live with them, leading to unexpected consequences.
The Adventurer
Calder hb 0714506974 £5.95
At Home
Calder hb 0714500941 £5.99

MEEK, JAMES

Set in contemporary Edinburgh, Meek's first novel, *McFarlane Boils the Sea*, describes 24 hours in the life of Laura McFarlane who is pregnant, relating her fall from the trendy scene into other, more unusual things. Meek paints a fragmented and surrealistic picture of nightclubs, run-down B&Bs and colourful characters. *Drivetime* is a twisted modern take on the Grand Tour, in which the main character, desperate for a new start, drives across Europe on an assignment from a wealthy stranger. His trip is a surreal voyage that Meek delivers in an intelligent and humorous fashion. Meek's short stories are bizarre and unsettling, with a twisted sense of reality and morbid undertones, yet they are often very funny.

Drivetime
Polygon pb 0748662057 £8.99
Last Orders And Other Stories
Polygon pb 0748661271 £8.99
McFarlane Boils The Sea
Polygon pb 0748660062 £7.95

MILLAR, MARTIN

Martin Millar, the self-styled punk novelist, writes in an unbridled and frequently hilarious style. *Lux The Poet* is representative of much of his work in both style and content. The book relates the adventures of a street poet who manages to get mixed up with a ruthless genetic engineering programme, and whose aim is to rescue his girlfriend Pearl and recite poetry to the nation on TV. He sets about his tasks armed only with his good looks (a Lana Turner face and Betty Grable legs) and a Star Wars toothbrush. The story is set in Brixton during the time of the riots and written with a style and flourish that led the *Literary Review* to describe Millar as a 'Tom Sharpe with a head full of cocaine and poetry'.

Collected Martin Millar
Fourth Estate pb 1857029100 £9.99
Dreams of Sex and Stage Diving
Fourth Estate pb 1857022130 £5.99
The Good Fairies of New York
Fourth Estate pb 1857022173 £5.99
Lux The Poet
Fourth Estate pb 0947795626 £5.99
Milk Sulphate and Alby Starvation
Fourth Estate pb 1857022149 £5.99
Ruby and the Stone Age Diet
Fourth Estate pb 1857022165 £5.99

MITCHISON, NAOMI

Born in Edinburgh and educated at the Dragon School, Oxford, she married Labour politician and subsequent Baron Richard Mitchison in 1916. Although based in Kintyre she has travelled widely, becoming the 'Mmarona' (mother) of the Botswanan Bakgatha tribe in the 60s. She has written over 70 books including children's stories, biographies, science fiction and novels, some of which are set in Scotland. Sadly a large number of her books are currently out of print. Her first novels are among her most popular and are a mixture of classical mythology and history. An insightful and eminent writer, she is noted for these intimate evocations of ancient cultures. One of these early historical works, *The Blood of the Martyrs*, is a powerful recreation of the world of Ancient Rome set during Nero's reign of terror, and concerning the destruction of one group of early Christians. Similarly *The Corn King and the Spring Queen* is set on the shores of the Black Sea over 2000 years ago and is a brilliantly realised novel of an ancient civilisation in which love and beauty vie with cruelty and dark magical forces. In a different vein, and recently re-released, is *Lobsters on the Agenda*, a humorous novel set in a small fishing village in the 1950s. Written in a lilting dialogue, it examines various conflicts of interest and loyalty in the local population, expressed in community gatherings over the course of a week.

The Blood of the Martyrs
Canongate pb 0862411920 £4.95
Bull Calves
Little, Brown pb 1860493742 £7.99
The Corn King and the Spring Queen
Canongate pb 0862412870 £6.95
Lobsters On The Agenda
House Of Lochar pb 1899863206 £9.99

> "In Scottish culture nothing beats a good-going funeral. It takes the mind off other things . . ."
> Naomi Mitchinson

MORIN, CAROLE
Lampshades
Indigo pb 0575401419 £5.99

Lampshades is about a sixteen year old who livens up her boring Scottish reality with a distasteful and colourful fantasy world that centres on the Nazis. She dresses up in SS uniform and is obsessional about cleanliness. Yet the more extreme Carole Morin makes her central character, the more she reveals what is behind this mask. A witty, clever and startling book.

MORRISON, NANCY B.

The Gowk Storm
Canongate pb 0862412226
£4.99

Set at the end of the 19th
century in a remote Highland
manse, Nancy Brysson
Morrison's compelling
coming-of-age story is an
intimate study of the social
limitations placed on women
and a celebration of the wild
beauty of the surrounding
countryside.

MORTON, TOM

Red Guitars In Heaven
Mainstream pb 1851586539
£7.99

This is Tom Morton's first
novel, a dark and humorous
tale of pornography,
fundamentalist evangelism,
rock'n'roll and Highland
culture. Anarchic and fun,
with its tongue firmly in its
cheek.

MUIR, WILLA

(1890–1970)

**Imagined Selves: Imagined Corners, Mrs Ritchie, Selected
Non-Fiction**
Canongate pb 0862416051 £8.99

It is slowly being recognised that Willa Muir was one of
Scotland's finest intellectuals this century. This collection of her
work includes her two novels as well a selection of her non-
fiction. The pieces show the contradiction inherent in herself
and her writings: a writer obsessed by Scotland in both her
subject and style who disliked much of what Scotland was and
is; and a strong feminist who largely sacrificed her identity,
being seen primarily as 'Edwin Muir's wife'. Fiction and
autobiography are so intertwined in her work that it is
sometimes difficult to distinguish between the two. Willa Muir
is a much neglected author who deserves more attention.

"The Congo's no' to be compared wi' the
West o' Scotland when it comes to insects",
said Para Handy. "There's places here that's
chust deplorable whenever the weather's
the least bit warm. Look at Tighnabruaich! -
they're that bad there, they'll bite their way
through corrugated iron roofs to get at ye!"
Neil Munro, Hurricane Jack of the Vital Spark

MUNRO, NEIL (1864–1930)

Neil Munro was born the illegitimate son of an Inverary kitchen maid. He left school at 13 and subsequently took up a career in journalism, eventually becoming the assistant editor of the *Glasgow Evening News*. His first novel, *John Splendid*, was published in 1898, and like much of his work concerns the impact of both economic and social change on the Highlands. He is however best remembered for his comic creation Para Handy, a West Highland puffer skipper who originally appeared in his weekly columns in the *Glasgow Evening News*. The droll adventures of the *Vital Spark* crew won him a huge readership. This creation, which Munro thought little of at the time, proved to be his most lasting work, and has been adapted for film, stage and television. The definitive collection of the much loved tales based around the skipper and crew of the *Vital Spark*, which includes all three volumes of the stories published during Munro's life, as well as eighteen recently discovered and never previously published tales, is the Birlinn edition. Munro's other comic characters Erchie MacPherson (Kirk deacon and part-time waiter) and Jimmy Swan (an enigmatic commercial traveller) show quite clearly that he had more than one string to his comic talents. These are humorous tales of daily life set in the West of Scotland at the turn of the century and they have been cult favourites for several generations now. Possibly Munro's best non-comic work, *The New Road* is set in 1733 and based around a new military road. The main villain, Simon Fraser of Lovat, is a chilling study in evil and the road itself is both the main plot motif and a metaphor for the changes happening in the Highlands. *Doom Castle* is a vivid historical novel giving a powerful depiction of the Highlands in the years just after the 1745 Rebellion. A French aristocratic agent is sent to kill a British agent who has been betraying exiled Jacobites. The dashing swordsman Victor de Montaiglon has only two clues: the name the agent used and the fact that he is in Argyll. He has a letter of formal introduction to the mysterious Laird of Doom Castle who might be able to help him. Neil Munro's other work is heavily political in content and poetic in style and has its own distinctive character. After his son died in the First World War his output became sparse. He died in 1930 in Helensburgh.

Para Handy
Birlinn pb 1874744025 £7.99
Doom Castle
B & W pb 1873631510 £6.99
Erchie And Jimmy Swan
Birlinn pb 187474405X £8.99
Jaunty Jock
House Of Lochar pb
189986315X £7.95
John Splendid
B & W pb 1873631448 £6.99
The Lost Pibroch And Other Shieling Stories
House Of Lochar pb
1899863109 £7.95
The New Road
B & W pb 1873631340 £6.99

MURRAY, DONALD S.

Special Deliverance
S.C.P. pb 1898218994 £5.95

A wide-ranging collection of short stories from the Western Isles that use traditional and more contemporary themes, such as the effects of the evacuation of St Kilda and the influence Gorbachev's stay in the Western Isles had on his Icelandic summit with Reagan.

OLIPHANT, BILL

Therapy of Camels
Chapman pb 0906772494 £7.95

Oliphant's light-hearted fiction is based on his experiences of life in Glasgow. It displays a fine sense of anarchic wit as well as being innovative and imaginative.

OLIPHANT, MARGARET (1828–1897)

Born in East Lothian and raised in Liverpool and Glasgow, Margaret Oliphant started to write at the age of 16 and went on to write almost a hundred novels. Although she only sporadically lived in Scotland, many of her books have Scottish themes. After her husband died leaving the family in debt, she relied entirely on her literary income to support them, a fact she felt had a bearing on the quality of some of her works. Her first works have become known under the collective heading of 'The Carlingford Chronicles'. They are comic observations on the clerical and domestic life. Much of her work is about Victorian society's subjugation of women and its refusal to offer women the same opportunities for personal achievement as men. Some of Oliphant's best works are her supernatural stories, which have a psychological underpinning which still chills today. Her work has recently been re-evaluated and recognised for its ironic exposure of the injustices of Victorian society. She is affectionately known as 'the feminist Trollope'.

A Beleaguered City
Greenwood Press hb 0837131375 £42.75
Curate In Charge
Sutton pb 086299327X £3.95
Effie Ogilvie
S.A.P. pb 0707307368 £9.50
Stories of The Seen and Unseen
Society Of Metaphysicians
(spiral bound) 1858100151 £11.50

OWENS, AGNES (b.1926)

Agnes Owens is an underrated writer whose work is marked by her insightful style, often applied to people trapped by poverty, passion or the everyday practicalities of life. Her writing is witty, honest and often gentle in tone. Her latest work, *For The Love Of Willie*, is an excellent example of many of these traits. It describes an inmate of a mental hospital writing a novel based on a dark romance she had when just sixteen, during World War II. As she writes she tries to get her fellow inmate to read her book, which brings to light a startling revelation about her life. Owens relays the story with compassion and care, and in so doing skilfully reveals some of our deeper desires and drives.

For The Love Of Willie
Bloomsbury hb 074754011X £10.99
People Like That
Bloomsbury pb 0747530904 £5.99
A Working Mother
Little, Brown pb 0349106215 £5.99

PAIGE, FRANCES

Kindred Spirits
HarperCollins pb 0006498825
£5.99

The fourth and final installment in the Mackintosh sisters' saga finds Anna Laidlaw emotionally content after the family storms and unrest of the past, but her twin Jean is experiencing a very different existence: the dormant passions that caused tragedy when she was a young girl are once again coming to the fore. Traumas of everyday life are examined in an enthralling fashion in Frances Paige's best-selling novels.

RAIFE, ALEXANDRA

Alexandra Raife is a recently discovered writer in the mould of Mary Stewart. Her work is both entertaining and engrossing. Drumveyn is a contemporary family saga set on the fictional Scottish estate of Drumveyn. After the death of Sir Charles Napier his widow finds herself at a crossroads in her life. *Grianan,* Alexandra Raife's third novel, revolves around the country house hotel of Grianan. A young woman returns to her childhood home, now a hotel run by her aunt, to heal herself after a broken engagement, but there are several surprises waiting there for her.

Drumveyn
Penguin pb 0140251146 £6.99
Grianan
Penguin pb 0140263683 £6.99
The Larach
Penguin pb 014025370X £5.99

RAMSAY, EILEEN

Eileen Ramsay is a popular author of Scottish family sagas. *Walnut Shell Days* is a cleverly constructed historical story set in the Scottish countryside of the early 1900s, full of emotional intensity and with several clever plot twists. Her latest book is *Harvest of Courage.* A young woman's experiences of land, love and the bitter effects of World War I on her idyllic Scottish rural life are at the core of the novel.

The Broken Gate
Little, Brown pb 0751507482
£5.99
Butterflies In December
Little, Brown pb 075151649X
£5.99
Dominie's Lassie
Little, Brown pb 0751511323
£4.99
Harvest of Courage
Little,Brown hb 0316641464
£16.99
Walnut Shell Days
Warner pb 0751520985 £5.99

REID, JAMIE

Home on the Range
Mainstream pb 1851587942
£6.99
Easy Money
Mainstream pb 1851585621
£8.99

Easy Money is a fast-paced story written around the world of horseracing, featuring the adventures of the flamboyant figure of Glaswegian self-made millionaire Lex Parlane, known in his own publicity as 'the most famous Scotsman since Rabbie Burns'. Reid's second novel, *Home on the Range,* introduces the charismatic professional gambler Connor 'Doc' Mulcahy, who is determined to gain revenge on an English bookmaker. As the initially successful revenge plan starts to fail, the stage is set for a dramatic showdown in this novel which is part adventure and part political allegory.

REID, JOHN M.

Homeward Journey
Canongate pb 0862411785
£3.95

A love affair between two very different individuals in the years between the World Wars is the basis of John MacNair Reid's novel. A young man falls in love with the first girl he meets while having a night out on the town in reaction to the death of his mother. In essence the novel is a study of concealment and deception.

ROBERTSON, JAMES

Ragged Man's Complaint
B & W pb 1873631243 £6.99

This is James Robertson's second collection of short stories, which reveal an author building on the considerable talent he displayed in his first collection, *Close*, now out of print. They are subtle and menacing stories of hope and fear, and some contain a feeling of unease and foreboding. A safari park's veneer is stripped away to reveal bitterness and brutality; a couple of hitchhikers are alone on an empty back road; an invasion of frogs threatens to cause insanity. There are often absurd or surreal overtones, yet beyond the strangeness Robertson illuminates deeply hidden areas of the human psyche.

Scottish Ghost Stories
Little, Brown pb 0751513938 £4.99

ROBERTSON, JAMES I.

The Lady of Kynachan
Bantam Press pb 0552142980 £5.99

This novel, based on the author's own ancestral papers, concerns the 1745 uprising. David Stewart inherits the Highland estate of Kynachan and marries the woman of his dreams, Jean Mercer. Although deeply in love, he rushes to Bonnie Prince Charlie's side when summoned to fight for the cause. Tragedy strikes on the field of Culloden, and as the British Government sets out to destroy the Highland ways it is left to Jean to save her children, the estate and the people of Kynachan. A romantic tale of adversity and the seeds of new hope.

ROBERTSON, WILLIE

Calum's Way Of It!
Argyll pb 1874640823 £4.99

A collection of comic stories featuring West Highlands and Islands policeman Calum, who is the bane of his Inspector's life and very much a law unto himself.

ROSE, DILYS

Dilys Rose is one of the pivotal figures in the Scottish literary scene. She has been compared to Katherine Mansfield and her work has received numerous prizes, including both the McVities and Saltire awards. Born in Glasgow, she took a degree in English and Philosophy at Edinburgh University. After a short time teaching she went on to travel widely. Her travel experiences were at the heart of her first collection of short stories, *Our Lady of the Pickpockets*. Themes in her work include society's peripheral characters and the dispossessed, particularly those affected by culture clash. Her writing is marked by her talent for describing fragile and transitory moments in life. She has written several plays and works of poetry as well as fiction. *War Dolls* is Rose's latest book, a new collection of short stories which reveal her continuing concern with outsiders trying to retain control of their lives despite disturbing factors working against them. The stories include a teenager's struggle to relate to his father's Scottish machismo, a tourist in Brazil getting too close to the ruling elite, and a documentary maker's chilling encounter with a Mexican freedom fighter. Throughout Rose illuminates the connections and contradictions between people, and suggests that the few moments of joy that might occur in their lives are there to give meaning and sense to the remaining chaos. All the stories are told in Rose's cool, emphatic style.

Our Lady of the Pickpockets
Mandarin pb 0749391014 £5.99
Red Tides
Minerva pb 0749396334 £5.99
War Dolls
Headline pb 0747273030 £9.99

ROSS, BESS

Strath (Neil Gunn Prize Winner)
Canongate pb 086241668X
£8.99

This novel, set in a 17th century Highland village, concentrates on the everyday lives of the central characters while simultaneously tackling the broader social issues of the time. George Mackay Brown described Bess Ross as 'a new Scottish writer of undoubted talent'.

RUSH, CHRISTOPHER

A Twelvemonth And A Day
Canongate pb 0862414393
£4.99

Christopher Rush's *A Twelvemonth And A Day* has the sea coursing through every page. In this tale of a devout fishing community's adventures there are storms, wrecks and sharks, the mysterious, supernatural aspect of the ocean also playing a part. An emotionally resonant work that captures the awe and majesty of the ocean as if it were a genie in a bottle.

Last Lesson of the Afternoon
Canongate pb 0862416493
£6.99

SCOTT, J.D.

The End of an Old Song
Canongate pb 0862413117
£4.95

The decline of an old house is used to symbolise the passing of a way of life in J.D. Scott's tale of two young men who cannot break free from a young girl.

"Never mind my grace, lassie; just speak out a plain tale, and show you have a Scotch tongue in your head."
Sir Walter Scott,
The Heart of Midlothian

SCOTT, SIR WALTER (1771–1832)

Born in Edinburgh, Scott contracted infantile paralysis at the age of eighteen months, which left him lame in his right leg for the rest of his life. His family sent him to the Borders to recuperate, and it was at this early stage in his life that he gained a love of the region and its traditions. He returned to Edinburgh aged four and after completing his studies, entered legal practice in 1786, eventually becoming an advocate in 1792. His work brought him into contact with the major literary figures of the time and he was already well versed in the Border Ballads and numerous writers, including Walpole, Percy, Fielding and Smollett. His first literary efforts were in the field of ballad writing and collecting. These ballads were published by Kelso-based publisher James Ballantyne under the title *Minstrelsy of the Scottish Border*. This book was to make him one of the most popular poets of his day, probably his most famous poem being 'The Lady Of The Lake'. A man full of energy, he continued to write and work as a lawyer, and set about building a baronial castle at Abbotsford. He was also know as a passionate antiquarian.

He tried novel writing as a response to Byron's growing popularity as a poet. His first novel, *Waverley*, anonymously published, was an instant success, and he was to follow it with a series of equally popular novels, at first labelled only 'By the Author of Waverley', hence the Waverley Novels. This first of Scott's novels shows his dual feelings towards Scottish history. Set in 1745, it concerns the adventures of Edward Waverley, a British Army officer posted to Scotland. He meets up with Jacobite sympathiser, Baron Bradwardine, a friend of his uncle, and gains the affections of the Baron's daughter Rose. However, events lead him north to meet up with two Highland warriors and there he falls in love with Flora, the sister of one of the warriors. Waverley then decides to support the Jacobite cause after his loyalties are called into question by his regiment. As the story continues, Waverley has to finally decide between the Jacobite and Hanoverian causes, and between Rose and Flora. Minor characters are well developed, his use of spoken Scots is assured and masterful and the plot structure is excellent.

After the publication of *Waverley* the author was referred to as 'The Great Unknown' and 'The Wizard Of The North', although many did know his identity. In 1826 his publisher, with whom he had heavily invested, went into massive debt and Scott was declared bankrupt. He spent the remaining six years of his life writing his way out of this predicament, saying "This right hand shall work it all off!". Much of this later output was considered by Scott as hack work, but some of the works were of excellent quality; for example, *The Chronicles Of The Canongate* which includes *The Fair Maid Of Perth*. His health failed in his later years, and he undertook a tour of the Mediterranean in a Government-supplied frigate for health reasons. He died in Edinburgh in 1832.

Sir Walter Scott

Scott's work is wide-ranging, including poetry and biography, but it is his fiction for which he is best remembered. The novels cover a large variety of subjects, from historical adventures set in Scotland to those set in England and Europe, and they are set in times ranging from Scott's recent past to the Middle Ages. His vision of Scotland still informs the world on the country's romantic image. He had an ambivalent attitude to Scottish history, appreciating the order brought about by the 1707 Union, yet having a romantic sympathy for the Jacobite cause. Edwin Muir famously summarised Scott by saying he 'thought in English and felt in Scots'. During his life he experienced massive popularity but this suffered a steady decline in the 20th century. However his work is currently being reassessed, with definitive editions of the Waverley Novels only recently being undertaken. These are the Edinburgh UP editions of the Waverley Novels which offer the most accurate representation of what Scott originally wrote and intended to be read, before production errors occurred. They include explanatory notes and full glossaries. This project started in 1993 and is expected to take over ten years to complete.

The Edinburgh Edition of the Waverley Novels:
The Antiquary (Ed. D. Hewitt)
EUP hb 0748605371 £27.50
The Black Dwarf (Ed. PD Garside)
EUP hb 0748604510 £19.50
The Bride of Lammermoor (Ed. JH Alexander)
EUP hb 0748605711 £25.00
Guy Mannering (Ed PD Garside)
EUP hb 0748605681 £27.50
Ivanhoe (Ed G. Tulloch)
EUP hb 0748605738 £30.00
Kenilworth (Ed. JH Alexander)
EUP hb 0748604375 £25.00
A Legend of the Wars of Montrose
EUP hb 074860572X £22.50
(Ed. JH Alexander)
Redgauntlet (Ed. GAM Wood & D. Hewitt)
EUP hb 0748605800 £29.50
Saint Ronan's Well (Ed. M. Weinstein)
EUP hb 0748605355 £27.50
The Tale of Old Mortality (Ed. DS Mack)
EUP hb 074860443X £25.00

The Antiquary
Penguin pb 0140436529 £7.99
The Bride of Lammermoor
OUP pb 0192817914 £5.99
The Heart of Midlothian
OUP pb 0192815830 £2.99
Ivanhoe
OUP pb 0192831720 £2.99
Old Mortality
Penguin pb 0140430989 £5.99
The Pirate
Shetland Times pb 1898852170 £8.99
Quentin Durward
OUP pb 0192826581 £6.99
Redgauntlet
OUP pb 0192816683 £6.99
Rob Roy
Penguin pb 0140435549 £4.99
Waverley
Penguin pb 0140430717 £4.99

SCOTT, WILLIAM

The Bannockburn Years
Luath Press pb 0946487340 £7.95

William Scott's novel is an intricate work centring around a solicitor's consideration of standing for a Scottish independence party. The plot involves a medieval manuscript about the War of Independence, and a World War II fighter pilot. Scott uses his novel as a vehicle to explore Scotland's future.

SHEA, MICHAEL

Michael Shea is best known in his literary incarnation as an author of stylish political thrillers. (He was in the past the Queen's Press Secretary and now has a wide range of business interests.) His latest novel, *The Berlin Embassy*, concerns behind-the-scenes diplomacy in the British Embassy in Berlin. *State of the Nation* is set in a future independent Scotland which is on the brink of violent civil war after a global recession has caused record unemployment. In this volatile situation an American journalist uncovers evidence that American-based multi-nationals are orchestrating much of this recession in an effort to take over the Scottish economy. Shea's works nearly all share a heavy degree of political intrigue and this book is no exception.

The Berlin Embassy
HarperCollins hb 0002254727 £16.99
The British Ambassador
HarperCollins pb 0006493238 £5.99
Spin Doctor
HarperCollins pb 000649322X £4.99
State of the Nation
HarperCollins pb 0006498787 £5.99

SHEPHERD, NAN (1893–1981)

Born and raised in Aberdeenshire where she lived most of her life, Nan Shepherd was educated at Aberdeen University after attending local schools. She lectured at Aberdeen College of Education until she retired in 1956. She wrote three novels: *The Quarry Wood, The Weatherhouse* and *A Pass In The Grampians;* one volume of poetry, *In The Cairngorms,* and a volume of non-fiction called *The Living Mountain.* She was awarded an Honorary Degree at Aberdeen University in 1964, and died in Aberdeen. *The Grampian Quartet,* as the prose works would later be known, cover much the same territory as Lewis Grassic Gibbon's *A Scots Quair,* although *The Quarry Wood* was published four years before Grassic Gibbon's *Sunset Song.* They are a major work of modern Scottish fiction. Written in a vigorously realistic fashion they accurately depict the often restrictive life of rural Scotland and the consequences for women who devote their lives to the care of sick relatives. Shepherd accurately conveys the inner feelings of her characters, and focuses on the possibility of women finding emotional attainment outside marriage.

Grampian Quartet
Canongate pb 0862415896 £8.99

SHERIDAN, SARA

Truth Or Dare
Arrow pb 0749326905 £5.99

Sara Sheridan's first novel is a thoroughly contemporary tale of two close female friends on the run. The action moves about in location, taking in London, Glasgow, Belfast and Dublin. At the heart of the book is the girls' relationship and the story overall reads like a fictional road movie.

SMITH, ALI

Free Love
Virago pb 1860491901 £6.99
Like
Virago pb 1860493173 £6.99

Ali Smith's first collection of short stories, *Like,* is very personal. There is a sense of trying to deal with wounds from the past and moving on to a better future. In the title story, a girl finds her first 'free love' while in Amsterdam, leaving her girlfriend to stray into sex with a prostitute. Like many of the stories, it is delicately told and suggests the opening of new realms of physical and emotional freedom. Her debut novel, *Free Love,* is about two people who seem at first diametrically opposed but as the plot moves on it becomes apparent they have some very strong connections. A large part of the book's success lies in Smith's distinctively voiced examination of what it is like to live in the latter part of the 20th century.

SMITH, IAIN CRICHTON

Born on the island of Lewis, Iain Crichton Smith has pursued a long and successful career as both poet and novelist. He has published work in both English and Gaelic. The tragedy of the Highland Clearances is powerfully recreated in his master work, *Consider the Lilies*. The focus of the novel is an old woman being evicted from her croft and abandoned by the Free Church of Scotland. By bringing the historical occurrence of the Clearances down to a personal, emotional level, Crichton Smith widens our understanding of these events and creates in turn a universal message. *Listen to the Voice* is a collection of his short stories which proves that he is one of the most talented Scottish writers of our time, capable of writing fine works dealing with powerful forces and emotions as well as comic pieces which reveal a wickedly dry sense of humour.

Consider the Lilies
Canongate pb 0862414156
£4.99
Listen to the Voice
Canongate pb 0862414342
£5.99

SMOLLETT, TOBIAS (1721–1771)

Born in Dalquharn in Dunbartonshire, Smollett became an apprentice doctor in 1735. He joined the Navy and after leaving practised as a surgeon in London. Smollett was well known for his quick temper and sharp tongue. It was this aspect of his character that he used to create the style of writing for which he became famous. His grotesque parodies often read like an 18th century Irvine Welsh. *Roderick Random,* his first novel, is a fierce political satire that positively wallows in gross imagery and wicked characterisation, a robust comedy about sailors' lives during the War of Jenkins' Ear of 1739-41. He eventually landed in gaol for libel after replying to Admiral Knowles' pamphlet defending his competence in this affair. Needless to say the book was hugely successful and made Smollett famous. He went on to produce several novels in the same style, lampooning various aspects of British life. His last novel, *Humphrey Clinker,* emerged from his tour of Scotland in 1766. The humour in the Scottish sections reveals Smollett's love for his own country. His style, which mixed vicious honesty with outrageously funny and overblown characters, coupled with a willingness to show social reality, warts and all, influenced many writers such as Dickens, Thackeray and Scott. The success of his books allowed him to abandon surgery and take up travelling. He died in Italy in 1771.

The Adventures of Roderick Random
OUP pb 0192812610 £5.99
Humphrey Clinker
Penguin pb 0140430210 £4.99
The Life & Adventures of Sir Launcelot Greaves
Penguin pb 0140433066 £6.99

SPARK, DAME MURIEL

Born in Edinburgh, the daughter of an engineer, Muriel Spark was educated at James Gillespie's School For Girls (on which she based the school in *The Prime Of Miss Jean Brodie*). She emigrated to America after her marriage in 1938 but returned to London in 1944 after the marriage broke down. She became editor of the *Poetry Review* in 1947 and from this time onwards devoted her time to writing. Since the early 1960s she has lived either in New York or Italy. In 1954 she became a Catholic, an event that is of great importance in her books. She received a DBE in 1993. Muriel Spark has produced works in various fields such as poetry, biography (notably of Wordsworth and Emily Bronte) and so far one volume of autobiography, as well as her novels, the most famous of which is undoubtedly *The Prime Of Miss Jean Brodie*. Her novels are often short and elegantly written. Although few of her works are set in Scotland, her Scottish upbringing and background informs and permeates her writing at all times. *The Prime of Miss Jean Brodie* is much more dramatic and complex than the excellent film adaptation might suggest. It is at heart a study of Calvinism set in an Edinburgh girls' school. Like her namesake, 18th century William Brodie who was a respectable citizen by day but a criminal by night, Jean Brodie has a divided personality, holding to utterly contradictory ideas and philosophies. In her own vision of the 'crème de la crème' (a thinly veiled view of Calvinist doctrine) there are the elect and the damned. It is one of her own 'elect' who brings about her downfall. The novel is also notable for its memorable descriptions of Edinburgh. Her recent work and winner of the 1997 David Cohen British Literature Prize, *Reality And Dreams,* is one of Muriel Spark's most richly absorbing and complex novels. It examines the fine divide between reality and fantasy. A movie director is recovering after an accident and as he fades in and out of consciousness he starts to imagine a film he wants to make. These visions give way to an obsession that will have a profound effect on his family and friends.

The Abbess of Crewe
Penguin pb 0140040749 £5.99
The Bachelors
Penguin pb 0140019103 £6.99
The Ballad of Peckham Rye
Penguin pb 014001909X £5.99
Collected Stories of Muriel Spark
Penguin pb 0140177949 £8.99
The Comforters
Penguin pb 0140019111 £6.99
Driver's Seat
Penguin pb 0140034641 £5.99
A Far Cry From Kensington
Penguin pb 0140108742 £5.99
The Girls of Slender Means
Penguin pb 0140024263 £5.99
Hothouse by the East River
Penguin pb 0140040021 £5.99
Loitering With Intent
Penguin pb 0140179623 £5.99
The Mandelbaum Gate
Penguin pb 0140027459 £6.99
Memento Mori
Penguin pb 0140113029 £6.99
Not To Disturb
Penguin pb 0140037748 £5.99
The Only Problem
Penguin pb 0140179615 £6.99
The Prime of Miss Jean Brodie
Penguin pb 014002235X £5.99
Public Image
Penguin pb 0140031316 £6.99
Reality and Dreams
Penguin pb 0140123105 £6.99
Robinson
Penguin pb 0140021574 £5.99
Symposium
Penguin pb 0140123091 £6.99
The Takeover
Penguin pb 0140045961 £6.99
Territorial Rights
Penguin pb 0140145575 £6.99

SPENCE, ALAN

Spence, one of the most respected writers of his generation, is also one of the most individual and shares the interest Neil Gunn possessed in Eastern ideas and mysticism. *The Magic Flute* follows the lives of four Glaswegian boys. It combines gritty realism and humour with a Zen-like clarity, an approach he was to develop and expand in his later works. *Way to Go* is his long-awaited second novel and is set in the Glasgow funeral trade, looking at the way the Scottish people regard death. Funny, poetic and moving, it takes a deep look into many different aspects of modern Scottish urban life. *Its Colours They Are Fine* is a collection of powerfully moving and poetic stories about Glasgow street life.

Its Colours They Are Fine
Phoenix pb 1857997530 £5.99
The Magic Flute
Phoenix pb 1857997816 £6.99
Stone Garden & Other Stories (McVitie's Prize Winner)
Phoenix pb 1857994531 £5.99
Way To Go
Phoenix hb 1897580487 £15.99

"One's prime is elusive. You little girls, when you grow up, must be on the alert to recognise your prime at whatever time of your life it may occur. You must then live it to the full."

Muriel Spark, The Prime of Miss Jean Brodie

STEVENSON, ROBERT LOUIS (1850–1894)

Robert Louis Stevenson was born the son of a distinguished engineer in Edinburgh. He was frequently ill as a child and throughout his life, possibly from T.B. He began studying engineering at Edinburgh University, moving on, however, to the study of law. At the age of twenty he announced his intention to become a writer. His first major published work was *An Inland Voyage,* a travel book that described a canoe trip in Belgium and France. He wrote several other travel pieces before progressing to longer fiction. *Treasure Island* was his first major novel and brought him almost instant fame. Originally intended for his 12-year-old stepson, this exciting and flamboyant adventure story is one of the most famous children's novels ever. Written in Stevenson's trademark crisp and beautifully balanced prose, its delights have enthralled readers young and old alike for over a hundred years. The exploits of Jim Hawkins, Blind Pew and Long John Silver look set to enchant readers for many generations to come. It was followed by *Kidnapped* in which Stevenson's mastery of the novel is superbly demonstrated. The story takes place after the failed Jacobite uprising of 1745 and the subsequent Appin murder case in which James Stewart and his foster-brother Alan Breck Stewart were wrongly accused of murdering Colin Campbell of Glenure, who had evicted James from his farm. The dramatic adventures of David Balfour and Alan Breck Stewart make for a truly classic read. In the sequel to *Kidnapped,* David returns to Edinburgh to collect his uncle's estate, and there he falls for the proud, beautiful Catriona. Later came *The Strange Case Of Doctor Jekyll And Mr. Hyde* with which Stevenson achieved critical and financial recognition. A self-professed bohemian, he constantly flouted conventions and regarded Jekyll and Hyde as a novel that exposed Victorian hypocrisy. A prolific writer throughout his life he wrote many adventure tales such as *The Black Arrow.* This is set during the War of the Roses. It is a tale of love, brutal battles and a quest for revenge. Regarded by many critics as a pot-boiler and Stevenson's weakest work, this novel still has much to recommend it including a well-structured plot, a wealth of incidents, and lush, descriptive passages written with lucidity and care. Stevenson's last work, the tragically unfinished *Weir of Hermiston* might possibly have become his greatest. Based around the life and times of Lord Braxfield, the hanging judge, the novel is a powerful study of a father-son relationship in which Archie, Lord Hermiston's son, comes into conflict with his father, eventually being wrongfully arrested for murder. The conclusion of the book was to have shown Lord Hermiston passing the death sentence on his own son. The novel is rich in Scots dialogue, displaying Stevenson's impressive command of language, and his deep appreciation of Scottish character and landscape, a trait evident in many of his works.

Although fascinated by Scotland's history and people, ill health kept Stevenson away for long periods of time. In France he met Fanny Osbourne, an American ten years older than him, and married her in America in 1880. There he wrote *The Silverado Squatters,* an account of the first days of his marriage, which he spent in a mining camp, returning to Edinburgh after the book's completion. In 1885 Stevenson and his family started a period of travel, first to America then to the South Pacific, looking for a suitable place to settle. He finally settled on the island of Upolu in Samoa where he built a house on the Vailima estate.

Stevenson wrote several accounts of his journeys in the Pacific which were collected under the title *In The South Seas*. He wrote numerous works from 1885 till his untimely death in Samoa in 1894.

Along with his fictional work Stevenson wrote many biographical and poetic pieces including *A Child's Garden Of Verses*, an exploration of childhood fantasies that conveys the fears and pleasures of childhood. The book is perhaps best appreciated by adults but will also appeal to many children. He is widely regarded as one of the best letter writers in the English language. His vivid descriptions of his native land were heightened by his absences from it. His constant struggle against illness, and his frequent travelling and early death created a lasting romantic myth around him. Stripped of the myth, Stevenson's wide-ranging work stands on its own and includes some of the finest pieces written by a Scotsman.

The Black Arrow
B & W pb 187363112X £5.99
The Body Snatcher & Other Tales
Dent pb 0460878816 £2.00
Catriona
Harvill pb 1860460127 £8.99
The Dynamiter
Sutton pb 0862990920 £3.99
The Ebb-Tide
EUP hb 0748604766 £25.00
The Ebb-Tide
Orion pb 0460675353 £2.99
**Essays And Poems
(Ed. Claire Harman)**
Everyman pb 0460872249 £1.99
**In The South Seas
(Ed N. Rennie)**
Penguin pb 0140434364 £6.99
Kidnapped and Catriona
OUP pb 0192817264 £2.99
Kidnapped
Penguin pb 0140434011 £2.99
The Master of Ballantrae
Penguin pb 0140434461 £3.99
The Master of Ballantrae
OUP pb 0192816357 £2.99
The Scottish Novels
Canongate pb 0862415330 £5.99
Shorter Scottish Fiction
Canongate pb 0862415551 £4.99

South Sea Tales
OUP pb 0192824392 £5.99
The Strange Case of Doctor Jekyll and Mr Hyde
Penguin pb 0140431178 £2.50
The Strange Case of Doctor Jekyll and Mr Hyde, and Weir of Hermiston
OUP pb 019281740X £2.50
Tales of Adventure
Canongate pb 0862416876 £7.99
Tales of the South Sea
Canongate pb 0862416434 £7.99
Treasure Island
Penguin pb 0140620834 £1.00
Treasure Island
OUP pb 0192816810 £2.50
**Treasure Islands: A Robert Louis Stevenson Anthology
(Ed. Jenni Calder)**
N.M.S. pb 0948636599 £6.95
**Weir of Hermiston
(Ed C. Kerrigan)**
EUP hb 0748603731 £30.00
Weir of Hermiston
Penguin pb 0140431381 £4.99
The Wrong Box
OUP pb 0192824260 £4.99

"Books are good enough in their own way, but they are a mighty bloodless substitute for life."
Robert Louis Stevenson, Virginibus Puerisque

Drink, Drugs and Debauchery in Scottish Literature

by James Robertson

What is the most famous drug-taking scene in Scottish literature? Not, I think, anything written by **Irvine Welsh,** despite the phenomenal success of *Trainspotting*. The episode that is recognised worldwide as a defining moment in substance abuse occurs in **Robert Louis Stevenson's** story of 1886, *The Strange Case Of Dr Jekyll And Mr Hyde:*

'I had long since prepared my tincture; I purchased at once, from a firm of wholesale chemists, a large quantity of a particular salt, which I knew, from my experiments, to be the last ingredient required; and, late one accursed night, I compounded the elements, watched them boil and smoke together in the glass, and when the ebullition had subsided, with a strong glow of courage drank off the potion.

The most racking pangs succeeded: a grinding in the bones, deadly nausea, and a horror of the spirit that cannot be exceeded at the hour of birth or death. Then these agonies began swiftly to subside, and I came to myself as if out of a great sickness. There was something strange in my sensations, something indescribably new, and, from its very novelty, incredibly sweet . . .'

Of course, Stevenson's morality tale is not really about drug-taking, but about the tension between instincts for good and evil within humans. The mysterious potion merely releases Jekyll's repressed but natural potential for wickedness in the monstrous form of Edward Hyde. This, in an age which has largely rejected the notion of innate sinfulness, might seem quite old-fashioned. And yet the vocabulary and the images which so appealed to the Victorian popular imagination have resonated for over a century, even to the way in which drug-taking is often discussed today. When Jekyll confesses, 'I knew myself, at the first breath of this new life, to be more wicked, tenfold more wicked, sold a slave to my original evil; and the thought, in that moment, braced and delighted me like wine', it brings to mind those lurid government TV commercials where some unspecified 'drugs' cause young people, lured on by the promise of unimaginable pleasure, to do wicked and nightmarish things to one another.

The transformation of the civilised doctor into the snarling, violent Hyde resembles the effects more of abuse of alcohol than of any other drug. Drink, of course, has long held an established place in Scottish letters. It informs the poetry of those 18th-century celebrants of Edinburgh lowlife, **Allan Ramsay** and **Robert Fergusson.** It is everywhere in **Robert Burns** from the line 'Freedom an' whisky gang thegither' to 'Tam o' Shanter'. In fiction, drinking scenes are commonplace to the point of being almost obligatory, especially in novels written by men, from **Walter Scott** to **Duncan McLean.** Sometimes excessive alcohol gets folk into fights, as in **Neil Gunn's** *The Silver Darlings,* when it brings rivalries and jealousies to the surface among deep, undemonstrative Caithness and Lewis fishermen. Sometimes it performs a more positive function, enabling people to celebrate in style: think of the great wedding scene in **Lewis Grassic Gibbon's** *Sunset Song,* or the 'ancient and now forgotten pastime of High Jinks' indulged in by Mr Pleydell and his legal cronies in **Scott's** *Guy Mannering.* Its comic potential has been exploited, though never exhausted, from **James Hogg** to **Neil Munro's** *Para Handy* and **Jeff Torrington's** exuberant novel of 1960s Glasgow, *Swing Hammer Swing!* A drink can be both a draught of terror or, as the medieval poet **Robert Henryson** described in *The Testament Of Cresseid,* a warming glass in winter:

I mend the fyre and beikit me about,

Than tuik ane drink, my spreitis to comfort,

And armit me weill fra the cauld thairout...

Like it or not, alcohol seems to underpin certain ideas about what Scotland is and has been. It was through a supposedly befuddled haze that **Hugh MacDiarmid** explored the metaphysical, poetic and political dimensions of Scottish identity in the 2,680 lines of *A Drunk Man Looks At The Thistle.* In spite or perhaps because of its inherent dangers, we are very fond of a drink.

The riotous back-room, the smoke-filled howff, the dour and functional city bar, all these are familiar scenes in our literature. But they are almost always masculine scenes. The historical reason for this is that, until relatively recently, many women would never have set foot in, or would not have been permitted to set foot in, anywhere as insalubrious, morally questionable - and male-dominated - as a pub. Drink and other drugs, however, have been just as important to women as to men, although sometimes not for the best reasons. The weaver poet **Janet Hamilton** (1795-1873) recognised disapprovingly that alcohol abuse was not restricted to men when she wrote:

Oh, the dreadfu' curse o' drinkin'!
Men are ill, bu tae my thinkin',
Leukin' through the drucken flock,
There's a Jenny for ilk Jock.

John Galt had the Reverend Balwhidder in *Annals Of The Parish* note the arrival of the 'new luxury' of tea-drinking among females in 1761, and that the older women gathered guiltily to partake in groups 'in out-houses and by-places, just as the witches lang syne had their sinful possets and galravitchings.' The social and psychological environments of male and female drug-taking were marked out early on.

And what of that other legally condoned drug, nicotine? **Jessie Kesson,** whose novels and short stories set in the North-East are filled with references to the small pleasures that made a hard life bearable, once said: 'If God said to me, "All the drink in the world is finished, Jessie," I would say: "A pity about that, God. I enjoy a drink a bitty." But if he said all the fags in the world were finished, I'd be under the first bus.' Smoking may now be politically incorrect, but its place in literature is assured, from **James VI's** condemnation of the habit in his *Counterblaste To Tobacco* (1604), to **Norman MacCaig's** dry assessment of how long it took him to write a poem: 'Two fags. Unless it's a wee one then it's one fag.'

All this indicates something about stimulants and depressants that the literary idea of their transformational powers sometimes obscures. Drugs are part of our culture and we have been using and abusing them for centuries. They are not so much 'open sesames' to other worlds and experiences (although they can be) as elements of daily reality. There are more drugs, and more kinds of drugs, available now than ever before: no doubt the literature of the future will chart how they take their place in people's lives, and - to return to Jekyll and Hyde - with what good or bad results.

James Robertson is currently at work on his first novel. He has written an acclaimed collection of short stories, Ragged Man's Complaint, *a book of Scottish ghost stories and a collection of poetry called* Sound Shadow.

STEWART, MARY

Rose Cottage
Hodder & Stoughton pb
0340695617 £5.99

Mary Stewart's unique brand of romantic suspense is evident in this, one of her more recent works. The main character, Kate Herrigan, is asked to visit her childhood home before it is sold, but there is evidence of a break-in and rumours of prowlers and even ghosts. While Kate solves the mystery of Rose Cottage she encounters unexpected romance. Mary Stewart is perhaps best known for her Arthurian novels, but her style of romantic saga writing has ensured that her other works are of a similar high quality.

Airs Above The Ground
Headline pb 0340024585 £5.99
The Crystal Cave
Headline pb 0340151331 £6.99
The Gabriel Hounds
Headline pb 0340043539 £5.99
The Hollow Hills
Headline pb 0340186119 £5.99
The Ivy Tree
Headline pb 0340011157 £5.99
The Last Enchantment
Headline pb 0340258292 £5.99
Madam, Will You Talk?
Headline pb 0340012625 £4.99
The Moon Spinners
Headline pb 0340013613 £5.99
My Brother Michael
Headline pb 0340013958 £4.50
Nine Coaches Waiting
Headline pb 0340014393 £5.99
The Prince And The Pilgrim
Headline pb 0340654112 £5.99
The Stormy Petrel
Headline pb 034057724X £5.99
This Rough Magic
Headline pb 0340022027 £5.99
Thornyhold
Headline pb 034050045X £5.99
Touch Not The Cat
Headline pb 034021984X £5.99
The Wicked Day
Headline pb 0340352140 £5.99
Wildfire At Midnight
Headline pb 034001945X £4.50

STIRLING, JESSICA

The Wind From The Hills
Hodder & Stoughton hb
0340671963 16.99

This sequel to *The Island Wife* follows the fortunes of sisters Innis and Biddy Campbell who are in love with the same man. Set on the island of Mull during the 19th century, this Scottish family saga is one of Jessica Stirling's many best-selling works.

Creature Comforts
Hodder & Stoughton pb
0340657936 £5.99
The Dark Pasture
Hodder & Stoughton pb
0340707453 £5.99
Hearts of Gold
Hodder & Stoughton pb
0340657944 £5.99
The Hiring Fair
Hodder & Stoughton pb
0340707445 £5.99
The Island Wife
Hodder & Stoughton pb
0340671955 £5.99
The Marrying Kind
Hodder & Stoughton pb
0340657626 £5.99
Penny Wedding
Hodder & Stoughton pb
0340618213 £5.99
Shadows on the Shore
Pan pb 0330333550 £4.99
The Spoiled Earth
Hodder & Stoughton pb
0340707437 £5.99
Treasures On Earth
Hodder & Stoughton pb
0340657928 £5.99
The Workhouse Girl
Hodder & Stoughton pb
034066603X £5.99

SUTHERLAND, LUKE

Jelly Roll
Anchor pb 1862300305 £6.99

A very original first novel set around a struggling band's tour of the Highlands, this is a darkly comic tale of a musician's descent into the nine circles of hell and of the personality clashes involved in a constantly touring band. A story full of sex, drugs and rock 'n roll.

TANNAHILL, REAY

A Dark And Distant Shore
Penguin pb 0140067639 £6.99
Fatal Majesty: The Drama Of Mary, Queen Of Scots
Orion hb 0752804936 16.99
Passing Glory
Penguin pb 0140127704 £6.99
Return Of The Stranger
Orion pb 0752802844 £5.99

A Dark and Distant Shore is an historical saga that concerns a young woman's fight to reclaim her family castle in the Scottish Highlands. Covering nearly a century with many views of far-flung outposts of the Victorian empire, this work brings to mind Margaret Mitchell's *Gone With The Wind. Fatal Majesty* is a fictionalised account of the complex web of political and royal manoeuvrings that were at the centre of Mary Queen of Scots' life and death.

THOMPSON, ALICE

Justine
Canongate pb 0862416035 £12.00
Justine
Virago pb 1860493068 £6.99

This challenging and unrelenting first novel was the joint winner of the James Tait Black Memorial Prize. The novel takes a post-modernist look at sex, desire, control and power. Set in contemporary London, it explores the areas of sexuality touched on by the Marquis de Sade and goes on to skilfully subvert de Sade's views. In the original Canongate edition the facing pages were left uncut, requiring readers to cut them open themselves.

TORRINGTON, JEFF

Jeff Torrington's seriously funny *Swing Hammer Swing!* won the 1992 Whitbread Book of the Year award. The novel describes a week in the life of Gorbals' resident Tom Clay and is set in the 60s, when urban renewal projects were tearing down the old slum tenements. Torrington's central character sets off on a mini-voyage of self-discovery, and in the process Torrington draws a remarkably atmospheric picture of the Gorbals and its underclass residents at the time. His second novel, *The Devil's Carousel*, is a dark comedy describing the repetitive world of 70s' car manufacturing in Scotland. With a rich cast of memorable characters, the novel generates a wide range of different emotional states.
The Devil's Carousel
Minerva pb 0749397624 £6.99
Swing Hammer Swing!
Minerva pb 0749397470 £7.99

TRANTER, NIGEL

Born in Glasgow, Nigel Tranter trained as an accountant and turned to full-time writing in 1936. He is one of the most prolific authors Scotland has known, with over a hundred books to his name. His entertaining fictionalised accounts of Scottish history are for many Scots their first meaningful encounter with their past. His books bear the hallmark of a man superbly versed in his subject, with a rounded understanding of the characters behind the events. This is clear from *The Bruce Trilogy* and *The Wallace* which offer Tranter's own particular take on two of the most famous heroes of Scottish history. He has written about most periods of the nation's history. Since Tranter has been so prolific it is difficult to single out particular books. The three following are simply representative of his huge backlist of titles. *Balefire* is set after the Flodden massacre. Abel Ridley, a Scottish laird, is spared his life after promising an English knight a huge ransom, but this is only the beginning of his fight to survive. *Balefire* is a tense story of the 16th century Border wars with a pervasive atmosphere of fear and chaos, told with Tranter's usual flair and verve for character and plot. *The Flockmasters* is a tale from the Clearances. Alastair MacRory returns to Scotland to recuperate from a wound suffered in the Peninsular War. He is horrified to find his fellow clansmen being ruthlessly evicted by flockmasters to make way for herds of sheep, and decides to fight the unscrupulous businessmen taking the land. In *Kettle of Fish* Adam Horsburgh, a schoolmaster, decides to openly defy the 1857 Tweed Fisheries Act that bans salmon fishing for fifty miles off the mouth of the Tweed. However his actions precipitate a salmon war, with poaching gangs descending from all around. This is one of Tranter's lighter historical adventures with a strong feeling for time and place. His non-fictional works are mainly about Scotland's architecture, and he has a keen interest in the political affairs of the nation.

Balefire
B & W pb 1873631057 £5.99
Black Douglas
Hodder & Stoughton pb
0340164662 £5.99
Bridal Path
B & W pb 1873631022 £5.99
The Bruce Trilogy
Hodder & Stoughton pb
0340371862 £12.99
Captive Crown
Hodder & Stoughton pb
0340248734 £5.99
Chain of Destiny
Hodder & Stoughton pb
0340212381 £5.99
Children of the Mist
Hodder & Stoughton pb
0340570997 £5.99
Columba
Hodder & Stoughton pb
0340508264 £5.99
Crusader
Hodder & Stoughton pb
0340579277 £5.99
David the Prince
Hodder & Stoughton pb
0340279109 £5.99
Druid Sacrifice
Hodder & Stoughton pb
0340599847 £5.99
Fast and Loose
B & W pb 1873631294 £5.99
The Flockmasters
B & W pb 1873631456 £5.99
Flowers of Chivalry
Hodder & Stoughton pb
0340520280 £5.99
Folly of Princes
Hodder & Stoughton pb
0340234717 £5.99
Freebooters
B & W pb 1873631731 £5.99
The Gilded Fleece
B & W pb 1873631138 £5.99
Gold For Prince Charlie
Hodder & Stoughton pb
0340187670 £5.99
Harsh Heritage
B & W pb 1873631650 £5.99

Highness In Hiding
Hodder & Stoughton pb
0340625864 £5.99
Honours Even
Hodder & Stoughton pb
0340625848 £5.99
Island Twilight
B & W pb 1873631227 £5.99
James V Trilogy
Hodder & Stoughton pb
0340637668 12.99
Kenneth
Hodder & Stoughton pb
0340566388 £5.99
Kettle of Fish
B & W pb 1873631464 £5.99
Lion Let Loose
Hodder & Stoughton pb
0340586982 £5.99
The Lion's Whelp
Hodder & Stoughton pb
0340659998 £5.99
Lord In Waiting
Hodder & Stoughton pb
0340625872 £5.99
Lord of the Isles
Hodder & Stoughton pb
0340368365 £5.99
Macbeth the King
Hodder & Stoughton pb
0340265442 £5.99
Macgregor Trilogy
Hodder & Stoughton pb
0340405724 12.99
Mail Royal
Hodder & Stoughton pb
0340535393 £5.99

The Marchman
Hodder & Stoughton pb
0340659955 £5.99
Margaret The Queen
Hodder & Stoughton pb
0340265450 £5.99
Master of Gray Trilogy
Hodder & Stoughton pb
0340666757 12.99
The Montrose Omnibus
Hodder & Stoughton pb
0340407638 £9.99
The Patriot
Hodder & Stoughton pb
0340349158 £5.99
Poetic Justice
Hodder & Stoughton pb
0340625821 £5.99
The Price of a Princess
Hodder & Stoughton pb
034060994X £5.99
The Queen's Grace
B & W pb 1873631103 £5.99
A Rage of Regents
Hodder & Stoughton pb
0340659971 £5.99
A Stake in the Kingdom
Hodder & Stoughton pb
034063765X £5.99
The Stewart Trilogy
Hodder & Stoughton pb
0340391154 12.99
The Stone
B & W pb 1873631014 £5.99
Tapestry of the Boar
Hodder & Stoughton pb
0340601051 £5.99

Tinker's Pride
B & W pb 1873631308 £5.99
True Thomas
Hodder & Stoughton pb
0340328150 £5.99
Unicorn Rampant
Hodder & Stoughton pb
0340386355 £5.99
The Wallace
Hodder & Stoughton pb
0340212373 £5.99
Warden of the Queen's March
Hodder & Stoughton pb
0340545976 £5.99
The Wisest Fool
Hodder & Stoughton pb
0340202998 £5.99
Young Montrose
Hodder & Stoughton pb
0340162139 £5.99

M. & A. Pritchard's Tranter's Terrain *(Neil Wilson pb 1897784236 £5.99) is a companion to Tranter's historical novels.*

TROCCHI, ALEXANDER (1925–1984)

Trocchi was the foremost British beat writer, a major figure in contemporary Scottish writing who has heavily influenced the new wave of Scottish writers. He founded the influential magazine *Merlin* which published writers such as Beckett and Genet, and wrote a small number of novels. *Young Adam,* his first novel, is a contemporary classic of Scottish literature. Set on a barge travelling along the canal that runs between Glasgow and Edinburgh, it is in essence an existential thriller. *Cain's Book* is Trocchi's graphic account of his experiences in New York: hooked on drugs, but still writing. For a short time Trocchi made a living by writing erotic fiction for the legendary Olympia Press. One of these fictions is *Helen and Desire,* the story of a young woman's sexual odyssey, written from the perspective of the female central character. This is a major underground book that has at last made it into the mainstream. Trocchi had moved to America in the 50s but was forced to return due to heroin addiction. He famously feuded with Hugh MacDiarmid at the Edinburgh International Writers' Conference in 1962 over their respective literary achievements. He died in 1984 in London. Nearly all of Trocchi's shorter pieces are included in *A Trocchi Reader* published by Polygon.

Cain's Book
Calder pb 0714542334 £8.99
Helen And Desire
Rebel Inc. pb 0862416299 £6.99
Invisible Insurrection of a
Million Minds: A Trocchi Reader
Polygon pb 0748661085 £9.99
Thongs
Blast Bks US pb 092223311X £6.99
White Thighs
Blast Bks US pb 0922233144 £7.99
Young Adam
Rebel Inc. pb 0862416248 £6.99

URQUHART, FRED
Full Score: Selected Short Stories
Mercat Press pb 008037719X
£6.99

Twenty short stories selected from over fifty years' work, some of which are set in and around the fictitious town of Auchencairn. Even these localised works contain themes and issues of universal relevance, and all his work reveals his gifted insight and his ear for dialect.

"I often wondered how far out a man could go without being obliterated."
Alexander Trocchi, Cain's Book

URQUHART, THOMAS (c.1611-1660)

Urquhart was born in Cromarty, the son of a major land-owner. He was educated at King's College, Aberdeen and then spent some years in Europe. Before returning to Scotland in 1636 he fought on Charles I's side against the Covenanters, a decision that forced him to flee to London where he was subsequently knighted. It was while in London that he published *Epigrams Divine And Moral*. The following year, after his father's death, he returned to Scotland where he wrote *Trissotetras,* a study in mathematics. After the coronation of Charles II, Urquhart turned back to the Royalist cause which led in 1651 to his brief imprisonment and the loss of his estates, as a result of which he departed for Europe. His later works include *Pantochronochanon* in which he traces his family tree back to a descendant of Adam. *The Discoverie Of A Most Exquisite Jewel* is an attack on the Scottish clergy which argues for the need for a universal language, which Urquhart tried to invent. The idea of a universal language was further explored in *Logopandecteison*. Urquhart's most acclaimed work is his racy translation of Rabelais' comic masterpiece *Gargantua and Pantagruel,* which shows his dexterity of language and his ribald wit. Urquhart's choice of subject matter for his writing was radically different from the historical and religious themes of previous writers, and his unique, humorous and eccentric character is evident throughout his work. Legend has it that he died laughing on hearing of the restoration of Charles II.

The Jewel (Ed RDS Jack & RJ Lyall)
S.A.P. hb 0707303273 £8.75
Gargantua and Pantagruel by F. Rabelais
Translated by Sir Thomas Urquhart
Everyman hb 185715181X £10.99

Photograph by Jessie Simmons

WALLACE, CHRISTOPHER

The Pied Piper's Poison
Flamingo hb 0002256274
£16.99

A first novel of remarkable power and poetry set in a refugee camp in Southern Poland, just after the end of the Second World War. A young Scottish doctor is sent to identify the cause of a mysterious and horrific outbreak of plague in the camp. A compelling and intelligent novel that is unsettling and disturbing.

WALLACE, RANDALL

Braveheart
Signet pb 0451185730 £5.99

Randall Wallace's novel was the starting point for Mel Gibson's cinematic epic on William Wallace. What it lacks in historical accuracy it more than makes up for in passion, vividly relating the story of Wallace's struggle to unite the Scottish people against the ruthless English king, Edward I, in a tale of romance, intrigue and above all, heroic action.

WARNER, ALAN

Morvern Callar established Warner as a name to watch. It relates the story of a young woman in a remote Highland sea-port whose boyfriend commits suicide, and her subsequent journey of the spirit. Bleak and macabre, erotic and lyrical, this accomplished first book is a remarkable literary creation. It has recently been adapted for film by the BBC. His second novel *These Demented Lands* is a radical departure from his first, even though it is a sequel and includes the heroine Morvern Callar. The plot concerns events at the island honeymoon hotspot of the Drome Hotel. The novel's various colourful characters are all engaged in their own peculiar actions. A DJ is trying to set up a huge rave on the nearby airstrip while an aircrash investigator gathers pieces of wreckage and assembles them at the same site. Meanwhile various eccentric characters are converging on the hotel for the forthcoming rave. His most recent book is *The Sopranos*. The choir of Our Lady Of Perpetual Succour School For Girls is travelling to the national finals in the big city. After throwing the competition the sopranos have big plans–body-piercing, pub crawling and then on to the man-trap disco where a recently docked submarine crew on shore leave is due. However their plans don't go quite as expected. Alan Warner's third novel shows that he is one of the most innovative and original writers on the Scottish scene.

Morvern Callar
Vintage pb 0099586118 £5.99
The Sopranos
Cape pb 0224051083 £9.99
These Demented Lands
Vintage pb 0099577917 £5.99

"... the loxogonospherical triangles whether amblygonospherical or oxygonospherical are either monurgetick or disergetick."

Sir Thomas Urquhart

WELSH, IRVINE

Irvine Welsh's *Trainspotting* hit the Scottish literary scene like an incendiary bomb. Since its publication it has been frequently copied in terms of style and content. Situated in the parts of Edinburgh few tourists dare visit, his rich, grotesque take on the city's drug underworld is an urban masterpiece. There have been several theatrical productions and of course the movie that fast became one of the most successful in British cinema history. He followed up this success with *The Acid House,* a collection of short stories which are hard-hitting and feature a wide range of styles and feelings from sharp realism to demented fantasy and from the comic and sad to the horrific and shocking. Welsh has recently finished writing the screenplay for the forthcoming film of this collection. *Ecstasy* is a collection of three tales that have as their locus the themes of sex'n'-drugs'n'dance. Inventively disgusting, they display Welsh's prodigious talent. *Marabou Stork Nightmares* is a frightening, often funny and frequently grotesque tale of contemporary Scottish life. The story takes place in the world of Edinburgh-based casuals with nightmarish flashbacks to a real or imagined African childhood. Welsh's latest book, *Filth,* finds him taking on the crime genre. Written in his familiar intense and extreme style, the novel has its heart Detective Sergeant Bruce Robertson, a wonderful creation: misanthropic, corrupt and sleazy. He's just about to set off for his Christmas break in Amsterdam (a week of top quality sex and drugs) when a messy murder case fouls up his plans. As he dives head first into the lower reaches of degradation and evil, his only source of truth and conscience is his own anus. Once again Welsh provides a wild and outrageous novel at turns disturbing and very funny.

The Acid House
Vintage pb 0099435012 £5.99
Ecstasy
Vintage pb 0099590913 £5.99
Filth
Cape pb 022404118X £9.99
Irvine Welsh Omnibus
Cape pb 0224050036 £9.99
Marabou Stork Nightmares
Vintage pb 009943511X £5.99
Trainspotting
Minerva pb 0749336501 £6.99

WHITE, KENNETH
The Blue Road
Mainstream hb 1851582797
£12.95

One of Kenneth White's 'way books', this prose narrative is set in Labrador and quickly moves on from the more traditional concerns of the novel into a study of man's primal relationship with the earth.

WHITE, KIRSTY
My Little Oyster Girl
Orion pb 1857970977 £4.99

A family saga that relates the tale of Catriona, the daughter of a Skye crofter. When her mother dies she struggles to keep the family in food, moving to Glasgow just before World War I. Eventually she rises up to become a successful businesswoman, but still has to find love. It is a story of hard work and perseverance triumphing over tragedy.
Tia's Story
Orion pb 1857974913 £4.99

WHYTE, CHRISTOPHER

Leagues away from Irvine Welsh's hard-man school of Scottish fiction, Christopher Whyte's novel, *Euphemia MacFarrigle and the Laughing Virgin*, is set in the genteel parts of Glasgow held in the arms of the Catholic Church, a place of social niceties and sexual prejudice. It is satirical comedy on the contemporary Catholic Church that shines with wit and intelligence. In *The Warlock of Strathearn* Archibald MacCaspin, retired schoolmaster, deciphers an obscure 17th century manuscript. The decoded narrative concerns a young man with supernatural powers. His constant conflict with his evil grandmother is resolved in a violent fashion. A novel full of fantastical elements that explores the psychodrama of life using magical realism. His most recent work, *The Gay Decameron*, is set at a gay dinner party in Edinburgh. In it Christopher Whyte weaves the men's untold stories into and around the evening's events to produce a funny, erotic and elegaic tale of gay lives in the late 20th century.

Euphemia MacFarrigle & The Laughing Virgin
Indigo pb 0575400382 £5.99
The Gay Decameron
Gollancz hb 0575065052 £16.99
The Warlock of Strathearn
Gollancz pb 0575065060 £9.99

WILLIAMS, GORDON

From Scenes Like These
B & W pb 1873631677 £6.99

Gordon Williams is regarded by many as one of the most innovative post-war Scottish writers. This work is one of his early semi-autobiographical novels, a raw and powerful tragedy in which Duncan Logan, the main protagonist, is growing up in the bleak years just after World War II. His life has no focus and he can see nothing of worth for himself in the future. As he desperately struggles to escape his brutal present all he can find is violence and betrayal. Williams has several other hard-hitting works to his credit including *The Straw Dogs* and *The Upper Pleasure Garden*.

WITHALL, MARY

Mary Withall writes intelligent sagas with a lot of historical and sociological comment. They are set mainly in western Scotland, particularly in the Oban area. *Beacon on the Shore, The Gorse in Bloom* and *Where the Wild Thyme Grows* form a trilogy set around 1900. Her subsequent work, *Field Of Heather,* although not part of this trilogy, is loosely connected to it.

Beacon on the Shore
Coronet pb 0340640502 £5.99
Field of Heather
Coronet pb 0340717467 £5.99
The Gorse in Bloom
Coronet pb 0340640529 £5.99
Where the Wild Thyme Grows
Coronet pb 0340640545 £5.99

YOUNG, SANDY

Son of the Glen
House Of Lochar pb
1899863168 £6.99

Young's book is a novel of Highland life that spans the years from the Second World War to the present day as told by a shepherd's son. The author has drawn on his own experiences in the writing of this carefully constructed evocation of the Scottish agricultural community.

Capital Crimes

by Ian Rankin

When I arrived in Edinburgh in the late 1970s, it seemed that while the capital had more than its fair share of publishing houses, any actual *writing* worth bothering about was being done in Glasgow. While I struggled to find both theme and voice in my short stories and (putative) novels, the 'model' of the Edinburgh novel remained **Muriel Spark's** *The Prime Of Miss Jean Brodie,* published over a quarter of a century before. And prior to Spark... well, there were some books from earlier in the century, books largely forgotten and out of print, and then it was back to **Stevenson** and **Scott.**

This may seem like a gross simplification, but at the time *nothing* seemed to be happening in Edinburgh. Glasgow, meanwhile, was proving to be 'smiles better' in all manner of ways. There was **William McIlvanney,** of course, but also **Alan Spence, Alasdair Gray, Jim Kelman, Agnes Owens**... If you wanted to write a worthwhile Scottish novel, it looked like you had to hike west.

My first published novel was set in the west-central Fife of my childhood and adolescence, and showed a teenager keening for something better, something he thought he could find (don't laugh) in Edinburgh. My second novel was set in the city itself, but the hero, far from being a confused laddie from Cardenden, was a hard-bitten and cynical police detective. Actually, when writing *Knots & Crosses,* I'd no idea the crime genre still existed. I knew of a few individual works, but practically the only crime novels I'd read were the Shaft series (as a youth) and, more recently, **McIlvanney's** Laidlaw novels.

To me, **McIlvanney** was a 'proper' writer, and this made it all right for me to write what I thought was a serious book from a policeman's point of view. My initial aim was to write about the side of Edinburgh the tourist seldom sees, the side *I* knew. I wanted to write about an urban, up-to-date Edinburgh with more than its fair share of 80s problems. But my model (at least in the first two Rebus books) was still traditional: **Stevenson's** *Dr Jekyll And Mr Hyde.* While Scotland has a grand tradition of adventure writing and gothic storytelling, there's no tradition of the whodunnit (**Conan Doyle** being the exception rather than the rule), and hence no dead weight of expectation resting on the shoulders of would-be practitioners.

In 1990 I left Edinburgh, first for London and then for France, returning in 1996 to a city much changed - not least by **Irvine Welsh's** *Trainspotting.* Suddenly, in the eyes of the world, Edinburgh had become a real three-dimensional city rather than a living museum or tourist theme park. But something unexpected had happened along the way.

Edinburgh is suddenly the city of capital crimes. Writers such as myself, **Alanna Knight** and **Marten Claridge** make our homes here. **Quintin Jardine** and **Frederic Lindsay** live in the vicinity, and a new breed of Scottish crime writer seems attracted to the place too. **Paul Johnston** won the prestigious John Creasey Award for his first novel, *Body Politic,* a serial killer hunt set in a totalitarian Edinburgh of the near-future. **Christopher Brookmyre** won a similar award for his first novel *Quite Ugly One Morning* which fuses a Welshian sensibility to the kind of comedic chase novel usually more associated with American masters such as Carl Hiaasen. **Carol Anne Davis's** first novel, *Shrouded,* is a chilling account of one man's journey through obsession towards madness and murder - and will make anyone think twice about their local funeral parlour's embalming option.

Another east coast writer, **Iain Banks,** chose to set *Complicity,* his stalk and slash whodunnit, in the Athens of the North, while the historical novelist and Edinburgh resident **Dorothy Dunnett** has a sideline writing the 'Dolly' series of traditional whodunnits....

Have I left anyone out? Almost certainly, for new Edinburgh crimes seem to be hitting the bookshelves every month. These books are not just popular at home: crime novels have a huge international market, appealing to fans the world over, and introducing them to aspects of Scottish daily life far removed from the shortbread-tin and the eightsome reel. My own books are translated into a range of languages, everything from Latvian to Japanese, while other crime writers spend a good chunk of each year on tour around the bookshops of the USA, Canada and Australia.

The irony in all of this is that Edinburgh languishes way behind Glasgow in the true-crime stakes. There were six murders in the capital in 1997, contrasted to sixty-six in Strathclyde. City comparisons show Glasgow to have a murder rate three times that of Edinburgh, making the west coast city much the more dangerous place *per capita*. So Edinburgh's mean streets may not be so mean after all, which doesn't explain what seems a dearth of Glasgow crime writing. It's six years since **McIlvanney's** last Laidlaw novel. **Peter Turnbull,** the ex-pat Yorkshireman responsible for the 'P Division' procedurals, has flitted back to Leeds, where his latest novel is set. **Bill Knox** remains active, and **Ron McKay** writes the occasional west coast thriller...and that's about it. **Frederick Lindsay,** who *has* written about Glasgow, has moved the action to Edinburgh for his latest police novel, *Kissing Judas.*

Perhaps nascent Glasgow writers have been scared off by the dual threat of Jack Laidlaw and the seemingly eternal Taggart, afraid to be regarded as mere clones. Then again, it may be that the very nature of Scotland's titular capital - detached, furtive, clandestine - lends itself to novels of intrigue, while Glasgow - brash, vibrant, passionate - does not.

James Ellroy coined an oxymoron to describe my own novels. He called them 'Tartan *noir'*. The journey into the darker recesses of the human soul continues.

Ian Rankin is the author of the 'Inspector Rebus' series of crime novels. He has been the recipient of a Hawthornden fellowship, the Raymond Chandler Prize, and three 'Dagger' awards, including, in 1997, the prestigious Gold Dagger Award for the best crime novel of the year for his book Black & Blue. *That book was also shortlisted for the American 'Edgar' Award - a first for a Scottish crime novel. Rebus's most recent outing is in* The Hanging Garden.

Crime Fiction

BEATON, M.C.

M.C. Beaton's Hamish Macbeth novels recently had their profile dramatically increased thanks to the wonderful BBC adaptations starring Robert Carlyle as the genial police constable of the Highland town of Lochdubh. The books have been cult favourites for quite some time and it may come as no surprise to discover that they are very different from their TV equivalents, due largely to the even more pointed and outrageous black comedy of Beaton himself.

Death of a Cad
Transworld pb 0553407929
£3.99
Death of a Gossip
Transworld pb 0553407910
£3.99
Death of a Glutton
Transworld pb 0553409727
£3.99
Death of a Hussy
Transworld pb 0553409670
£3.99
Death of an Outsider
Transworld pb 0553407937
£3.99
Death of a Perfect Wife
Transworld pb 0553407945
£3.99
Death of a Prankster
Transworld pb 0553407937
£3.99
Death of a Snob
Transworld pb 0553409689
£3.99

BROOKMYRE, CHRISTOPHER

From its opening, when journalist Jack Parlabane stumbles across a grotesquely murdered and mutilated doctor, to its conclusion *Quite Ugly One Morning* keeps up an exhilarating pace. Christopher Brookmyre mixes razor-sharp dialogue with colourful villains, wicked black humour and a high octane story line. His second novel *Country of the Blind* takes up where the first left off, with journalist Parlabane once again the centre of the action. This time a Tory newspaper tycoon has been murdered, seemingly as part of a botched burglary. However Parlabane suspects something more sinister. This thrilling novel establishes Christopher Brookmyre among Scotland's premier division writers.

Country of the Blind
Abacus pb 0349109303 £6.99
Quite Ugly One Morning
Abacus pb 0349108854 £6.99

CAVE, PETER

Peter Cave's Taggart TV tie-
in novels retain the series' distinctive atmosphere and Taggart's much loved dour and stubborn character.
Taggart: Fatal Inheritance
Mainstream pb 1851586288 £5.99
Taggart: Forbidden Fruit
Mainstream pb 185158627X £5.99
Taggart: Gingerbread
Mainstream pb 1851585567 £4.99
Taggart: Nest of Vipers
Mainstream pb 1851585559 £4.99

DOYLE, SIR ARTHUR CONAN

It may come as a surprise to some readers that the creator of the archetypal English gentleman detective was in fact Scottish. Doyle used his background in medicine as a heavy source of inspiration. By his own admission he based Holmes on one of his Edinburgh medical teachers, Dr. Joseph Bell. Using the simple narrative formula of Watson retelling the stories gives the reader a feeling of intimacy with the characters. The books are also characterised by the interplay between Holmes with his razor-sharp eccentric intellect and Watson's more conventional and everyday empiricism. These are only two of the elements that have ensured the stories' long-standing popularity.

The Adventures of Sherlock Holmes
OUP pb 0192823787 £3.99
The Casebook of Sherlock Holmes
OUP pb 0192823744 £3.99
His Last Bow
OUP pb 0192823817 £3.99
The Hound of the Baskervilles
OUP pb 0192823779 £3.99
The Memoirs of Sherlock Holmes
OUP pb 0192823752 £3.99
The Return of Sherlock Holmes
OUP pb 0192823760 £3.99
Sherlock Holmes
OUP pb 019281530X £3.99
The Sign of Four
OUP pb 0192823795 £3.99
A Study In Scarlet
OUP pb 0192823809 £3.99
The Valley of Fear
OUP pb 0192823825 £3.99

DUNNETT, DOROTHY

Dorothy Dunnett's light and enjoyable crime thrillers feature the abysmally dressed portrait painter and amateur detective Johnson Johnson. These easy-going adventures are set in some very exotic locations. Originally named after Johnson's boat *Dolly* and published under Dunnett's maiden name Halliday, they have recently been re-issued under these new titles.
Rum Affair
Arrow pb 0099846500 £3.99
Tropical Issue
Arrow pb 0099846608 £3.99

HOLMS, JOYCE

Two of Joyce Holms's mysteries are available. *Foreign Body* is the second 'Fizz' Fitzgerald and Tam Buchanan murder mystery, set in the Scottish Highlands. It finds the intrepid duo investigating the murders of a hiker and an 82 year old woman. The close-knit community of a small Highland town is affectionately recreated in this enjoyable and briskly paced work.
Foreign Body
Headline pb 074725561X £5.99
Payment Deferred
Headline pb 0747255601 £5.99

JARDINE, QUINTIN

Quintin Jardine worked in journalism and PR before he turned to writing a series of novels featuring the tough, high-flying Edinburgh police chief Bob Skinner. The latest book in the much acclaimed series is *Skinner's Ghosts*. Skinner believes he has put the worst of his past behind him, but when a former Government Minister's widow is killed and her son kidnapped, he is not so sure. With each new novel Jardine's creation develops in maturity as his character unfolds before us. Jardine has also created a new crime-stopping duo in Oz Blackstone and Primavera Phillips.
A Coffin For Two
Headline pb 0747254613 £5.99
Blackstone's Pursuits
Headline pb 0747254605 £5.99
Skinner's Festival
Headline pb 0747241406 £4.99
Skinner's Ghosts
Headline hb 0747219443 £16.99
Skinner's Mission
Headline pb 074725043X £5.99
Skinner's Ordeal
Headline pb 0747250421 £5.99
Skinner's Round
Headline pb 0747250413 £5.99
Skinner's Rules
Headline pb 0747241392 £5.99
Skinner's Trail
Headline pb 0747241414 £5.99

JOHNSTON, PAUL

Body Politic (Winner of John Creasey Memorial Dagger Award)
Hodder & Stoughton pb 0340694912 £5.99

Body Politic is set in the year 2020 in an Edinburgh which has become an independent walled city heavily reliant on its year-round Festival and tourist trade for its livelihood. When this main source of revenue is threatened by a series of brutal murders, reluctant investigator Quint Dalrymple is sent in. The resulting book straddles the genres of science fiction and crime.

KNIGHT, ALANNA

Alanna Knight's absorbing crime novels stylishly evoke the atmospheric city of Edinburgh during the nineteenth century. An omnibus edition is available which includes three novels featuring her investigative hero, Jeremy Faro: *A Quiet Death, To Kill A Queen* and *The Evil That Men Do*. In *The Coffin Lane Murders* a brutal murder marks the beginning of Alanna Knight's latest Inspector Faro mystery in which he has to deal with a serial killer.
The Coffin Lane Murders
Macmillan hb 0333689127 £16.99
Inspector Faro's Casebook : The Second Omnibus
Pan pb 0330348558 £7.99

LINDSAY, FREDERIC

Frederic Lindsay's unsettling crime novel, *Kissing Judas*, twists and turns, changing in location and direction. Set in Edinburgh, Ireland and the Loire Valley, it has a main character Jim Meldrum, who, like many fictional Scottish detectives, is emotionally and personally damaged by his job. He is haunted by the murder of a blind man fifteen years ago because of his doubts about the guilt of the man convicted for it, Hugh Keaney. Keaney's hunger strike makes him determined to uncover the truth. Lindsay has written several other works including the televised *Brond* (now out of print) and is an intelligent writer with insight into psychological motives and actions. In *A Kind Of Dying* Lindsay has produced another intelligent pyschological thriller, the second crime novel to feature Jim Meldrum, which contains many of the strengths of its predecessor.

After The Stranger Came
Deutsch hb 0233987797 £13.99
A Charm Against Drowning
Deutsch hb 023398254X £10.95
Jill Rips
Deutsch hb 0233980172 £9.95
A Kind Of Dying
Hodder & Stoughton hb 0340695358 £16.99
Kissing Judas
Hodder & Stoughton pb 034069534X £5.99

McDERMID, VAL

Gold Dagger Award winner Val McDermid is fast becoming a major international crime author. She has written three quite distinct series. The Lindsay Gordon books are set in Scotland and *Booked For Murder* is the fifth in the series. This time the Scottish investigator agrees to explore the death of crime writer Penny Varnavides, whose murder has been carried out exactly the same way as the one described in her forthcoming book. This points to three suspects: Penny's agent, her editor and her ex-girlfriend. The action moves from Gordon's Californian retreat to the high-energy world of London publishing. McDermid's Manchester-based private investigator Kate Brannigan has become one of Britain's most popular crime characters. She first appeared in *Dead Beat* (1992). Her adventures are marked by fast-paced, complex and meticulously crafted plots. *Star Struck* is the sixth novel in this sequence. McDermid has also written two thrillers involving clinical psychologist Tony Hill. *The Mermaids Singing* is a powerfully written psychological thriller that revolves around the tortured mind of a serial killer and the efforts of Tony Hill to stay alive and help capture this murderer.

Photograph by Jessie Simmons

Lindsay Gordon series

Booked For Murder
Women's Press pb 0704345951
£5.99
Common Murder
Women's Press pb 0704345927
£5.99
Final Edition
Women's Press pb 0704345935
£5.99
Report For Murder
Women's Press pb 0704345919
£5.99
Union Jack
Women's Press pb 0704345943
£5.99

Kate Brannigan series

Blue Genes
HarperCollins pb 0006498310
£5.99
Clean Break
HarperCollins pb 0006497721
£4.99
Crack Down
HarperCollins pb 0006490085
£4.99
Dead Beat
Vista pb 0575600020 £4.99
Kick Back
Vista pb 0575600071 £5.99
Star Struck
HarperCollins hb 00023258531
£6.99

Tony Hill series

The Mermaids Singing (CWA Gold Dagger Award Winner)
HarperCollins pb 0006493580
£5.99
Wire in the Blood
HarperCollins pb 000649983X
£5.99

MCILVANNEY, WILLIAM

Tough Glasgow policeman Jack Laidlaw is an extension of McIlvanney's non-crime fiction: the same interest in working class values and ordinary people is present. McIlvanney's memorable way with figures of speech, as well as his ability to carefully establish character and place, have led to his Laidlaw works being compared with those of Raymond Chandler. All of this makes for a crime writer whose novels are well worth getting to know.

Laidlaw
Sceptre pb 0340576901 £6.99
The Papers of Tony Veitch
Sceptre pb 0340576898 £6.99
Strange Loyalties
Sceptre pb 0340574607 £6.99

MINA, DENISE

Garnethill
Bantam Press hb 0593043510 £15.99

A powerful, hard-hitting first novel set in present day Glasgow. When a fast-talking, hard-drinking Glaswegian woman finally decides to end her relationship with a married man she is shocked to find his body strapped to a chair in her living-room, his throat slit. Suspected by the police of being involved, she decides to investigate the murder herself, uncovering a trail of extortion, rape and blackmail. An intense and disturbing crime novel that handles its central characters with care and sensitivity.

RANKIN, IAN

Ian Rankin's crime novels are set in and around present-day Edinburgh. His hero, John Rebus, is a tough cop, full of contradictory emotional drives and with a troubled past. Since Rebus was first introduced, Rankin has developed his character over the course of several novels, filling out his complex personality. He has created a very credible detective who works in a realistic and brutal world. Rankin's plots are well-constructed and believable, and even his supporting characters are rounded, balanced and all too human. He won the 1997 Golden Dagger Award for *Black and Blue*, which has expanded his popularity and reputation considerably. This is a superb piece of crime fiction. Rankin's grasp of dialogue, location and authenticity is excellent. The novel moves around four cases but has at its core just one killer: Bible John. Rankin's most recent book is *The Hanging Garden* which finds Inspector Rebus investigating a war crimes

suspect and a rising local crook. The two cases seem unrelated, but Rankin's complex, multi-layered work weaves these and several other story threads together into a cohesive and convincing whole, in this sophisticated and satisfying novel. His work has a powerful resonance and he is becoming recognised as one of the best crime writers at work in Britain today.

Black and Blue
Orion pb 0752809482 £5.99
The Black Book
Orion pb 1857974131 £5.99
A Good Hanging and Other Stories
Orion pb 0752809431 £5.99
The Hanging Garden
Orion hb 0752807218 £16.99
Hide and Seek
Orion pb 0752809415 £5.99
Knots and Crosses
Orion pb 0752809423 £5.99
Let It Bleed
Orion pb 0752804014 £5.99
Mortal Causes
Orion pb 1857978633 £5.99
Strip Jack
Orion pb 0752809563 £5.99
Tooth and Nail
Orion pb 0752809407 £5.99

SCOTT, MANDA

Manda Scott is one of the most exciting of new crime writers. *Hen's Teeth* is a gripping crime thriller that was nominated for the 1997 Orange Prize for Fiction. Glasgow-based Doctor Kellen Stewart is faced with a problem: she has just found out her ex-lover is dead. With the help of a friend she tries to uncover the truth behind the death. Why is the dead woman's body packed with Temazepam, and was it suicide or something more sinister? This is a fascinating thriller full of colourful characters and unexpected twists and turns.

Hen's Teeth
Women's Press pb 0704344963 £6.99

WISHART, DAVID

Classics scholar David Wishart puts his talents to good use in the comic and engrossing Marcus Corvinus mysteries. Set during Roman times, the series' hero is a world-weary amateur sleuth and keen bon viveur to boot. Wishart uses his classical knowledge to add historical depth to his books. However their real strength lies in the careful plot constructions, memorable characters and humour.

Germanicus
Sceptre pb 0340684453 £6.99
I, Virgil
Sceptre pb 0340635118 £5.99
Nero
Hodder & Stoughton pb 0340667028 £6.99
Ovid
Hodder & Stoughton pb 0340646837 £5.99

Science Fiction

BANKS, IAIN M.

The majority of Iain M. Banks' science fiction is set in his future world of 'the Culture', a society in which technology has advanced so far that machines have become sentient and long surpassed human intelligence. A relationship has developed between these benevolent machine intelligences and the human population, which allows people to live in the lap of luxury for incredibly long life-spans. However, this seemingly utopian society has numerous problems of its own. Banks' science fiction is space opera on a vast scale in which brilliantly imaginative plot lines are mixed with very believable characterisations. His latest SF work, *Inversions*, finds Banks embarking on a different style, less dependent on technology and more on character and atmosphere. The book consists of two closely linked stories of love, betrayal, deceit and secrecy. One is the story of a king's new physician who has more enemies than she first realises, while the other concerns a body-guard based in another palace across the mountains. The chapters deal consecutively with the two stories as each climbs to its own devastating end. Once again Banks' imaginative and innovative style shines through in this exciting and very original work.

Against a Dark Background
Orbit pb 1857231791 £6.99
Consider Phlebas
Orbit pb 1857231384 £6.99
Excession
Orbit pb 185723457X £6.99
Feersum Endjinn
Orbit pb 1857232739 £6.99
Inversions
Orbit hb 1857236262 £16.99
The Player of Games
Orbit pb 1857231465 £6.99
State of the Art
Orbit pb 1857230302 £5.99
The Use of Weapons
Orbit pb 185723135X £6.99

DOYLE, SIR ARTHUR CONAN

The Lost World (Ed. Ian Duncan)
OUP pb 0192833529 £4.99
The Lost World and The Poison Belt
Sutton pb 075090822X £5.99

The Lost World is a classic piece of science fiction by the author of the Sherlock Holmes stories. A plateau in South America has been frozen in time and a scientific expedition headed by Professor Challenger sets out to explore its wonders, which include ape-men and prehistoric creatures. A larger than life, exciting tale in which the laws of evolution are suspended. The tale of *The Poison Belt* begins on the anniversary of Professor Challenger's first adventure. He calls together his fellow explorers from that expedition, mysteriously asking them to bring oxygen. What follows is another work of vintage science fiction and a rattling good yarn.

GIBBON, LEWIS GRASSIC

Three Go Back
Polygon pb 0748662030 £7.99

Gibbon is, of course, best known for *A Scots Quair,* but he worked in a number of different genres. His science fiction work starts with the survivors of an airship crash coming to on a vast beach to find that they have travelled back in time to the lost continent of Atlantis. The work is an unexpected departure from Gibbon's usual subject matter and themes, yet it has many qualities to recommend it, not least his vision of prehistoric life.

LINDSAY, DAVID

Although born in London, Lindsay spent his formative years in Jedburgh. The horrors he experienced in World War I spurred him to write his first novel, *A Voyage to Arcturus,* a much over-looked cult classic that has inspired writers as various as C.S. Lewis and Clive Barker. In a visionary tour de force, largely set on a planet circling the star Arcturus, Lindsay creates a world of intense new experiences. On the planet the narrator endures many strange and extraordinary events. At the conclusion of the book a fierce and terrible discovery shakes the hero to the core. Lindsay revels in spiritual and emotional extremes - his aim is to delve beyond the flesh and blood of normal reality and illuminate the powerful inner world he sees within us all. Lindsay's second novel, *The Haunted Woman,* explores some of the same fantastical elements as its predecessor. A young woman moves from hotel to hotel with her aunt until by chance they visit 'the Judge's' ancient and mysterious house where they discover another world with profound and disturbing characteristics. Lindsay's intense, surrealist style makes this a distinctly unusual novel.

The Haunted Woman
Canongate pb 0862411629
£3.95
A Voyage to Arcturus
Canongate pb 086241377X
£6.99

MACLEOD, KEN

Using a similar approach to his close friend Iain M. Banks, Ken MacLeod takes advanced scientific theories and ideas and pushes them into the future, changing them along the way to suit his own distinctive worlds. These ideas include radically redefined political groupings, sophisticated nano-technologies and cloning. He writes vigorously intelligent works that are coupled with cool, modern science fiction. His second book, *The Stone Canal* is set on a Martian colony. It moves from the recent past to the distant future where cloning has been perfected and the Third World War has occurred. His third novel, *The Cassini Division*, shows the work of a quickly maturing writer. The involved plot concerns a power struggle between humans and post-human AIs who have created a wormhole into the far future. The book asks difficult questions about the nature of intelligence and the boundaries of sentience and humanity. It shows MacLeod building on the successes of his past and adding ever more layers of intellectual and philosophical depth to his work, without ever losing sight of his quickfire plotting and richly dark humour.

The Cassini Division
Orbit hb 1857236033 £15.99
The Star Fraction
Orbit pb 0099558815 £5.99
The Stone Canal
Orbit pb 0099559013 £5.99

Fiction Anthologies

There are many fine anthologies of Scottish fiction available. **The Oxford Book of Scottish Short Stories** (ed. Douglas Dunn OUP pb 0192825216 £7.99) is one of the finest anthologies available, selected by an accomplished writer in this genre. **The New Penguin Book of Scottish Short Stories** (ed Ian Murray Penguin pb 0140064117 £6.99) is an anthology that includes some of Scotland's best short stories over the last two centuries. **The Picador Book of Contemporary Scottish Fiction** (ed. Peter Kravitz Picador pb 0330335510 £7.99) bears witness to the literary renaissance that has taken place in Scotland over the last few years. **The Devil And The Giro: The Scottish Short Story** (ed. Carl McDougall Canongate pb 0862413591 £9.99) is a collection of fifty short stories from various time periods which shows that the short story form has been flourishing in Scotland for some considerable time. **Classic Scottish Short Stories** (ed. James Reid OUP pb 0192826867 £5.99) consists of twenty-two stories from some of Scotland's most influential authors over the last 150 years that illustrate the full range of Scottish writing. **A Tongue In Yer Heid** (ed. James Robertson B&W pb 1873631359 £6.99), subtitled 'A Selection Of The Best Contemporary Short Stories In Scots', is a lively collection featuring some of Scotland's best new writers. Two further anthologies of new writing are **The Flamingo Book of New Scottish Writing 1997** (Flamingo pb 0006550509 £5.99) and **The Flamingo Book of New Scottish Writing 1998** (Flamingo pb 0006551181 £6.99). The 1998 volume is the twenty fifth in an annual series of new Scottish stories that celebrates the wide range of writing talent currently working in Scotland. **Scottish Short Stories 1800-1900** (ed. Douglas Gifford Calder pb 0714506575 £5.95) is a collection of the work of ten writers, including Sir Walter Scott and Robert Louis Stevenson. *The Clocktower Press* is a small Scottish literary magazine which published some of Scotland's most experimental and subsequently famous names in literature before they broke through into mainstream publishing. **Ahead of its Time** (ed. Duncan McLean Clocktower Press pb 0224050249 £9.99) celebrates the achievements of the magazine and features new works by Irvine Welsh, Alan Warner, James Kelman and Janice Galloway. **Children Of Albion Rovers** (ed. Kevin Williamson Canongate pb 0862417317 £5.99) is a collection of novellas from some of the most exciting and dynamic new writers in Scotland: Irvine Welsh, Alan Warner, Laura J. Hird, Paul Reekie, James Meek and Gordon Legge. The ancient skill of story writing was much prized by the Celts. **Within The Hollow Hills: An Anthology Of New Celtic Writing** (ed. John Matthews Floris Books pb

0863155251 £8.99) is a collection by modern authors which shows that the tradition is still very much alive. Many of the stories show direct links with their bardic predecessors' mysterious and supernatural tales. Finally there is a book which reveals the treasures of early Scottish writing. **The Mercat Anthology Of Early Scottish Literature 1375-1707** (ed. Jack & Rozendaal Mercat Press pb 1873544655 £15.99) offers a selection of material from a largely neglected area of Scottish literature, and includes everything from courtly love poems to flyting, that peculiarly Scottish habit of verse insult. Each extract is glossed and explanatory notes are also provided for those unfamiliar with early texts. This anthology is an ideal introduction to some of the greatest Scottish literature.

Scotland is, of course, rich in traditional tales and folklore and in storytelling inherited from the Celtic tradition. Many fine anthologies demonstrate the variety of these traditions. **A Celtic Miscellany** (trans. K.H.Jackson Penguin pb 0140442427 £8.99) is a collection of medieval Celtic literatures from various sources. **The Penguin Book of Scottish Folk Tales** (ed. Neil Philip Penguin pb 014013977X £8.99) consists of over a hundred folk tales that celebrate Scotland's rich storytelling tradition, collected from all over Scotland and featuring stories from many periods in time. **Scottish Traditional Tales** (eds. Bruford & MacDonald Polygon pb 0748661506 £12.95) is an authoritative and original collection of tales gathered from a wide variety of sources over the past fifty years. **Deirdre And Other Great Stories From Celtic Mythology** (ed. Eoin Neeson Mainstream pb 1851589929 £8.99) is written in a modern style and is a collection of some of the most potent stories in Celtic mythology. Written primarily for adults, this collection might well be of interest to older children as well.

Some excellent anthologies look at particular areas of the country and their storytelling traditions. **Popular Tales of the West Highlands Vols. 1 & 2** (Birlinn pb 1874744157 and 1874744165 £12.99 each) and **More West Highland Tales Vols. 1 & 2** (Birlinn pb 187474422X and 1874744238 £12.99 each) are a treasure trove of Gaelic oral culture collected in the 1800s by John Francis Campbell, one of the great Victorian scholars. His efforts not only raised the prestige of the storyteller but also preserved many of these tales. The books give the original Gaelic texts with English translations alongside. **West Highland Tales** (Canongate pb 0862412781 £7.99) is an illustrated selection of Fitzroy Maclean's favourite tales from his native land. **Selected Highland Folk Tales** (ed. Macdonald Robertson House Of Lochar pb 1899863060 £8.99) is a collection of Scottish folklore assembled over the course of a quarter of a century and including stories on all the major themes such as fairies, witchcraft and haunted houses. The wide range of subject and theme should ensure that the collection contains many items of interest for native Scots and visitors alike. **Stories From South Uist** (Birlinn pb 1874744262 £6.99) is a collection of forty two tales from one of the greatest Gaelic storytellers, Angus McLellan, translated by John Lorne Campbell. The tales have many connections with myths and legends of other European locations including Scandinavia and Greece, yet retain their own particular identity. **The Ghost O'Mause and Other Tales and Traditions of East Perthshire** (ed. Maurice Fleming Mercat Press pb 1873644442 £9.99) well represents the rich story-telling tradition of East Perthshire in a collection of folk tales, songs and historical traditions. **Tales Of Galloway** (ed. Temperley Mainstream pb 1851580263 £4.99) is an anthology of classic stories originally told in crofts and rural cottages in Galloway. **An Arran Anthology** (ed. Hamish Whyte Mercat Press pb 1873644671 £9.99) gathers together writings ranging from murder mysteries to poetry with the linking theme being their connection with Arran. The collection includes works by Wordsworth, Sir Walter Scott and Iain Banks.

Many anthologies use a particular theme to approach Scottish literature and folklore. **Scottish Love Stories** (ed. Susie Maguire Polygon pb 0748662022 £9.99) explores the many faces of love in an anthology which includes some of the biggest names in Scottish literature including James Kelman, Janice Galloway and Muriel Spark. Some of the stories feature unusual objects of desire such as tea and biscuits and Tintin. The sea has always been one of the central features of the Scottish experience, inspiring many writers and poets. **The Sea: An Anthology** (eds. Armstrong & Osborne Canongate pb 086241783X £12.99) is the most comprehensive anthology on the subject and the editors have selected works that cover all aspects of the sea from myths and legends to war at sea. The collection includes poetry, fiction and non-fiction. **Scottish Sea Stories** (ed Murray Polygon pb 0748662081 £9.99) includes some of the most famous names in Scottish literature in an anthology that captures the sounds, smells and many moods of the ocean. **Glimmer of Cold Brine** (ed. Lawrie et al Mercat Press pb 0080365795 £4.99) is a collection of sea stories, poems, prayers and superstitions that traverse the centuries. It tells of the many Scottish lives that have been shaped by the sea, and includes a wide range of contributions from well-known Scottish writers along with others who are lesser known. **Haunted Scotland** (ed. Adams. Mainstream pb 185158952X £7.99) is a collection of new and more traditional ghost stories from all over Scotland, that support the notion that Scotland is indeed a haunted land. *Blackwood's Magazine*, originally named *The Edinburgh Monthly Magazine* was initially published in 1812. It continued publishing until 1980. Among its contributors were many of the great literary names of the time, from John Galt to John Buchan. **Tales of Terror from Blackwood's Magazine** (ed.

Morrison & Baldick OUP pb 019282366 £5.99) is a collection which features, among others, Walter Scott and James Hogg. **An Anthology of Scottish Fantasy Literature** (ed. Colin Manlove Polygon pb 0748662138 £10.99) demonstrates Scotland's fascination for imaginary worlds which has been one of the prime sources of inspiration for many of its artists. Manlove's anthology explores this rich seam of material and includes work by writers as diverse as Robert Burns, James Hogg, Alasdair Gray and Iain Banks. Finally, the conflict between hostile English governments and local cottage whisky makers gave rise to many incidents. **Tales of Whisky And Smuggling** (ed. Stuart McHardy House Of Lochar hb 0948403861 £9.99) is a collection of stories based on real events and containing tales that combine humour and tragedy.

Scottish Talking Books

by Joe Gordon, Waterstone's, 13-14 Princes Street, Edinburgh

What are talking books? For those unfamiliar with this increasingly popular medium, talking books are books which have been adapted for audio cassette or CD. For the most part they are simple readings by authors, or more commonly, actors, of existing novels, plays and poems. They can range in complexity from a simple voice-only reading, through narration with music and sound effects or even full cast dramatisations. Scottish audio books are still relatively few in number, but it is an expanding field. Even so the range of differing titles available is already broad, covering such diverse productions as **Billy Connolly's** live performances, **Alasdair Gray's** ground-breaking novel *Lanark,* classic fiction from **Robert Louis Stevenson** and **Sir Walter Scott,** poetry from **Robert Burns** and **Hugh MacDiarmid**, and the new wave of younger Scottish writers such as **Irvine Welsh.**

Audio books have the advantage of letting the listener hear how the words should be spoken, which is of course very important for those not familiar with the Scots language, be it the older Broad Scots of Robert Burns or more modern colloquial phrases employed by Irvine Welsh in *Trainspotting.* This makes them popular with overseas visitors, who often listen to the tape while reading the book to help their pronunciation of our often colourful language. Several publishers currently produce Scottish talking books, from large scale publishers such as Penguin to Edinburgh mainstays Canongate and the specialist Scots language society, Scotsoun.

Penguin have several interesting Scottish titles available on cassette. Classical fiction is present in the form of a wonderful abridgement of **Robert Louis Stevenson's** *Kidnapped,* read by Robbie Coltrane who seems quite caught up in this adventurous yarn. Penguin also cater for younger listeners with a junior adaptation of **Stevenson's** *Treasure Island,* read by another Scottish comedian turned actor, Alan Cumming. This exciting retelling may help parents encourage children to explore Stevenson further.

Penguin have released a Scottish edition of their fine series of short stories. This selection, edited by Ian Murray, contains twelve short tales by writers including **Lewis Grassic Gibbon, Alasdair Gray, George Mackay Brown, Neil M. Gunn, Iain**

Crichton Smith and **Naomi Mitchison.** History has also had an audio makeover in the shape of a four-cassette adaptation of **John Prebble's** fascinating exploration of the 1745 uprising and its aftermath for the Highlanders in *Culloden,* read by David Rintoul.

The BBC audio collection includes a children's edition of **Stevenson's** *Treasure Island* with a good cast which features Iain Cuthbertson, while a reading of **Sir Walter Scott's** *Ivanhoe,* issued to tie in with the TV adaptation is less convincing, although it does have the benefit of being narrated in the suave tones of Christopher Lee. Two classic Scots comedies are covered with Gregor Fisher telling the tale of **Neil Munro's** immortal Clyde puffer 'The Vital Spark' in *Para Handy Tales.* Although not quite as faithful to the novels as the Canongate adaptations, this is a lively reading by Fisher. The irrepressible Stanley Baxter brings his formidable comic skills to bear on an excellent reading of **Compton MacKenzie's** hilarious *Whisky Galore.* This tale of canny Highlanders and their contraband whisky cargo is well enhanced by Stanley Baxter's gift for comic timing and his range of characterisations. The other mainstay of the BBC's Scottish catalogue is Sherlock Holmes. Here the BBC have probably the most comprehensive range of **Sir Arthur Conan Doyle's** great detective available on tape with *The Adventures Of Sherlock Holmes, The Casebook Of Sherlock Holmes, The Memoirs Of Sherlock Holmes* and *The Return Of Sherlock Holmes,* all spanning three volumes of dramatised action, each with Clive Merrison as Holmes. Completing the Holmes set is the two-volume *His Last Bow.*

The innovative publishers Naxos are one of the few who make their audio output available on compact disc as well as tape. As with their other material their Scottish productions are modern, digitally recorded readings, enhanced with well chosen classical music. Jonathan Oliver utilises his Shakespearian trained voice to give a powerful reading of **Sir Walter Scott's** great chivalric novel *Ivanhoe.* John Sessions tells the tale of **Stevenson's** *The Strange Case Of Dr Jekyll And Mr Hyde,* gleefully changing voices to portray the unfortunate schizophrenic doctor, creating a suitably eerie effect. Once more, of course, **Stevenson's** *Treasure Island* arises. Of the several versions of this ripping yarn available on audio however, the Naxos edition is certainly one of the best.

Edinburgh publishers Canongate have an excellent selection of their classical range available on cassette. Unlike most others listed here Canongate have an extensive range of Scottish titles. Among the most important are *Smeddum And*

Other Stories and *Scenes From Sunset Song,* both by **Lewis Grassic Gibbon** and read by Eileen McCallum. With Gibbon still a popular choice for a school text this audio reading may help students with this classic Scots novel. **Alasdair Gray's** excellent and innovative novel *Lanark* is available in two abridged volumes, read by the author himself. Also available is *Some Unlikely Stories.*

    Neil Munro's Para Handy is well represented by Canongate with *The Vital Spark* and *In Highland Harbours,* both two-volume sets, read by Robert Trotter. Perhaps not as lively as Gregor Fisher's reading, nonetheless Trotter's Para Handy has just the right voice for the purist, and the cassette adaptation is very true to the novels. **Neil Munro's** dry and darkly comic tales of Glasgow life are available also, in *Erchie My Droll Friend,* again read by Robert Trotter. The gainfully employed Trotter has turned his talents to **Robert Louis Stevenson.** Canongate have *The Strange Case Of Dr Jekyll And Mr Hyde* predictably, but also less common Stevenson audio titles in the shape of *The Bodysnatcher And Other Stories,* perfect listening material before going on a ghost tour of Edinburgh's Old Town, and *Travels With A Donkey In The Cevennes,* RLS's diary of his wandering in this wild region. It may not be Bill Bryson but when did he last ride a donkey a hundred and twenty miles?

    Two other giants of 20th Century Scottish literature are represented by Canongate. *Consider The Lilies* by **Iain Crichton Smith** is very well narrated by Eileen McCallum. Octogenarian Scots author **Muriel Spark** has her dark novel *The Driver's Seat* brought to life by no less a figure than Dame Judi Dench. Along with HarperCollins' cassette of *The Prime Of Miss Jean Brodie* this is one of the few of Spark's novels to have made the leap to audio thus far.

    No recommended list of Scottish audio titles would be complete of course without **Robert Burns**, our national bard. As with Stevenson and Scott, various publishers have tackled Rabbie. Canongate have a very fine cassette with Bill Torrance among others reading Burns' poetry and songs. HarperCollins have a Burns cassette which comes complete with a miniature Gem Guide to the poet, a perfect gift. Audio Books And Music have a fine anthology in *The Best Of Scottish Poetry,* which boasts more than 30 readings of poets as diverse as **Burns, James Hogg, Edwin Muir, Hugh MacDiarmid, Norman MacCaig** and **George Mackay Brown.** The readings are by a variety of Scots actors including Alan Cumming, Hannah Gordon and *This Life*'s Daniela Nardini.

Scotsoun, a specialist society dedicated to the dissemination of the Scots language, have a number of cassettes of verse, prose, folksong and Scots language course tapes available. Predominantly a mail order society, Scotsoun is also available from a few bookstores. Among their broad range are recordings of the poet **Hugh MacDiarmid** and **Stevenson, Bruce Leeming's** *A Scots Haiku*, and **Edwin Morgan** and **George Mackay Brown** reading a selection of their favourite Scots poetry.

For those who prefer a more contemporary flavour, Reed Audio have two volumes of classic **Billy Connolly** live performances, although there are no bleeps to censor the famous Glaswegian's more colourful colloquialisms, so be warned. Reed has also released a vibrant audio version of **Irvine Welsh's** mega-hit *Trainspotting*. In a similar vein Random House have produced a lively adaptation of **Welsh's** bestseller *The Acid House* (which also features Irvine Welsh and Iggy Pop in conversation as a bizarre bonus).

A final entry is reserved for the works of **Nigel Tranter**, the Lothian's elder statesman of historical fiction. Tranter's novels are brought sweepingly to life by Novel Sound. The great epics of *The Wallace* and *The Bruce Trilogy* are excellently and dramatically read, with choice use of sound effects to enhance scenes. *Tales And Traditions Of Scottish Castles*, *Highness In Hiding* and *Footbridge To Enchantment* have also been produced, all boasting an introduction by the author himself, with more titles to follow. These tales, short and long, contain great narratives and the full richness of Scotland's history, told in an exciting and accessible manner.

Folklore

Beith, Mary
Healing Threads: Traditional Medicines of the Highlands And Islands
Polygon pb 0748661999 £9.99

A history of Highland folk medicine from the earliest of times that provides a full directory of remedies, cures and practices.

Bennett, Margaret
Scottish Customs from the Cradle to the Grave
Polygon pb 0748661182 £11.95

A collection of traditional Scottish customs that cover childbirth and infancy, love, courtship and marriage, and finally death and burial, drawn from a broad range of sources from the 16th century to the present day.

Campbell, Steuart
The Loch Ness Monster: The Evidence
Birlinn pb 1874744610 £6.99

The most comprehensive study of all the evidence relating to the Loch Ness monster, written by a scientist who is an expert on the paranormal. The book is bang up-to-date with its information and allows readers to decide for themselves, based on the evidence presented.

Darwin, Tess
The Scots Herbal
Mercat Press pb 1873644604 £12.99

A comprehensive guide to the way in which wild plants have been used in Scotland from prehistoric times to the present day.

Douglas, Hugh
The Hogmanay Companion
Neil Wilson pb 1897784129 £5.99

A complete guide to everything you wanted to know about New Year's Eve.

Edwards, Owen Dudley
Burke and Hare
Mercat Press pb 1873644256 £9.99

A thorough and careful reconstruction of the infamous murders and their aftermath.

Foreman, Carol
Glasgow Curiosities
John Donald pb 0859764850 £7.95

A collection of bizarre, little-known true stories originating from Glasgow.

Gerber, Pat
Stone of Destiny
Canongate pb 0862416701 £6.99

Since Edward I took the Stone of Destiny from Scotland in 1296 there have been persistent rumours that he removed the wrong stone. Pat Gerber's story attempts to discover if the real stone was the one taken to Westminster so long ago.

Grant, I.F.
Highland Folk Ways
Birlinn pb 1874744424 £9.99

This well-illustrated book describes the crafts, customs and methods that were used in the Highland way of life, from clothes, food and cooking utensils to fishing and farming implements and weapons. The detailed descriptions emerge from Grant's discussions with the increasingly small numbers of men and women who remember using these items, as well as from her own research.

Gray, Affleck
The Big Grey Man of Ben MacDhui
Birlinn pb 1874744203 £6.99

Scotland's second-highest mountain is rumoured to have a strange creature living on its slopes. Many mountaineers have seen footprints, shapes and some have reportedly seen the creature itself. Gray sets out in search of the truth, a search that will take him to the Himalayas and the Harz mountains as well as the Cullins.

Halliday, Ron (Ed.)
McX: Scotland's X-Files
B & W pb 1873631774 £6.99

Strange happenings in the skies, countryside and waters of Scotland are examined in this exploration of paranormal events in Scotland from the past and present.

Hutchinson, Roger
Polly: The True Story Behind Whisky Galore
Mainstream pb 1840180714 £7.99

The events surrounding the sinking of the *SS Politician* were the inspiration for Compton Mackenzie's famous novel *Whisky Galore*, and have subsequently entered modern Scottish mythology. This book uses eye-witness accounts and official papers to create a history of the actual events, and if anything the reality only enriches the story.

Lamont-Brown, R.
Scottish Folklore
Birlinn pb 1874744580 £6.99

This work provides an A-Z of locations throughout Scotland and the folklore associated with them. It also traces the roots of the Scottish folklore tradition and examines recurring themes and influences. A vital reference for anyone interested in the subject.

Livingstone, Sheila
Scottish Customs
Birlinn pb 1874744416 £6.99
Scottish Festivals
Birlinn pb 1874744785 £6.99

Two instalments in the *Traditional Scotland* series, looking at the origins of Scottish traditions and festivals respectively. The author uses extracts from works of literature to illustrate some of the customs, and gives details of dates for the festivals.

Macgregor, Forbes
Greyfriars Bobby: The Real Story At Last
Gordon Wright pb 090306569X £3.50

An updated version of Forbes Macgregor's best-selling book about the famous Skye terrier and his master John Gray.

**Mackenzie, Alexander &
Sutherland, Elizabeth
The Prophecies of the
Brahan Seer**
Constable pb 0094784604
£9.99

Scotland's own version of
Nostradamus, the Brahan
Seer, had his prophecies
handed down initially by the
Gaelic oral tradition. They
were eventually collected and
written down in 1877 by
Alexander Mackenzie. As
familiar to the Highlanders as
the prophet Isaiah, the Seer
is a mysterious figure thought
to have come from the Isle of
Lewis in the 16th or 17th
century. He is best known
for his series of prophecies
concerning the Highlands.
In this re-issue of the original
1877 book, Elizabeth Sutherland's commentary examines
to what extent each prophecy
has been fulfilled.

**McOwan, Rennie
Magic Mountains**
Mainstream hb 1851587071
£14.99

Tales of supernatural beings
roaming the Scottish mountains have abounded since
the earliest of recorded
times. In this work Rennie
McOwan explores our Gaelic
and Norse heritage with
particular reference to these
stories and comes up with a
thorough study of ancient
Scottish mountain beliefs.

**Martin, Andrew (Ed)
Scottish Endings: Writings
On Death**
N.M.S. pb 0948636866 £7.99

A wide range of tales, stories
and hard factual information
on death in Scottish history,
including executions, ghosts,
murders and bizarre burial
arrangements, presenting
both well-known and more
obscure information.

**Roberts, Alasdair
Midges**
Birlinn pb 1874744637 £4.99

The savage bloodlust of the
Highland midge is renowned
throughout the world. This
entertaining and well-illustrated book covers a wide
range of topics relating to the
ruthless beastie, such as how
did Bonnie Prince Charlie
and Queen Victoria cope,
and what are the hidden perils of camping in relation to
this nefarious insect? There is
also a vitally important section
on useful repellents and
midge-bite remedies.

**Smith, Robert
Aberdeen Curiosities**
John Donald pb 0859764729
£7.95

An entertaining collection
telling of some of the strange
happenings and eccentric
characters of Aberdeen. Find
out, among other things,
about the rat permanently
housed in a chapel and the
soldiers who dropped their
trousers in the main street...

Thomson, James U.
Edinburgh Curiosities:
A Capital Cornucopia
John Donald pb 0859764494
£7.50
Edinburgh Curiosities 2
John Donald pb 0859764796
£7.95

A trawl through the more
bizarre and curious events in
Edinburgh's history has created these wonderful books full
of unusual, well-written and
meticulously researched
stories.

Tranter, Nigel
Tales and Traditions of
Scottish Castles
Neil Wilson pb 1897784139
£7.99

An illustrated guide to the
myths, legends and historical
facts surrounding some of
Scotland's most famous castles.

Willsher, Betty
Scottish Epitaphs and Images
Canongate pb 0862415918
£5.99
Understanding Scottish
Graveyards
Canongate pb 0862415608
£4.99

Scottish Epitaphs is a lavishly
illustrated book that features
epitaphs from all over
Scotland and from various
points in time. Their
sometimes complex symbolic
imagery is lucidly explained
by the author. The guide to
graveyards explores the different fashions in sculpture
and inscription over the
centuries and their
symbolic meaning.

Wilson, Alan J. et al
Ghostly Tales and Sinister
Stories of Old Edinburgh
Mainstream pb 1851584560
£5.99

A collection of over a
hundred eerie tales put
together by three experts on
the subject. Wilson and his
co-compilers are historians
who provide tours around
Edinburgh's Old Town,
pointing out places where
some of the capital's more
infamous residents carried
out their exploits. This
illustrated collection includes
such well-known characters
as Deacon Brodie, Burke and
Hare, along with other more
obscure figures such as Major
Weir and Agnes Fynnie. It
will tell you all you want to
know about Edinburgh's
darker side.

History

A personal introduction to Scottish history

by Nicola Royan, Waterstone's, Perth

I came to Scottish history primarily through early Scottish literature. My discovery of **Barbour** and **Dunbar** among many others was a revelation, for previously I had never even heard of Scottish literature before Burns. To understand the writing it helps to understand the circumstances of the writers and thus the history of the realm. In doing so one discovers that Scottish identity has been a long time in the making, for *Braveheart* is not a twentieth century phenomenon. A sound understanding of history enables one to separate romance from reality and to appreciate the achievements of the people of early Scotland.

A useful place to start a study of early Scottish history is the *New History Of Scotland Series* published by Edinburgh University Press, particularly the first four volumes (see full details in General History section). All the titles in the series are engaging and informative on the cultural and social changes as well as the battles and parliaments. Visiting historical sites also helps bring the past to life, and among the best guides to archaeology are those published by Historic Scotland, which cover topics from the earliest settlements to 18th century fortresses. Among the best titles on the subject are **Sally Foster's** *Picts, Gaels and Scots* (Batsford hb, 0713474866, £5.95) and **Anna Ritchie's** *Viking Scotland* (Batsford pb, 0713472251, £5.95). For the advanced enthusiast, the range of books on archaeological sites and monuments by the Royal Commission on the Ancient and Historical Monuments of Scotland (RCAHMS) are an excellent source of information.

Because of the nature of early Scottish society we know most about the kings and nobles. *Scotland's Kings and Queens* by **Richard Oram** (HMSO pb, 0114957835, £12.99) is a useful illustrated introduction to the long line of monarchs and in **Stewart Ross's** *Monarchs of Scotland* (House Of Lochar pb, 0948403381, £7.95) the author reconstructs each monarch's character and outlines their contribution to Scottish history. There are more detailed biographies of figures such as independent Scotland's longest-reigning King in *William The Lion 1143-1214* by **D.D.R. Owen** (Tuckwell pb, 1862320055, £14.99). Of Scotland's heroes, Bruce has fared particularly well in **Geoffrey Barrow's** *Robert The Bruce and the Community of the Realm Of Scotland* 3rd ed. (EUP pb, 0852246048, 14.95), and also in **Barbour's** *Bruce* (Canongate pb, 0862416817, £8.99) still worth reading, even after some 600 years. Wallace is served by accounts by **James Mackay** in *William Wallace: Brave Heart* (Mainstream pb, 185158823X, £9.99) and in **Andrew Fisher's** *William Wallace* (John Donald pb, 0859761541, £8.95). Whereas the modern accounts are primarily concerned with offering as much certain knowledge of their subjects as they can, **Barbour** and **Blind Harry**, the writer of the epic *Wallace,* were as occupied by the political messages embodied by their heroes. The nature of these messages and the means by which Barbour and Harry bequeathed them to the nation is the subject of an absorbing study by **R. James Goldstein,** *The Matter of Scotland* (University of Nebraska Press hb, 0803221444, £38.00).

No matter how much one strives to separate romance from reality, I suspect part of the attraction of early Scotland will always lie in castles and abbeys, kings and knights. The reality, however, is often just as exciting and even more interesting, for it plays the greater part in how the Scots even now think of themselves.

General History

There are numerous texts which cover Scottish history as a whole. Four of the best studies are:-

DONALDSON, GORDON (ED)
The Edinburgh History Of Scotland
Mercat Press pb

DUNCAN, A.A.M.
Vol.1 The Making of the Kingdom
0901824836 £15.95

NICHOLSON, RANALD
Vol.2 The Later Middle Ages
0901824844 £15.95

DONALDSON, GORDON
Vol.3 James V To James VII
0901824852 £15.95

FERGUSON, WILLIAM
Vol.4 1689 To The Present
0901824860 £15.95

One of the most detailed and scholarly series on Scottish history, remarkable for its range and depth of information. Although originally published in the 60s still an authoritative survey of Scottish history.

Edinburgh University Press has produced a series that builds into a unique and highly informative history of Scotland. Each book, written by an eminent scholar in the field, looks at some of the defining issues of that particular time. More discursive and general than the Edinburgh History of Scotland, they nonetheless provide a clear overview of the periods covered. They also benefit from more recent research. Equally academic, they would be ideal for the non-specialist looking for a general idea of the course of Scottish history.

New History Of Scotland Series:

SMYTH, ALFRED P.
Warlords And Holy Men: Scotland AD 80-1000
EUP pb 0748601007 £9.95

BARROW, G.W.S.
Kingship And Unity: Scotland 1000-1306
EUP pb 074860104X £9.95

WORMALD, JENNY
Court, Kirk And Community: Scotland 1470-1625
EUP pb 0748602763 £9.95

MITCHISON, ROSALIND
Lordship To Patronage: Scotland 1603-1745
EUP pb 074860233X £9.95

LENMAN, BRUCE
Integration And Enlightenment: Scotland 1746-1832
EUP pb 0748603859 £9.95

CHECKLAND, OLIVE & SYDNEY 2nd ed.

Industry And Ethos: Scotland 1832-1914
EUP pb 0748601023 £9.95

HARVIE, CHRISTOPHER

No Gods And Precious Few Heroes: Scotland Since 1914. 3rd ed.
EUP pb 0748609997 £9.95

COOKE, A. et al (Ed.)

Modern Scottish History: 1707 To The Present
Tuckwell Press pb
Vol.1 The Transformation Of Scotland, 1707-1850
1862320683 £14.99
Vol.2 The Modernisation Of Scotland, 1850 to Present
186232073X £14.99
Vol.3 Readings, 1707-1850
1862320780 £14.99
Vol.4 Readings, 1850 to Present
1862320837 £14.99
Vol.5 Major Documents
1862320888 £14.99

A five volume distance learning course specially prepared for the Open University which includes transcribed documents and uses the talents of some of Scotland's leading historians in its creation, among them T.C. Smout, Nigel Tranter, Christopher Harvie and C.A. Whatley.

DEVINE, T.M. & MITCHISON, R. (Eds)

People And Society In Scotland
Vol. 1 1760-1830
John Donald pb 0859762106 £15.00

FRASER, W.H. & MORRIS, R.J. (EDS)

Vol. 2 1830-1914
0859762114 £16.00

DICKSON, A.D.R. & TREBLE, J.H. (Eds)

Vol. 3 1914 To The Present
0859762122 £15.00

The economic and social factors that shaped modern Scotland are explored in this scholarly series.

Chemical Workers by Stephen Adam from
The People's Palace Book of Glasgow

There are several excellent one-volume surveys of Scottish history that will appeal, variously, to readers at all levels of interest, each having its own specific approach and areas of speciality. **Michael Lynch's** *Scotland: A New History* (Pimlico pb, 0712698930, £10.00) is one of the more recent single volume accounts of Scottish history, and also one of the best. As well as containing all the essential dates and deeds, it is strong on the wider social and cultural developments, for example the growth of the burghs and the impact of movements such as the Reformation. Well written, it also provides suggestions for further reading and is an excellent introduction to the subject. More traditional in style and approach is **J.D. Mackie's** *A History Of Scotland* (Penguin pb, 0140136495, £7.99). In this account Mackie charts Scotland's long-standing defence of its independence in matters religious, economic and constitutional, from the time it first emerged as a nation to the recent past, while also showing that the Scots had many areas of interest closely interlocked with their neighbours. First written in 1964, this 1997 edition is revised by Bruce Lenman and Geoffrey Parker. In *Scotland: A Concise History* (Gordon Wright pb, 0903065878, £6.95) **James Halliday** concentrates on factors, events and opinions that have shaped Scottish history, rather than providing a narrative history of the events themselves. His work is succinct and aimed at a general readership rather than the history specialist. **Nigel Tranter's** highly readable history *Story of Scotland* (Neil Wilson pb, 1897784074, £7.99) covers the years prior to the establishment of the nation and right up to the 20th century. Acclaimed diplomat and soldier **Fitzroy Maclean's** *Scotland: A Concise History* (Thames & Hudson pb, 0500277060, £8.95) tends to concentrate on the many bloody conflicts that the Scots have been involved in. Straightforward, clear and concise, it is an excellent introduction to Scotland's past. **Gordon Donaldson's** *Scotland: The Shaping of a Nation* (Rev. ed., House Of Lochar pb, 189986329X, £8.99) examines the events, institutions and political and social trends that have formed Scotland. It ranges in time from the early centuries right up to the present and covers among other subjects Anglo-Scottish relations, the monarchy, politics and the church. *The Lion in the North: One Thousand Years of Scotland's History* (Penguin pb, 0140056459, £7.99) by renowned Scottish historian **John Prebble** is his account of the chaos that often surrounded the years of Scotland's independence, a history with its fair share of both idealistic and treacherous acts. Prebble covers the time from the initial unification of the country under Kenneth mac Alpin in the 9th century to the defeat of the Jacobites at Culloden.

As a social history, **T.C. Smout's** *A History of the Scottish People 1560-1830* (HarperCollins pb, 0006860273, £9.99) and its accompanying volume *A Century of the Scottish People 1830-1950* (HarperCollins pb, 0006861415, £8.99) together form the best-selling classic social history of Scotland. Smout's books manage to be simultaneously scholarly, informative, thought-provoking and highly readable. In *Scottish Voices 1745-1960* by **T.C. Smout** and **Sydney Wood** (HarperCollins pb, 0006862160, £8.99), the authors use first-hand accounts, reportage and contemporary documents from the 18th century onwards to chart the changes in Scottish society over the years. They select themes such as work, religion, love and shopping to show ordinary people doing everyday things, creating a flavour of the Scottish experience in the recent and more distant past.

There are a few volumes that concentrate on the evolution of Scottish identity. *Image And Identity: The Making And Remaking of Scotland Through the Ages* (John Donald pb, 0859764095, £16.00) edited by **D. Broun et al** focuses on institutional and political development. It examines the constantly changing images of Scottishness that have been crafted and re-crafted over the ages. Similarly **William Ferguson's** *The Identity of the Scottish Nation: A Historic Quest* (EUP pb, 0748610715, £14.95) examines the changing ideas of Scottish nationhood from the Scottish Origin Legend expressed by medieval chroniclers to contemporary ideas of national identity and all constructs of nationality in-between. The Scots' awareness of their identity has been manifested in many forms. In *Scotland: An Unwon Cause* edited by **P.H. Scott** (Canongate pb, 0862417007, £9.99) a series of major texts, both political and literary, are gathered together to show the development of Scotland's view of itself over the years. Texts such as 'The Act Of Union' and 'The Declaration Of Arbroath' are printed, along with notes and a contemporary discussion, providing not only primary source material but also a modern overview. Very different in mood and style from the more academic studies is **Ludovic Kennedy's** *In Bed With An Elephant* (Corgi pb, 0552144746, £6.99). While covering some of the same ground as the books above, the work is a blend of four genres: history, travel, political tract and autobiography, that are connected by the central theme of Scotland's stormy relationship with England over the ages. Ranging back and forth in time from the prehistoric settlement on Skara Brae to Home Rule, the book is vividly written in Kennedy's distinctive style.

Useful general reference books on Scottish history include *A Dictionary Of Scottish History* (John Donald pb, 0859760189, £9.95) edited by **G. Donaldson** and **R.S. Morpeth**. This volume lists the dates, facts and personal biographies crucial to Scottish history. With the same editors, *Who's Who In Scottish History* (Welsh Academic Press pb, 1860570054, £9.99) is another invaluable research tool, while for the serious student of early history **A. Anderson's** *Early Sources In Scottish History* (Watkins hb, 1871615054, £52.00) is vital.

Scotland's Past In Action Series:

Published by the National Museums of Scotland, this informative and attractively produced series highlights activities that have been significant in the shaping of Scotland.

Burnett, John
The Scots In Sickness And Health
N.M.S. pb 0948636920 £4.99

The wider history of health rather than medicine is examined in this informative tome which includes a study of the contributions of medical pioneers such as Joseph Lister and James Simpson. The book also looks at traditional practices such as the independent Gaelic medical tradition, as well as the latest developments in medical technology.
Sporting Scotland
N.M.S. pb 0948636661 £4.99

Dodds, Alastair
Making Cars
N.M.S. pb 0948636815 £4.99

Gauldie, Enid
Spinning And Weaving
N.M.S. pb 0948636688 £4.99

MacLean, Colin
Going To Church
N.M.S. pb 0948636882 £4.99

For hundreds of years the church has been one of the most powerful institutions in Scottish life. In this book Colin MacLean traces the experience of church-going in Scotland through to the present day, with a particular emphasis on the Church of Scotland, creating a vivid account of one of the key features of Scottish history.

Martin, Angus
Fishing And Whaling
N.M.S. pb 094863667X £4.99

Simpson, Eric
Going On Holiday
N.M.S. pb 0948636939 £4.99

Holidays have a long history in Scottish society. This book looks at the way in which the concept of a holiday has changed over the years, from the early holidays, fairs and festivals to the more recent idea of a holiday created largely by the Victorians.

Sprott, Gavin
Farming
N.M.S. pb 0948636696 £4.99

Withrington, Donald
Going To School
N.M.S. pb 0948636890 £4.99

Wood, James L.
Building Railways
N.M.S. pb 0948636823 £4.99

The Scottish nation's ability to fight and fighting spirit is evident down through the centuries. The bravery of the Scottish and Highland regiments in both World Wars has become the stuff of legend. This long history is covered in the following works:-

HENDERSON, DIANA

Highland Soldier: A Social History of the Highland Regiments, 1820-1920
John Donald hb 0859762173 £12.50

A very detailed study of the ten Highland regiments which gives a complete view of the soldiers' and officers' lives, covering such topics as recruiting, living conditions and music.

The Scottish Regiments
HarperCollins pb 0004710258 £9.99

MCCORRY, HELEN (ED)

The Thistle At War: Scotland's Battles
N.M.S. pb 0948636912 £7.99

An illustrated anthology of poems, diary entries, reminisences and fictionalised accounts of the Scottish experience of war. It is told from numerous points of view - from the experiences of fighting men to the observations of nurses, stretcher bearers, wives and children.

PREBBLE, JOHN

Mutiny: Highland Regiments In Revolt 1743-1804
Penguin pb 0140043284 £9.99

Between 1743 and 1804 sixteen Highland Regiments mutinied. The reasons for this are explored in John Prebble's passionate account of this tragic history at a time when Highland society was in crisis. Clansmen were being sold off by their chiefs to serve in the Regiments, where they often became victims of the army's harsh dicipline. Their only means of protest was mutiny and this in turn was to meet with the fiercest of punishments.

ROSS, GRAHAM

Scotland's Forgotten Valour
Maclean Press pb 1899272003 £7.95

The stories of Scottish soldiers who received the Victoria Cross since it was first established in 1856.

SADLER, JOHN

Scottish Battles from Mons Graupius to Culloden
Canongate pb 086241508X £9.99

John Sadler revisits many of the conflicts that shaped and defined Scotland's past. A natural storyteller, his accounts are vivid pieces of writing.

TAYLOR, WILLIAM

The Military Roads In Scotland
House of Lochar pb 1899863087 £9.95

Taylor analyses the military and political considerations behind these roads before looking at the roads them- selves. He examines the many difficulties experienced by General Wade and his successor Major Caulfield. This book will be of interest to both historians and walkers. This revised edition includes up-dated information and new appendices as well as maps.

Prehistory and Archaeology

The rich heritage of prehistoric sites in Scotland, especially in the Highlands and Islands, has attracted many archaeologists and enthusiasts to the country. New techniques are constantly revealing new information about these sites and the people who constructed them. We now have a more detailed and sophisticated understanding of the prehistoric world than ever before. This activity as well as the picturesque quality of standing stones such as those at Callanish and other similar sites have produced several excellent books on the subject for all levels of interest.

Scotland's First Settlers by **Caroline Wickham-Jones** (Batsford pb, 0713473711, £5.95) examines the earliest traces of people in Scotland, which date from the Stone Age nearly 9000 years ago. These people were nomads who fished and hunted to survive and whose way of life was to last four millenia, before the advent of settled farming. Wickham-Jones looks at the origins of these settlers, how they used the resources of the environment, and what can be learned about them from the remains they left behind. Following on from the early settlers, **Patrick Ashmore's** *Neolithic And Bronze Age Scotland* (Batsford pb, 0713475315, £5.95) provides a similar study of the growth and decline of the people who inhabited Scotland from 4000 to 750 BC, a people that created the great stone circles and ceremonial enclosures that still survive on many of the islands as well as the mainland. Ashmore describes the industry and agriculture of a time that saw the emergence of farming and continued to the start of the Iron Age. A shorter but nevertheless useful study of the same time period can be found in **Gordon Barclay's** *Temples And Tombs: Neolithic Scotland* (Canongate pb, 0862417805, £5.95) which covers the neolithic and early Bronze Age. Written with the general reader in mind, **Richard Oram's** *Scottish Prehistory* (Birlinn pb, 1874744696, £8.99) provides an archaeological guide from the seventh millenium BC up to the early historic kingdoms after the Celtic Iron Age, while *Ancient Scotland* by **Stewart Ross** (House Of Lochar hb, 0948403543, £16.00) affords an illustrated exploration of the tombs, forts, artefacts and standing stones from Scotland's ancient races, portraying the civilisations who created these objects and buildings. These early peoples left their distinctive mark on the Scottish landscape, as examined in **Iain Zaczek's** *Ancient Scottish Landscapes* (Collins & Brown hb, 1855854961, £14.99), a dramatic pictorial celebration of that legacy, studying the four ancient regions of pre-Christian Scotland. **Stuart Piggott's** *Scotland Before History* (EUP pb, 0748660675, £6.95) is a concise guide to Scotland's ancient cultures from the seventh millenium BC to the time of the Celts. Included is a gazetteer by Graham

Ritchie of over 250 major prehistoric monuments. Ritchie is also a co-author of *Oxford Archaeological Guides: Scotland* by **A. and G. Ritchie** (OUP pb, 0192880020, £10.99), a travel guide to over 200 sites of archaeological interest throughout Scotland, covering sites dating from earliest times to 1200 AD and complete with maps, plans and photographs. **Anna Ritchie** has also written *Picts* (HMSO pb, 0114934916, £5.95) and *Scotland B.C.* (HMSO pb, 0114934274, £4.95), both well-illustrated, clearly laid out introductions for the general reader to key themes in Scottish prehistory.

Three guides to prehistoric Scotland specifically cover individual islands in detail. **Noel Fojut's** *A Guide to Prehistoric and Viking Shetland* (Rev.ed., Shetland Times pb, 0900662913, £12.00) is designed for the interested amateur. It covers archaeological sites from early prehistoric times to the Norse settlement of the islands, a time span of over five thousand years. It includes chronological descriptions, a gazeteer of many sites and a series of suggested car tours. **Ian Donaldson-Blyth's** *In Search of Prehistoric Skye* (Thistle Press pb, 0952095025, £4.95), examines some of Skye's finest pre-historic sites in great detail to allow the visitor or amateur historian a more rounded understanding of their significance. In *Prehistoric Orkney* (Batsford pb, 0713475935, £5.95) **Anna Ritchie** studies one of the areas richest in archaeological evidence of ancient peoples. The many surviving monuments shed light on the development of the island's earliest inhabitants throughout prehistory.

Ideal for the layman, **Bill Finlayson's** *Wild Harvesters: Scotland's First Settlers* (Canongate pb, 0862417791, £5.95) is a user-friendly, compact and easily accessible guide to the first people who lived in Scotland from 8000 to 4000 BC. Likewise *Settlement and Sacrifice: The Later Prehistoric People of Scotland* by **Richard Hingley** (Canongate pb, 0862417821, £5.95) provides a very readable re-assessment of the people who lived in Scotland from 1500 BC to 200 AD. These titles are the start of a Canongate series looking at new archaeological discoveries in Scotland.

Roman

The Romans arrived in Scotland in AD 80. Although they never conquered Scotland, visible evidence of their invasion attempts is still plentiful. Scotland contains some of the best preserved Roman military sites in Britain, as well as the wall constructed to contain the Northern tribes' resistance. In *Roman Scotland* (Batsford pb, 71347890X, £5.95) **David Breeze** looks at the latest archaeological evidence and contemporary Roman documents to examine the Romans, three attempted invasions of Scotland, the effects of which are still visible in the remains of the forts and frontiers they built. The reasons for the Romans withdrawal and the forces ranged against them are illuminated in this informative and well illustrated book, and the author assesses the relationship between Rome and the northern tribes once the Romans had withdrawn. **Breeze** is also co-author with **B. Dobson** of the excellent *Hadrian's Wall* (Penguin pb, 0140135499, £8.99) which examines the history of the structure initiated at the time of Emperor Hadrian and eventually abandoned in the 5th century. Other Roman relics in Scotland are examined in **Lawrence J. Keppie's** *Scotland's Roman Remains* (John Donald pb, 0859761576, £8.50) which looks at the Romans in Scotland and their wider occupation of northern Britain. **Gordon Maxwell** has written two books on the subject. *A Gathering of Eagles: The Romans in Scotland* (Canongate pb, 0862417813, £5.95) provides a short introduction to the influence Roman rule had on Scotland. Written in a refreshing and informative way it highlights the problems the Romans experienced trying to control and contain a restless population *The Romans In Scotland* (Mercat Press hb, 0901824763, £16.99) is a more detailed study which will nevertheless appeal to the general reader as much as the specialist.

Early History: c.3rd - 10th Century

The withdrawal of the Romans from Britain left a 'Scotland' divided between British tribes in the south and the enigmatic Picts in the north. Two separate waves of immigration followed - Angles in the east, and Irish tribes (Scotii) in the west. The Scotii established their kingdom of Dal Riada in Argyll in the 6th century. Over the course of 200 years they merged with the Picts, entirely subsuming Pictish language and culture, making Gaelic the language of the new realm, Alba. Under pressure from Viking invaders in the 9th century, the Scots expanded their territories to the south - displacing both Britons and Angles by the late 10th century. At this point we see Scotland as the geographic and political entity (albeit without Isles and Caithness - lost to the Vikings) that we recognise today. A nation Celtic in culture, combining the traditional values of a warrior society with a high civilization based around the Celtic church in general and the figure of St Columba in particular.

The influence of Celtic culture was to affect many areas of Scottish history and society. The Celtic tribes' history was a long one, dating from before the arrival of the Romans to around the time of the 9th century. The true identity of the Celts, which has fascinated people for many years, is explored in **Barry Cunliffe's** informative and well-researched book *The Ancient Celts* (OUP hb, 0198150105, £25.00), which uses up-to-date research and information to give an intriguing new picture of the true nature of Celtic identity. For a more Scottish-centred overview of the Celtic tribes the following books are well worth investigating: *The Picts And The Scots* by **Lloyd and Jennifer Laing** (Sutton pb, 0750906774, £10.99) is an easily accessible look at the origins of these two peoples that traces their evolution and inter-connections from the time of the Roman occupation to the Dark Ages. **John Marsden's** *Alba of* *the Ravens: In Search of the Celtic Kingdom of the Scots* (Constable hb, 0094757607, £17.95) is aimed at providing the general reader with a highly detailed view of the Celtic world. This work is structured around six portraits of the Celtic kings, starting with Fergus Mor and ending with Macbeth.

There are few written records about the Picts. However *In Search of the Picts: A Celtic Dark Age Nation* (Constable pb, 0094750106, £12.95) by **Elizabeth Sutherland** collates the available information to draw up an account of the Picts and their way of life, using evidence such as their extraordinary sculptured stones, and in so doing finds a highly organised society with a love of art and a close relationship with nature. An ideal complementary work, also by **Elizabeth Sutherland** is *The Pictish Guide* (Birlinn pb, 1874744661, £7.99) in which all the known Pictish carved stones, fragmentary or complete, Christian or pagan, are listed. The guide includes descriptions of symbols and decorations with interpretations of their meanings.

The Orkney islands were the heartland of the Vikings' Scottish territory. *Orkneyinga Saga* translated by **Hermann Palsson** and **Paul Edwards** (Penguin pb, 0140443835, £7.99) is an early history of the Orkneymen of Norwegian extraction who established an Earldom of Norway in the Northern Scottish Isles over a thousand years ago. This edition is presented in an English translation with a useful introduction. Another translation of the saga is found in the Mercat Press edition edited by **Joseph Anderson** (Mercat Press hb, 0901824259, £10.99). Its introduction includes some details of the islands' earlier history as well as continuing the Earldom's history beyond the time period covered in the saga itself. *The Viking Age in Caithness, Orkney and the North Atlantic* edited by **C.E. Batey** et al (EUP pb, 0748606327, £14.95) vividly brings the Norse world to life with its detailed presentation of everyday existence. It covers a wide range of topics connected with the Viking Age, including ethnology, runic inscriptions and settlement patterns.

St Ninian and later St Columba laid the foundations of Celtic Christianity in Scotland. *St Nynia, with a translation of The Miracles Of Bishop Nynia* by **John MacQueen** (Polygon pb, 0748660488, £4.99) is a study of the written records of St Ninian, the earliest Saint associated with Scotland. It includes an English translation of an 8th century poem about the saint. **Daphne Brooke's** *Wild Men and Holy Places: St Ninian, Whithorn and the Medieval Realm of Galloway* (Canongate pb, 0862415586, £10.99) examines the pivotal role played by Galloway in the Celtic kingdom during the Dark Ages and Medieval period. It was in Galloway that St Ninian founded Scotland's earliest church. This carefully researched history of the people and places of this region is an accomplished work.

Columba founded a monastery on Iona in 563 and later had many churches built in the Hebrides. His monastery became a school for missionaries, and he was also very active in Scotland's politics. One of the earliest accounts of this saint was written in the 7th century by an Irish monk who became abbot of Iona. **Adomnan** of Iona's *Life Of Columba* edited by Richard Sharpe (Penguin pb, 0140444629, £8.99) was designed to glorify the saint and his foundation of Iona. It describes various miracles and prophecies of the saint, as well as his missionary journeys. Now in a new translation with an introduction to both Columba and his biographer, the book gives an insight into the nature of Celtic spirituality at its very source. A translation of Adomnan's work is included in *The Illustrated Life Of Columba* by **John Marsden** (Floris Books pb, 0863152112, £14.99). This book details the life and times of the 6th century saint, with many accompanying illustrations. John Marsden provides a historical overview of the time, as well as a detailed portrait of St. Adomnan himself.

Also by **John Marsden**, *Sea-Road of The Saints: Celtic Holy Men in the Hebrides* (Floris Books pb, 0863152104, £9.99) focuses on the many early Christians who visited these islands. They are full of places dedicated to holy men - crosses more than 1000 years old mark their history. This book is an account of these men, pioneering religious figures such as Brendan the Voyager and Saint Columba. Their personal histories are carefully researched and written, and presented in a way that breathes life into the legends.

Medieval Scotland

The Middle Ages in Scotland saw the start of the slow decline of Celtic Scotland, the rise of feudalism and the Wars of Independence. There are several good studies of Scotland during medieval times. Amongst them are *Medieval Scotland: Crown, Lordship And Community* (EUP pb, 074861110X, £16.95) edited by **Alexander Grant** and **K. Stringer**, a study of the central themes behind the development of the medieval Scottish kingdom. **John L. Roberts'** lucid and lively account of Celtic Scotland, *Lost Kingdoms: Celtic Scotland and the Middle Ages* (EUP pb, 0748609105, £14.95), tells of the Canmore kings embracing feudalism and the attempts of increasingly Normanised kings of Scots to impose their authority on the ancient Celtic kingdom. It covers the period from the Picts' and Scots' kingdoms to the downfall of the Clan Donald at the end of the fifteenth century. The book is an admirable combination of rigorous historical accuracy and enjoyable storytelling. In a similar way **Ronald Williams'** *The Lords of the Isles: The Clan Donald and the Early Kingdom of the Scots* (House Of Lochar pb, 1899863176, £9.99) covers the time from the Kingdom of Dal Riada in Argyll in AD 500 to the story of the Bruce. This work is written in a strongly narrative style while retaining detail.

In *Medieval Scotland* (Batsford pb, 0713474653, £5.95) **Peter Yeoman** builds up a very 'down-to-earth' picture of medieval life, revealing many of the everyday fundamentals of life in the burghs and in the country. The book also examines the major role played by parish churches, abbeys and friaries at this time. The text is accompanied by a range of well-chosen illustrations. The influence of the medieval church is the sole focus of **Mark Dilworth's** *Scottish Monasteries In The Late Middle Ages* (EUP pb, 0748605274, £12.95) This study is an authoritative account of 16th century Scottish monastic life which describes the importance of monasteries and their activities at a time when abbots played the role of feudal lords. Each monastic order is placed within its historical context, and related to its mother-house in France or elsewhere in Europe. The author also considers the monastic contribution to both sides of the Reformation.

Around this time there were strong political, cultural, artistic and religious connections between Scotland, Norway and the Western Isles. **R. Andrew McDonald's** *The Kingdom of the Isles: Scotland's Western Seaboard c.1100-c.1336* (Tuckwell Press pb, 1898410852, £16.99) studies these links and builds into a fully rounded history of the age, a rare book on this neglected area of Scottish history. *Scotland in the Reign of Alexander III* edited by **Norman H. Reid** (John Donald hb, 0859762181, £12.50) studies the period from 1249 to 1286, covering such topics as the Church, law and economics, as well as politics. In 1263 Alexander defeated the King of Norway and went on to annex the Hebrides and the Isle of Man. Through careful marriage links with Norway and Flanders, Scotland became a European kingdom, and the subsequent years are often seen as a golden age. However, Alexander died heirless and the dispute over succession opened the door to English interference at the hands of Edward I.

Wallace and Bruce's attempts to re-establish the independence of Scotland from Edward I and II in the Scottish Wars of Independence are covered in **Raymond C. Paterson's** *For The Lion: A History of the Scottish Wars of Independence 1296-1357* (John Donald pb, 0859764354, £9.95), a detailed and coherent summary of the era which saw the re-establishment of the Scottish nation. Likewise **Peter Traquair's** *Freedom's Sword: Scotland's Wars Of Independence* (HarperCollins hb, 0004720792, £16.99) covers the longest period of conflict between Scotland and England, starting with William Wallace and the rebellion he initiated, and including the career of Robert the Bruce. The broader effects and influences of English court politics are also studied. **Fiona Watson's** *Under The Hammer: Edward I And Scotland 1286-1307* (Tuckwell Press pb, 1862320209, £14.99) examines Edward I's failed attempt to annex Scotland, seeing the key aspect of these events as the relationship between the native population and the new administrators left behind after the battle. In this way Watson presents an unusual account of these times.

The Wars of Independence threw up two of Scotland's most enduring heroes: William Wallace and Robert the Bruce. Wallace's efforts against Edward I, coupled with Bruce's aspiration to be monarch, were to eventually lead to the re-emergence of a sovereign Scotland. Any overview of the 13th and 14th centuries must have these two national figures heavily involved. There are any number of excellent biographies of Wallace, among them **Peter Reese's** *Wallace: A Biography* (Canongate pb, 0862416078, £5.95) which is written in two distinct sections. The first deals with the history of Wallace and his time. Built from various sources including **Blind Harry's** epic 1478 poem, it emphasizes Wallace's importance in creating a Scottish sense of identity during some of its darkest days. The second section concerns the impact Wallace had on later generations, concluding that his martyrdom was a greater legacy to the Scots than any of his actions. A unique and credible biography by a well respected military historian. For other books on Wallace see Nicola Royan's Introduction to Scottish History at the start of the History section.

Robert Bruce and the Community of the Realm by **Geoffrey Barrow** (EUP pb, 0852246048, £14.95) is a classic account of Bruce's struggle to win the throne. Detailed and authoritative, it sets his story within the political context of a country forced to define and defend its right to independence. Bruce's involvement in the Wars of Independence is covered by **Ronald McNair Scott's** *Robert The Bruce: King Of Scots* (Canongate pb, 0862416167, £5.95), an in-depth biography of Bruce constructed with a strong narrative drive and as such a very fine read with numerous well told anecdotes and a rounded portrayal of this historical figure. The wider conflict at this time is examined in *The Wars of the Bruces: Scotland, England & Ireland 1306-1328* by **Colm McNamee** (Tuckwell Press pb, 1898410925, £14.99). While England's war with Robert the Bruce was happening, and the English army heavily committed to this conflict, Edward Bruce, king of Ireland, took advantage of the situation to capture the Isle of Man and raid the Welsh coast, while German and Flemish pirates joined the Scots in the North Sea to cripple England's vital wool trade. These events were to have major ramifications for the whole of the British Isles. The author uses a strong narrative thread to make this a very accessible read.

The Comyns were the most powerful baronial family in 13th century Scotland. Accused of betraying both William Wallace and Bruce, they have often been portrayed as the villains of Scottish history. In **Alan Young's** *Robert The Bruce's Rivals: The Comyns 1212-1314* (Tuckwell Press pb, 1862320535, £16.99) their role in 13th century power politics is examined in a clear and unbiased fashion. Closely linked to Bruce's success, the rise and fall of the Black Douglas dynasty was to have major ramifications for the late medieval Scottish kingdom. *The Black Douglases: War And Lordship In Late Medieval Scotland 1300-1455* by **Michael Brown** (Tuckwell Press pb, 186232025X, £16.99) specifically analyses the full scale and nature of their aristocratic power.

Raymond C. Paterson studies the conflicts between Scotland and England subsequent to the Wars of Independence in *My Wound Is Deep: A History of the Later Anglo-Scottish Wars, 1380-1560* (John Donald pb, 0859764656, £11.95) The various political and military battles during this time effectively amounted to a two hundred years' war in the Borders. **George M. Fraser's** *The Steel Bonnets* (HarperCollins pb, 0002727463, £9.99) focuses on the endless fighting of the Border Reivers over four hundred years ago. Fraser's book brings these rustlers and outlaws back to life, telling the story of the great raiding families who terrorised the border.

Another major figure of the Middle Ages was St. Margaret. **Alan J. Wilson's** *St Margaret, Queen Of Scotland* (John Donald pb, 0859763986, £9.95) is the definitive biography of Scotland's only royal saint. Daughter of an English nobleman and born in Hungary where her father was exiled, she married Malcolm III Canmore in c.1070. Her influence anglicized the royal court and brought Benedictine monks to Dunfermline. This study follows her life from childhood to her canonisation in 1249.

Edward D. Ives' biography *The Bonny Earl of Murray: The Man, The Murder, The Ballad* (Tuckwell Press pb, 1898410836, £14.99) looks at the subject of the haunting ballad. The Earl of Murray's murder in 1592 by command of George Gordon, Sixth Earl of Huntly led to public outrage. Ives examines the machinations surrounding the Bonny Earl's murder, seeing his death as an inevitable result of a power struggle between two influential Scottish families.

The Stewart Dynasty

No other family has had such a profound effect on Scottish history as the Stewarts, from medieval barons right up to the '45 Rebellion and its subsequent effects. The Stewarts' history is inextricably linked to that of Scotland, and a wide selection of books illustrates this rich connection. **Stewart Ross's** *The Stewart Dynasty* (House Of Lochar hb, 0946537925, £18.95) covers over 600 years of the dynasty in their various roles as barons, monarchs and pretenders to the throne. This carefully researched book looks at the full history of this family and also sheds new light on their passionate sexuality and (possibly inherited) bouts of depression. A very different view of the dynasty comes from **HRH Prince Michael of Albany,** the senior legitimate descendant of the Stuart kings. In his book *The Forgotten Monarchy of Scotland: The True Story of the Royal House of Stewart and the Hidden Lineage of the Kings and Queens of Scots* (Element hb, 1862042349, £16.99) he gives a controversial history of the Royal House of Stewart that reveals new information about historical conspiracies, the fate of the Stewarts after the '45 uprising and the evolution of Freemasonry, not to mention details previously not commonly known about Scotland's Auld Alliance with France. The dominant images we have of the Stuart dynasty are those of tragic, romantic figures and political incompetents. *Princes, Poets And Patrons: The Stuarts And Scotland* by **Alastair Cherry** (HMSO pb, 011493388X, £6.50) takes a very different line - by concentrating on the cultural impact of the dynasty the author concludes that the Stuarts made a considerable contribution to Scotland's arts which had a lasting effect on the nation's culture.

There are numerous books concentrating on individual members of the Stewart dynasty. The first three described here belong to the authoritative 'Stewart Dynasty In Scotland Series' published by Tuckwell Press. *The Early Stewart Kings: Robert II and Robert III 1371-1406* by **Stephen Boardman** (Tuckwell Press pb, 1898410437, £14.99) is firmly based on contemporary documentation. It is aimed at the general reader as much as the scholar, and critically examines the reputations the two kings have acquired through the course of history, finding that they deviate, often substantially, from historical fact. In *James I* (Tuckwell Press pb, 1898410402, £12.99) **Michael Brown** provides a major full-length study of this enigmatic monarch, while **Norman Mac-Dougall's** *James IV* (Tuckwell Press hb, 1898410410, 1 £6.99) examines a king who combined interest in the arts and sciences with an awareness of politics in Europe at large. His disastrous end at Flodden in 1513 was a sad conclusion to a remarkably successful kingship. This study examines all aspects of his reign.

James II by **Christine McGladdery** (John Donald hb, 0859763048, £12.50) is a scholarly and highly detailed biography, heavily sourced from contemporary accounts and official records. It studies the life of the king who put an end to the power of the rising Douglas family, and who was killed during an attempt to win Roxburgh Castle back from the English.

Undoubtedly the most tragic figure in the Stewart dynasty is that of Mary, Queen of Scots. **Antonia Fraser's** *Mary Queen Of Scots* (Mandarin pb, 0749301082, £9.99) is an insightful and acclaimed biography, in which the author's interest in and sympathy for her subject is evident. Fraser succeeds on many fronts - not only does she explore the emotional make-up of her heroine's character, but also carefully recreates the world in which she lived. This book won the James Tait Black Memorial Award. *Mary Queen Of Scots: A Study In Failure* by **Jenny Wormald** (Collins & Brown pb, 1855850230, £9.99) takes a more contentious line, as it is more concerned with Mary as a political figure and as a ruler. Mary's first husband is the subject of **Caroline Bingham's** discerning biography, *Darnley: Consort Of Mary Queen Of Scots* (Phoenix pb, 1857997794, £9.99). Darnley was married to Mary Stuart in 1565 at Holyrood House and was proclaimed 'Henry, King of Scots.' Their disastrous marriage did produce a future heir, James VI. After plotting with others to murder the Queen's Italian secretary, Darnley himself was mysteriously murdered, with many rumours suggesting Mary's involvement.

Antonia Fraser has also written a biography of Mary Queen Of Scots' son, whose reign united the Crowns of Scotland and England. *King James VI Of Scotland, I Of England* is a thorough, well laid out and illustrated study that highlights the king's successful rule of Scotland as well as his rule of England. The death of James' eldest son meant that the succession passed to his second son, the future Charles I. **Charles Carlton's** *Charles I: The Personal Monarch* (Routledge pb, 0415125650, £14.99) reveals an uncertain and perturbed individual who had personal difficulties fitting into the role of king during a time of political and social upheaval. In this subtle and well-constructed biography, Carlton confirms this image as well as giving the reader a clearer idea of the reasons behind some of the apparently inexplicable royal policies.

Prince Charles Edward Stuart is of course another immensely romantic figure in Scottish history, the Young Pretender who attempted to reclaim the thrones of Scotland, England and Ireland for the Stuarts. **Fitzroy Maclean's** very readable biography *Bonnie Prince Charlie* (Canongate pb, 0862415683, £5.95) looks behind the romantic myths surrounding the Prince, from his efforts to rally the clans behind him, to the massacre at Culloden and his eventual death, alone and demoralized in Rome nearly 40 years later. For studies dealing with his role in the 1745 Uprising, see the section on '17th & 18th Centuries: Jacobites.'

17th & 18th Centuries

The implications of the Union of the Crowns and a new centralising monarchy were played out through conflicts of Church and State, popular resistance and civil war. From the Bishops' Wars of 1639-40 through forced Union under Cromwell and the Darien disaster to parliamentary union in 1707 the reality of Scotland's status as an independent realm proved questionable. The influence of Celtic Scotland had been in gradual decline since the early Middle Ages. This process was accelerated by the loss of the Lordship of the Isles and the collapse of MacDonald supremacy in the south-west Highlands, which created a power vacuum allowing the rise of the politically astute Clan Campbell. The 17th and 18th centuries saw the last attempt of Celtic Scotland to assert itself politically in the ill-fated Jacobite Rebellions.

The civil wars of the mid-17th century and the Covenanting tradition created a whole new range of heroes and villains who have since passed into popular mythology. Montrose's romantic image as a warrior hero still lingers in the Scottish historical consciousness. **Edward J. Cowan's** *Montrose: For Covenant And King* (Canongate pb, 086241556X, £4.99) explores the soldier, poet and Covenanter who became a Royalist and heroically fought against hopeless odds, in an exciting retelling of his life story. Better known for his adventure novels, **John Buchan** a classic biography of the Scottish general. *The Marquis of Montrose* (Prion pb, 185375224X, £8.99) is written with all the flair used in his novels, and paints Montrose as a man noble in character with great strength of purpose, who proved himself a military genius. In *The Campaigns of Montrose* (Mercat Press hb, 0901824925, £5.95) **Stuart Reid** concentrates on Montrose's military record, examining his battles and his undeniable abilities as a strategist. The work is academically rigorous yet manages to convey a feeling of the sound and fury of 17th century warfare. *A Land Afflicted: Scotland And The Covenanter*

Wars, 1638-1690 by **Raymond C. Paterson** (John Donald pb, 0859764869, £9.95) also studies the warfare of this time, assessing the battles of Montrose and the continuing struggle after his death.

David Stevenson is a leading authority on 17th century Scotland. His *King Or Covenant? Voices From Civil War* (Tuckwell pb, 189841081X, £14.99) presents thirteen biographical studies of people caught up in the 'troubles' of the 17th century. Fascinating and highly readable, it offers fresh perspectives on an important period in Scottish history. He has also written *Highland Warrior* (Saltire pb, 0854110593, £12.99) a study of Alasdair MacColla, Montrose's right-hand man and inventor of the Highland charge, the tactic used to such devastating effect by Highland armies until the battle of Culloden.

Constitutional crises provoked by the Covenanters' resistance to royal authority spread from Scotland to influence the parliamentary stand-off in England, and Scotland was drawn into the English Civil War. Scottish armies fought against the monarchy but the execution of Charles I forced the Covenanting leadership to withdraw their support from Cromwell and accept Charles II as king. Cromwell invaded Scotland and followed his military success with political incorporation. **John D. Grainger's** *Cromwell Against The Scots: The Last Anglo-Scottish War, 1650-1652* (Tuckwell Press pb, 1862320640, £14.99) is a scrupulous history of the war which views the events in both their military and political dimensions.

Political instability and personal feuding in the Highlands formed the background to the conflicts of the wider civil war. **Ronald Williams** looks at the role of two powerful clans in *The Heather And The Gael: Clan Donald And Clan Campbell During the Wars of Montrose* (House Of Lochar pb, 1899863184, £11.99). Williams describes the savage hatreds and fierce loyalties which were at the heart of the war in the Highlands. **Paul Hopkins'** classic study *Glencoe and the End of the Highland War* (John Donald pb, 0859764907, £25.00) provides an excellent analysis of the late 17th century Highlands and the rise of Jacobitism. Hopkins gives a detailed account of the Highland War of 1689-92 as well as of the massacre itself, placing it in its historical context. He brings clarity and a balanced view to this complex period of Highland history. The dark events surrounding the massacre are described by **John Prebble** in *Glencoe: The Story of the Highland Massacre* (Penguin pb, 0140028978, £7.99). John Prebble retells the story with accuracy and vigour, seeing in the massacre a symbolic beginning of the end for the Highland way of life.

Act of Union

The 1707 Act of Union was put through in controversial circumstances. Widespread allegations of corruption, rioting in the streets of Edinburgh, rumours and political intrigue surrounded the historic signing away of Scotland's independence. Among the key figures of the time was Andrew Fletcher, who bitterly opposed the Act of Union. **Paul Scott's** *Andrew Fletcher And The Treaty Of Union* (Saltire pb, 0854110577, £12.99) provides a compelling portrait of the man and his passionate defence of Scotland's nationhood. A fascinating insight into the political manoeuvering behind the signing of the Act can be found in *'Scotland's Ruine':* **Lockhart Of Carnwath's** *Memoirs Of The Union* (ASLS hb, 0948877286, £25.00) edited by **Daniel Szechi**. Lockhart was one of the Scottish Commissioners chosen to vote on a Union agreement with England, and he was one of the few who voted against.

Jacobites

The Rebellions of 1715 and '45 tend to dominate readings of Highland history at this time. An account of the wider Jacobite cause is afforded by **Bruce Lenman's** *The Jacobite Risings In Britain 1689-1746* (S.C.P. pb, 189821820X, £14.95). Lenman's book charts the background to Jacobitism, and explains the circumstances which allowed it to grow, as much political action as romantic and conservative beliefs. This book is a good place to start for an understanding of the wider period as well as the individual rebellions.

The Jacobite risings have been viewed in different ways, from the inevitable fall of a clan system led by a foolish, vain rebel to a brave and valiant attempt by Scotland's rightful heir to regain his crown. What is certain is that the defeat at Culloden and the brutal policies of the Hanoverian regime resulted in a fundamental change in the nature of Highland society. The rebellion itself and its tragic finale at Culloden have been analysed in many accounts. Among the best is *Culloden and the '45* by **Jeremy Black** (Sutton pb, 0750903759, £9.99). This book charts the key events of the 1745 Rebellion, including the battle at Culloden, steering clear of romantic myths and legends. One of the most popular accounts is **John Prebble's** *Culloden* (Penguin pb, 0140253505, £7.99), a classic and readable chronicle of the battle and the events that followed, written from contemporary sources. **Michael Hook** and **Walter Ross's** study *The Forty-Five: The Last Jacobite Rebellion* (HMSO pb, 0114957215, £12.95) also has much to recommend it, using manuscripts, printed sources and images which are reproduced in the book. The authors aim to look beyond the romantic image that has obscured many of the facts about the Rebellion. *The Jacobite Army In England, 1745: The Final Campaign* (John Donald pb, 0859764885, £14.95) by **F.J. McLynn** concentrates on the Prince Regent's campaign in England and the conduct of his army there.

Two excellent histories of the '45 which take a refreshingly different approach are **Maggie Craig's** *Damn Rebel Bitches: The Women of the '45* (Mainstream hb, 1851589627, £15.95) which looks at the role women played on both sides, from spies and followers to victims of rape and persecution after Culloden; and *Lochiel of the '45: The Jacobite Chief And The Prince* by **John S. Gibson** (EUP pb, 074860507X, £12.95), a biography of Donald Cameron of Lochiel, who was Bonnie Prince Charlie's most faithful chief. After Culloden he was the man who fought to keep the rebellion alive until fleeing to France where he sought French support to restage the uprising. This work draws on Lochiel's own recently rediscovered account of the '45.

There are a number of eye-witness accounts of the Rebellion including *Witness To Rebellion:* **John Maclean's** *Diary Of The '45 And The Penicuik Drawings* (Tuckwell Press pb, 1898410747, £9.99) edited by **I.G. Brown** and **H. Cheape**. This account, by one of Bonnie Prince Charlie's officers, charts the course of the Rebellion until Maclean's death at Culloden.

Much has been written about Charles Edward Stuart. Two books that specifically concentrate on his role in the '45 Rebellion are *The Road To Culloden Moor: Bonnie Prince Charlie And The '45 Rebellion* (Constable pb, 0094761701, £9.99) by **Diana Preston**, a lively biography of the prince that attempts to find out why he has found such an enduring place in Scottish memory. The book takes a very penetrating look into the Young Pretender's personality and background, and gives us a unique view of the Jacobite uprising from this perspective. **A.J. Youngson's** book *The Prince And The Pretender: Two Views Of The '45* (Mercat Press pb, 1873644620, £12.99) provides two very different views of the Rebellion that paint Bonnie Prince Charlie on the one hand as a dashing leader and on the other as an egotistical adventurer.

As a postscript to the Jacobite Rebellion, the unsolved killing of Colin Campbell of Glenure was to have effects reaching to the highest levels of Scottish politics and society, and became the basis of Robert Louis Stevenson's *Kidnapped* and *Catriona*. **Seamus Carney** re-examines this compelling and dramatic story in *The Appin Murder: The Killing of the Red Fox* (Birlinn pb, 1874744211, £6.99) searching for the truths behind the murder.

"I will share the fate of my Prince, and so shall every man over whom nature or fortune hath given me any power."

Cameron of Lochiel (1695–1748)

Enlightenment

The 18th century saw a major flowering of ideas in Scotland. *The Enlightenment Reader* (Canongate pb, 0862417384, £10.99) edited by **Alexander Broadie** gives a wide overview of this defining time for Scottish and European culture. His book gives a general introduction and texts from Enlightenment thinkers arranged thematically from aesthetics to science. The influence Scottish thinkers like David Hume, Adam Smith and James Hutton had on their respective fields was immense, pushing forward the boundaries and rewriting the rules. This book is a crucial guide to one of the most dynamic times in Scottish history, a time when Scotland, and especially Edinburgh, was one of the intellectual centres of the world. Looking at Scotland's development after the Act of Union in 1707, **N.T. Phillipson** and **Rosalind Mitchison's** *Scotland in the Age of Improvement* (EUP pb, 0748608761, £12.95) explores the history of all the major social institutions during the 18th century, showing some of Scotland's remarkable cultural and economic achievements. Most accounts of Scotland's intellectual flowering focus solely on the Edinburgh literati. One book that corrects this imbalance is *The Glasgow Enlightenment* (Tuckwell Press pb, 189841095X, £14.99) edited by **A. Hook** and **R.B. Sher**. Adam Smith, who became a professor at Glasgow University, was only one of a group of intellectual and academic figures who made Glasgow a centre of the Enlightenment. This book examines the work of Smith and fellow scholars such as Francis Hutcheson and Thomas Reid.

The political establishment in the new Scotland or North Britain was dominated by corruption, intrigue and the exploitation of limited access to the rich pickings of England's overseas colonies. One man in particular became so adept in his manipulation of this system that he became known as the 'uncrowned King of Scotland'. In *The Dundas Despotism: Henry & Robert Dundas 1770s-1830s* (EUP pb, 0748603522, £9.95) **Michael Fry** looks at the personalities, politics and patronage of the time.

Clearances and Emigration

The Clearances did much to destroy Highlander culture and identity, forcing many to leave Scotland altogether. A rising population, changes in the social fabric of the Highlands and landlords determined to maximise the cash value of their property led to the forcible eviction and dispossession of thousands of people. Emigration became a way of life for communities, having a profound effect on the Highlands. The Clearances remain a highly emotive issue to this day. *The Making of the Crofting Community* (John Donald pb, 0859764060, £12.95) by **James Hunter** is a seminal history of the last two hundred years which gives a wider picture of the Clearances and charts the events that formed the modern Highlands and Islands. This book strips away the romantic myths surrounding the last 200 years of Scottish history and gives us a vital new account which is both original and accurate, highlighting popular resistance to the Clearances and the Crofters' War.

One of the major source books and a good starting point for any study of the Clearances, is **Alexander MacKenzie's** *The History of the Highland Clearances* (Mercat Press pb, 0901824968, £10.99). In *The Highland Clearances* (John Donald pb, 0859764664, £11.95) **N.S. Newton** sets out to examine many of the myths which surround the subject, making full use of facts and figures. Once again **John Prebble** provides an informative history on one of the key areas of Scotland's past in *The Highland Clearances* (Penguin pb, 0140028374, £7.99), re-examining these events in a dramatic narrative, with clarity and detail while retaining a sense of the suffering caused. A very different slant on the Clearances can be found in **David Craig's** *On The Crofters' Trail* (Pimlico pb, 0172673830, £10.00). Craig travelled through Scotland and Canada to collect the handed-down memories of the Highland crofters forced from their homes by greedy landlords. In their stories the full tragedy of the Clearances is revealed, as relayed to Craig by their descendants. This is a powerful and very personal book and a major contribution to Scotland's recent social history.

Scottish Emigration and Scottish Society (John Donald hb, 0859763706, £12.50) edited by **T.M. Devine** looks at emigration throughout Scotland with reference to changing political and social factors both abroad and within Scotland itself, covering the years from 1750 to 1914.

A work that looks specifically at migration within Scotland is *The Urban Gael: Highland Migration and the Highland Migrant, 1700-1900* by **Charles W.J. Withers** (Tuckwell Press pb, 1862320403, £20.00). Withers explores the massive exodus of Highlanders to the urban lowlands in the 18th and 19th centuries, which was to have a significant cultural impact on many Lowland locations. This work draws together much of the previously available information on this subject and supplements it with new material.

There are a few books that focus on the experiences of the emigrés after they arrived in their new countries, and the impact they made there. **Jim Hewitson** has written two books on this subject: *Tam Blake And Co: The Story Of The Scots In America* (Canongate pb, 0862415594, £9.99) and *Far Off In Sunlit Places* (Canongate pb, 0862417759, £12.99). In the first volume Hewitson tells of Tam Blake who arrived in America in 1540, the first Scot to do so, and then recounts the lives of some of those early Scottish settlers. In his follow-up book he examines the impact Scots had on Australia and New Zealand in the years up to World War II. Writing in an anecdotal fashion Jim Hewitson looks at both the positive and negative influences these incomers had on their new countries. Likewise **James Hunter** has written two books on Scots emigrants in North America. In *A Dance Called America: The Scottish Highlands, The United States & Canada* (Mainstream pb, 1851588078, £9.99) he explores in an enthralling and poignant fashion what happened to the evicted Highlanders once they arrived, while *Glencoe And The Indians* (Mainstream pb, 1840180013, £9.99) is a remarkable account which traces the fate of the McDonald family from their roots in the Highlands to their forced migration and integration into the Nez Perce Indians of America. It covers two centuries and tells of massacres and dispossessions on two continents, showing how history can and does repeat itself, particularly in the persecution of minority groups.

19th & 20th Centuries

Life in Scotland in the 19th century was dominated by the great Scots institutions of church, law and education. The Church of Scotland underwent a dramatic change when a substantial number of ministers deserted the General Assembly in protest at state interference. This became a defining moment for Scotland. *Scotland in the age of the Disruption* by **S. Brown** and **M. Fry** (EUP pb, 0748604332, £9.95) looks at the events and personalities surrounding the historic split which established the Free Church and divided the nation in 1843.

The universities of Scotland were also subject to change, expected to meet the demand for civil servants for the British Empire and to compete with English universties. **George Davie's** *The Democratic Intellect* (EUP pb, 0852244355, £14.95) is a study of the universities during the 19th century which examines the central role of philosophy in the Scottish academic tradition and the pressures which ultimately undermined that tradition. *The Democratic Intellect* is regarded as a classic of Scottish cultural history. Although it can be demanding for the non-specialist reader it illuminates many of the key ideas which run through Scottish life and history from the Reformation to the present. Davie presents a convincing case for the distinctiveness and worth of native Scottish traditions. In his sequel, *The Crisis of Democratic Intellect* (Polygon hb, 0948275189, £14.95), Davie examines why, after World War I, the universities' long-lasting movement away from a generalist education towards a more specialising system was suddenly put into reverse. Davie shows why Scotland re-established the primacy of intellect, rather than placing the practical on the same level as the theoretical, analysing the views of classicist John Burnet, poet Hugh MacDiarmid and philosophers Norman Kemp Smith and John Anderson, thereby advocating a general and critical education.

The 19th century saw many other changes in Scottish life, especially in terms of increasing industrialisation and its effects. These changes are admirably presented in **T.C. Smout's** social histories, as referred to in the General History section.

Other aspects of the social history of the time can be found in **Leah Leneman's** work on the changing place of women in Scottish society. *A Guid Cause: The Women's Suffrage Movement In Scotland* (Mercat pb, 1873644485, £14.99) tells the story of the campaign for women's suffrage in Scotland which reached its climax in the early part of this century. It is a well-researched and informative book on this much overlooked area of Scottish history. Other books on women's history include **E. Breitenbach's** *Out Of Bounds: Women in Scottish Society 1800-1945* (EUP pb, 0748603727, £15.95), an informative and scholarly read. **Tom Begg's** *The Excellent Women* (John Donald pb, 0859764044, £15.00) covers the time when some of the key figures in the Scottish women's movement were campaigning for the then Edinburgh School of Cookery, now Queen Margaret's College.

The Complete Odyssey: Voices From Scotland's Recent Past (Polygon pb, 0748661751, £12.99) by **Billy Kay** is a collection of personal experiences of working class life, ranging from Italian immigrants and Shetland whalers to Highland land raiders. Well laid out and extensively illustrated with period photographs, it rescues an important and often neglected part of Scottish history.

As early as the end of the 18th century the Orange Order was already established in Scotland. **William S. Marshall's** *The Billy Boys: A Concise History Of The Orange Order In Scotland* (Mercat Press pb, 1873644523, £12.99) is a serious and dispassionate account of the history of this often controversial body looking at its influence, activities and views since its arrival in Scotland.

Events that began in the the previous century (i.e. the Clearances and subsequent emigration of large numbers of the Highland population) continued to take place and influence Scottish affairs of this time. Three books that do focus particularly on this aspect of the 19th century are: **T.M. Devine's** *The Great Highland Famine: Hunger Emigration And the Scottish Highlands in the Nineteenth Century* (John Donald pb, 0859763722, £20.00) a book that sets the Highland famine within its wider economic context, and **Rev. C. MacDonald's** *Moidart: Among The Clanranalds* (Birlinn pb, 1874744653, £9.99). Charles MacDonald (1835-1894) was a priest in Moidart for over thirty years. When he wrote this history of the great family of the Clanranalds he drew on the works of professional historians, eye witness accounts and his own observations from over a quarter of a century, and in the process created a minor classic. **Osgood Mackenzie's** *100 Years In The Highlands* (Birlinn pb, 1874744297, £5.95) has become a standard reference work since its first publication in 1921. Born into the privileged classes in 1842, Mackenzie kept detailed memoirs which provide a social history of the Victorian Highlands The memoirs reveal the relationship between common Highlanders and the people in the 'big house'.

The imminent arrival of the Millennium provides a suitable vantage point for a detailed study of 20th century Scotland. One book that attempts this is *Scotland in the 20th Century* (EUP pb, 0748608397, £14.95) edited by **T.M. Devine** and **R.J. Finlay**. In this collection of articles leading commentators examine Scotland's development during this century, looking at the vast changes that have taken place and analysing the most significant trends. The book covers various aspects of history, political, economic and social, including popular culture. While the articles which cover devolution are now slightly out of date, the collection remains a valuable contribution to the understanding of modern Scotland. Profound changes in all areas of modern Scottish life are examined by **Arnold Kemp** in *The Hollow Drum: Scotland Since The War* (Mainstream hb, 1851585885, £14.99).

The two World Wars had wide-ranging effects on Scottish society. Both wars are covered in **Ian MacDougall's** *Voices From War* (Mercat Press pb, 1873644450, £3.99) which features accounts from Scots men and women, covering the full range of wartime experience, from conscientious objectors to combatants. One of the most dramatic events of World War I was the sinking of the German fleet in Scapa Flow. **Dan Van Der Vat's** book *The Grand Scuttle* (Birlinn pb, 1874744823, £9.99) relays the events when Admiral Ludwig Van Reuter, in charge of the German Imperial Navy, scuttled fifty two ships at Scapa Flow on 21 June 1919. The book looks at this dramatic postscript to World War I. The author includes previously unused archive material and many little-known facts about the sinking.

Reminiscences of Scots who survived World War II are at the core of **Seona Robertson** and **Leslie Wilson's** *Scotland's War* (Mainstream hb, 1851587004, £14.99) which uses testimonies and photographs from a wide range of people and sources, creating an account of what the war was like for many ordinary men and women. The role that the Hebrides played in World War II is largely unknown, yet the bases of the west coast were crucial in turning the war against the Nazi U-Boat Wolf Packs. **Mike Hughes** explores this aspect of the war in *The Hebrides At War* (Canongate pb, 0862417716, £9.99), using first-hand eye-witness accounts of the conflict from military and civilian personnel. He enhances these accounts with photographs from his large private collection of images from the period, many of them informally taken. The result is an intimate and human portrayal of this arena of war. The exiled Polish forces played an important part in World War II, as examined in *For Your Freedom And Ours: Polish Forces In Scotland 1940-46* by **Allan Carswell** (N.M.S. pb, 0948636548, £2.95). Not only did they defend the Scottish coast and fight bravely in many arenas of war, but after the conflict was over many settled in Scotland.

Working Class Experience

Scotland's heavy industries such as steel, coal and engineering have had a major impact on its culture and identity. Only relatively recently has the full importance of this heritage been recognised. Stenlake Publishing produce a wide range of illustrated history books on this very subject, with numerous areas of Scotland and various industrial subjects covered. A sample of this range includes **Guthrie Hutton's** *Lanarkshire's Mining Legacy* (Stenlake pb, 1840330155, £12.95), **Paul Murray's** *Methil - No More!* (Stenlake pb, 1872074383, £6.50) and **Alan M. Sherry's** *The Blackburn - Dumbarton's Aircraft Factory* (Stenlake pb, 1872074820,£ 6.50). These books use period photographs from a wide range of sources to vividly recreate these bygone industries. For a full list of Stenlake's extensive range please enquire at any Waterstones branch. Another book on Scotland's industrial past that is worth mentioning is *The Clyde: A Portrait Of A River* (Canongate pb, 0862415845, £9.99) by **Michael Moss,** a history in words and pictures of Glasgow's once thriving shipbuilding industry. Shipbuilding on the Clyde was traditionally a bastion of socialism, a subject explored in *Militant Workers: Labour And Class Conflict on the Clyde, 1900-1950* (John Donald pb, 0859763730, £9.95) edited by **R. Duncan** and **A. McIvor.** The Red Clydesiders caused such consternation to the British Government that tanks were put on the streets of Glasgow to keep the peace. This scholarly study of these events and beyond examines the dynamics and special nature of the Clydeside movement.

The Land and The Sea

Agriculture has always been one of the key occupations in Scottish life. **David Kerr Cameron's** trilogy on rural Scotland *Willie Gavin, Crofter Man* (Birlinn pb, 1874744173, £8.99), *Cornkister Days* (Birlinn pb, 1874744181, £8.99) and *The Ballad and the Plough* (Birlinn pb, 1874744793, £8.99) looks at the reality of farming life in the North-East, and the era of Scotland's great farmtouns. In *Cornkister Days* he talks passionately about the 'countryside's old culture' where the Clydesdale horse, the plough, the hired man and the cottar were at the core of the community. His nostalgia is tempered with a realisation of the harshness of that life and the hardships the communities endured. Author **Douglas Willis** has close links with the crofting tradition. His description in *The Story Of Crofting* (John Donald pb, 0859763447, £9.50) is a thorough and up-to-date study of this way of life. A social history of crofting in the Highlands that highlights the communities' linguistic, cultural and moral values is provided by **Francis Thompson's** *Crofting Years* (Luath Press pb, 0946487065, £6.95), written very much from the point of view of the crofters themselves. In rural Scotland the movement of livestock was of fundamental importance to the life of the people and drove roads were vital in this. **A.R.B. Haldane's** work on these roads *The Drove Roads Of Scotland* (Birlinn pb, 1874744769, £9.99) is regarded as a classic of Scottish history and interweaves folklore, social comment and economic history. In many senses a sequel to this, Haldane's *New Ways Through the Glens* (House Of Lochar hb, 1899863052, £7.99) covers the work Thomas Telford and his colleagues did in opening up the difficult terrain of the Highlands, constructing communication routes in Northern Scotland.

Another mainstay of Scottish employment is the fishing industry, which has been of vital importance since prehistoric times. **James R. Coull's** *The Sea Fisheries of Scotland: A Historical Geography* (John Donald hb, 0859764109, £30.00) gives a thorough overview of the fishing industry in Scotland, both past and present, from boat construction and fishing techniques to the effects of the European Community on the Scottish fleet. The crucial role of the fishing industry in many Scottish communities, as well as the historical development of fishing techniques and many other aspects of fishing are explored in *Fishing And Whaling* (N.M.S. pb, 094863667X, £4.99) by **Angus Martin. Robert Smith's** in-depth study of the Scottish whaling community *The Whale Hunters* (John Donald pb, 0859763935, £8.95) contains many first-hand accounts of the conditions on board whaling ships, and a crucial history of this now most unpopular and barbaric trade. On a lighter note **Wallace Lockhart's** *The Scots And Their Fish* (Birlinn pb, 1874744815, £5.95) examines the importance to Scotland of fish both in economic and cultural terms. This often humorous work also contains tales, legends, verse and many recipes.

Humour

Albury, David (comp.)
The Quiz-Master Scottish Quiz Book
Polygon pb 0748662170 £4.99

Pub quiz nights are one of the more popular leisure pursuits. This quiz book is packed with questions on all aspects of Scottish life and culture, and is an ideal source for staging your own pub or house quiz.

Baron Of Ravenstone
Scotland Bloody Scotland
Canongate pb 0862411165 £4.99

An irreverent and provocative comic view of Scottish history.

Baxter, Stanley
The Parliamo Glasgow Omnibus
Birlinn pb 1874744009 £4.99

Stanley Baxter's hilarious take on the Glasgow dialect is one of Scotland's comic masterpieces. This omnibus is an initiation into the secrets and delights of this mode of speech and is sure to improve your grasp of 'the Glesca patter'.

Besley, Rupert
Scotland For Beginners
Neil Wilson pb 1897784007 £5.95
Skye For Beginners
Neil Wilson pb 1897784767 £5.95

A humorous and affectionate send-up of all things Scottish illustrated by the cartoonist author, and his book on Skye which gives the island the same treatment.

Burnie, Joan
Scotland The Worst!
Canongate pb 0862415535 £4.99

A collection that celebrates the worst, most trivial and forgettable aspects of Scotland.

Hardie, Buff et al
Scotland The What?
Gordon Wright hb 0903065592 £12.95
Scotland The What?
Second Helping
Gordon Wright hb 0903065851 £12.95

Collections of songs and sketches from one of Scotland's most successful comedy teams.

McCorrisken, Walter
A Wee Dribble Of Dross
Birlinn pb 1874744122 £3.99
Hairy Knees And Heather Hills
Birlinn pb 1874744343 £4.99

McCorrisken is regarded as the new McGonagall. His much loved poetry uses the West of Scotland dialect, dreadful rhymes and his own unique style of philosophising. Hilariously funny works by someone who can only be described as one of the world's worst poets.

McGonagall, William
McGonagall: A Selection
Birlinn pb 1874744114 £4.99

The poetry of McGonagall is so awful that it transcends itself and becomes incredibly funny, causing McGonagall himself to become a national instituiion. This selection features the worst/best of his work including his most famous poems.
Collected Poems
Birlinn pb 1874744017 £8.99

Maguire, S. & Young, David J. (Eds)
Hoots! An Anthology Of Scottish Comic Writing
Polygon pb 0748662294 £10.99

A feast of Scottish humour including works from some of the finest comics and writers in Scotland including Ivor Cutler, Chic Murray, Irvine Welsh and Rab C. Nesbitt.

Morrison, Allan
Haud Yer Wheesht: Yer
Scottish Granny's Favourite Sayings
Neil Wilson pb 1897784600 £3.99

This book is a collection of over 500 observations on life from wordly-wise, elderly Scottish ladies. With gems of common sense from grannies all over Scotland, it is full of appeal for all ages.

Munro, Michael
The Complete Patter
Canongate pb 0862416191 £5.95

The richly expressive, often alliterative dialect that Glasgow has spawned is lovingly deciphered in this work. The illustrations are by John Byrne.

Munro, Michael
The Crack
Canongate pb 0862416183 £4.99

Glasgow's famous sense of humour is well represented in this fine collection.

Munro, Michael
The Old Firm Joke Book
Canongate pb 0862417430 £4.99

A collection of humour created by the rival fans of Scotland's two largest football teams.

Neill, Bud
Bud Neill's Magic
Zipo Books pb 190198401X £6.99

Bud Neill's pithy and affectionate cartoons of Western Scotland's culture are over fifty years old but still contain characters you would recognise walking the streets of Glasgow. This collection is a good introduction to his work.

Lobey's The Wee Boy
Mainstream pb 1851584056
£5.95

A collection of five Lobey Dosser adventures, the celebrated comic creation of Glasgow cartoonist Bud Neill. Compiled by Ranald MacColl.

Osborne, Brian D. & Armstrong, Ronald
Scotch Obsessions
Birlinn pb 1874744688 £6.99

A provocative and humorous investigation of the many varied obsessions Scottish citizens have held, complete with quotations to illustrate the points made.

Shields, Tom
Tom Shields: Free At Last
Mainstream pb 1851588809
£7.99

Free At Last is the third volume of Tom Shields' collected writings. Culled from his humorous columns in *The Herald*, his thoughts and observations range widely from football to philosophy and all subjects in between. His unique wit makes this a seriously funny book.

Whyte, Hamish & Robertson, Barbara
The Minister's Cat
Mercat Press pb 1873644108
£3.99

The Scots alphabet game complete with accompanying pictures by Barbara Robertson.

Literary Criticism

The Scotnotes Series from the Association For Scottish Literary Studies provides an invaluable introduction to many major Scottish writers and literary texts. The series is aimed primarily at students during the later high school years or attending university but will be of interest to anyone studying these authors or books:

Smith, Iain Crichton
George Douglas Brown's The House With The Green Shutters
ASLS pb 0948877030 £4.00

MacGillivray, Alan
George Mackay Brown's Greenvoe
0948877081 £4.00

MacLachlan, C.
John Buchan: Witch Wood, Huntingtower and The Thirty-Nine Steps
0948877340 £4.00

Simpson, Kenneth
Robert Burns
0948877227 £4.00

Jack, Ronnie DS
The Poems Of William Dunbar
0948877324 £4.00

Young, Douglas
Lewis Grassic Gibbon's Sunset Song
0950262994 £4.00

Baird, Gerald
The Poems Of Robert Henryson
0948877294 £4.00

Petrie, Elaine
James Hogg's The Private Memoirs And Confessions Of A Justified Sinner
0948877057 £4.00

Smith, Iain Crichton
Robin Jenkins's The Cone-Gatherers
094887726X £4.00

Thomson, Geddes
The Poetry of Edwin Morgan
0948877006 £4.00

Blackburn, John
The Poetry of Iain Crichton Smith
0948877219 £4.00

Robb, David
Muriel Spark's The Prime of Miss Jean Brodie
0948877146 £4.00

The Scottish Writers' Series, edited by David Daiches and David Robb and published by the Mercat Press, is a series that explores the work of some of Scotand's most famous poets and writers and evaluates their contribution to literature.

1. Walter Scott by Thomas Crawford
0707303052 £1.99
2. Hugh MacDiarmid by Kenneth Buthlay
0707303079 £1.99
3. Robert Henryson by Matthew P. McDiarmid
0707303060 £1.99
4. Robert Fergusson by David Daiches
0707303133 £1.99
5. John Galt by PH Scott
0707303648 £1.99
6. Lewis Grassic Gibbon by I. Campbell
0707303656 £1.99
7. Alexander Montgomerie by RDS Jack
0707303672 £1.99
8. Robert Burns by D. Low
0707303680 £1.99
9. John Davidson by M. O'Connor
0707303664 £1.99
10. J.M. Barrie by L. Ormond
0707305047 £1.99
11. George MacDonald by DS Robb
0707305233 £1.99

The History Of Scottish Literature, published by Mercat Press under the general editorship of Craig Cairns, is a comprehensive history providing a detailed general view of Scottish literature. Some of the most knowledgeable scholars in the field create a complete picture of Scotland's literature, including works in Latin and Gaelic, setting the writing in its proper cultural and intellectual context.

Jack, R.D.S. (Ed)
Vol.1 Origins To 1660
0080377254 £12.50

Hook, Andrew (Ed)
Vol.2 1660-1800
0080377262 £12.50

Gifford, Douglas (Ed)
Vol.3 Nineteenth Century
0080377270 £12.50

Cairns, Craig (Ed)
Vol.4 Twentieth Century
0080377289 £12.50

Some other books offer general interpretations of Scottish literature in particular periods. **The Mainstream Companion To Scottish Literature** (ed. Trevor Royle Mainstream pb 1851585834 £12.99) is a comprehensive reference guide to Scotland's literature, useful for a thorough understanding of Scottish writing, which covers all the major movements, events and writers. **Scottish Literature Since 1707** by Marshall Walker (Longman pb 0582028922 £20.99) is an introduction to Scottish literature for students and general readers alike, that places it in its historical context. Taking the year of Scotland's union with England as its starting point, it provides a critical interpretation of Scottish literature's distinctive idioms and themes. In his study Walker finds an energetic culture rich in characters whose writing is often highly politicized. Particular attention is paid to the major input of women writers. In **Scottish Writers Talking** (ed. Isobel Murray Tuckwell Press pb 189841078X £9.99) Norman MacCaig, Jessie Kesson, William McIlvanney, David Toulmin and George Mackay Brown talk about their life and work in a series of in-depth interviews. In another book edited by Isobel Murray and Bob Tait, **Ten Modern Scottish Novels** (Mercat Press pb 0080284930 £4.99) ten Scottish novels from the past fifty years are closely examined. In these works Murray and Tait find not one Scotland but many. They conclude that despite vast differences between the books there are a significant number of recurring themes which are then further explored. **The Modern Scottish Novel: Narrative and the National Imagination** by Craig Cairns (EUP pb 0748608931 £14.95) is a challenging and controversial study of the Scottish novel which explains the intellectual and artistic background behind the success of contemporary writers such as Irvine Welsh and Iain Banks. **Discovering Scottish Writers** (eds. Reid & Osborne Scottish Library Association pb 1898218846 £7.95) is a good introduction for anyone with a general interest in Scottish writing. It covers the lives and literary achievements of eighty of Scotland's finest writers. The book is highly informative and accessible, outlining the cultural, historical and literary importance of each writer and carefully avoids being dry or stale. A broad introduction to the cultural life of the nation is provided by **Scotland: A Concise Cultural History** (ed. Scott Mainstream hb 1851585818 £20.00), a collection of essays by some of the leading figures in their fields, covering every topic from philosophy to football and its place in Scottish life. It is designed not only to celebrate the diversity of Scottish life and its contribution to world culture, be it in music or engineering, but also to examine how the modern nation responds to that legacy.

There are some interesting works which concentrate on particular themes and particular aspects of Scottish literature. **A History of Scottish Women's Writing** (eds. Gifford & McMillan EUP pb 0748609164 £9.95) is a comprehensive analysis of Scottish women's writing from the earliest texts available to the present day, with over forty new essays on this field of literature. Some contributors examine groups of writers such as dramatists and 19th century poets, and topics such as the effect on women writers of the Kailyard school. Other essays focus on individual writers, among them

Nan Shepherd, Muriel Spark and Liz Lochhead. While drawing attention to important women writers of the past, including some now unjustly neglected, this study also assesses the vibrant contemporary scene and the new developments to be found there. **The Ballad And The Folk** by David Buchan (Tuckwell Press pb 1898410674 £9.99) is a fascinating account of the ballad tradition. The book has two distinct strands. First it looks at the ballad as a form of oral literature, and, secondly, it places the ballad tradition in its social context, focusing on the North-East of Scotland. David Buchan writes about what has been described as 'the ballad enigma' in a straightforward and lucid fashion. The importance of folk traditions in Scottish literature is hard to over-estimate. Hamish Henderson is a key figure in the recent revival of Scottish folklore and **Alias MacAlias: Writings on Songs, Folk And Literature** (Polygon pb 0748660429 £7.99) is a personal collection of work on the subject. Henderson gives a superb introduction to the living folk culture in Scotland. There are introductory pieces on tinkers, Glencoe, folksong recordings and the Clearances as well as formal essays on leading figures. **Scottish Skalds And Sagamen: Old Norse Influence On Modern Scottish Literature** by Julian D'Arcy (Tuckwell Press pb 1898410259 £14.99) looks at another tradition. The book examines how the Viking invasions made a lasting impression on Scottish language, history and culture, and how this influenced the work of nine major Scottish authors including Hugh McDiarmid, Naomi Mitchison and George Mackay Brown. Sense of place is important to Scottish literature and two books by Moira Burgess look in particular at Glasgow. **Imagine A City: Glasgow In Fiction** (Argyll hb 1874640785 £12.99) aptly takes its title from a quote from *Lanark*. The book itself is a comprehensive account of how Glasgow has been seen in fiction over the last two centuries. From the earliest depictions of Glasgow by Scott and Smollett to the romanticised views portrayed in the Kailyard school of writing, and on to the violent razor gang Glasgow of *No Mean City*, the book is more than literary criticism, it is a commentary on how writers have viewed the soul of this great city. **Reading Glasgow** (Book Trust Scotland pb 1901077004 £6.95) is a guide book that explores Glasgow's literary heritage. This small volume is packed with information on authors and includes many illustrations along with easy-to-follow maps. It is perfect for tourist or resident alike.

Books on individual Scottish writers are plentiful. Robert Burns is, unsurprisingly, well-chronicled. **Robert Burns and the Sentimental Era** by Carol McGuirk (Tuckwell Press pb 1898410879 £9.99) reveals Burns as a sophisticated individual who helped transform his own folk traditions, in turn giving the Scottish landscape and society a strong personal image. **Love & Liberty** (ed. Kenneth Simpson Tuckwell Press pb 1898410895 £16.99) is a collection of essays arising from the International Bicentenary Burns Conference in 1996 and addresses the question of how a poor tenant farmer rose to become a world poet, celebrating his international appeal. **Robert Burns: A Man For All Seasons**, compiled by John Young (S.C.P. pb 1898218609 £14.95), is a study of Burns' use of natural history in his writing. **Scott's Interleaved Waverley Novels** (ed. Ian Gordon Brown Mercat Press hb 0080350828 £19.50) is an introduction to and commentary on Scott's novels in the edition published by Robert Cadell in 48 volumes between 1829 and 1833.

Edwin Muir was, among other things, one of the most outstanding critics of his day. **The Truth Of Imagination** (Mercat Press hb 008036392X £14.99) shows his remarkable range of interests. The collection concentrates on his reviews of some of the most important writers of his time, including Tolkien, Faulkner and Greene. **The Golden Harvester: The Vision Of Edwin Muir** by James Aitchison (Mercat Press hb 0080364004 £14.99) is a comprehensive study of Edwin Muir's work, drawing on his novels, poetry, letters and other sources to chart the development of his work. The author studies Muir's use of myth and argues that he ventures far into the limits of experience to create his unique artistic vision. **Hugh MacDiarmid: Man And Poet** (ed. Gish EUP pb 0748604057 £14.95) is a critical assessment of one of Scotland's most important twentieth century poets, which draws together previously unpublished essays by prominent scholars, poets and friends to provide a new context for understanding MacDiarmid, his work and his position at the crux of modernism and post-modernism. MacDiarmid himself was a prolific writer of prose and criticism. In many respects his non-poetic works share the same interests and concerns as his poetry. His campaign to encourage a Scottish renaissance movement was high on his agenda. Linked to this were his efforts to revive the use of Scots. All of his work has a strong political aspect to it. During his life he was a member of the National Party of Scotland and the Communist Party: he was expelled from both - from the National Party for his communist leanings, and from the Communist Party for his nationalism. His non-poetic works strongly attack the stereotypical literature of the past and advocate the case for Scotland's nationhood to be achieved in part by a literary renaissance. As a whole these works are essential for a full understanding of MacDiarmid's achievements. Carcanet is to be congratulated for keeping in print the following titles :

Albyn: Shorter Books And Monographs
Carcanet hb 1857542339 £30.00
Contemporary Scottish Studies
Carcanet hb 1857541308 £25.00
Lucky Poet
Carcanet hb 1857540638 £18.95
The Raucle Tongue I: Collected Writings
Carcanet hb 1857542347 £25.00
The Raucle Tongue II:
Carcanet hb 1857542711 £35.00
Scottish Eccentrics
Carcanet hb 1857540131 £16.95

Music & Dance

Dance

There has been a recent resurgence in the popularity of ceilidhs, but not everyone is familiar with Scottish country dances apart from such favourites as 'The Dashing White Sergeant' and 'Strip the Willow', an ignorance which can severely cramp your style. There are several books available giving details of the various dances and their steps. *The Swinging Sporran* by **A. Campbell** and **R. Martine** (Penguin pb, 0140119957, £5.95) provides an excellent introduction to Scottish country dancing. Well-illustrated and with easy-to-follow instructions on all the major dances, it gives a good idea of just how much fun ceilidhs can be. Part of the Collins Pocket Reference Series, *Scottish Country Dancing* (HarperCollins pb, 000470987X, £5.95) is compiled by the **Royal Scottish Country Dance Society** and provides an excellent and easily portable guide to the subject. Of a similar size is Robbie Shepherd's *Let's Have A Ceilidh* (Canongate pb, 0862415136, £5.95) which again gives details of all the important dances and comes complete with musical arrangements. Finally, *Scottish Ceilidh Dancing* by **D. and M. Ewart** (Mainstream pb, 1851588450, £5.95) uses simple straightforward language to describe the sometimes intricate dance steps involved in country dancing. As for a history of the subject, **G.W. Lockhart's** *Highland Balls And Village Halls* (Luath Press pb, 094648712X, £6.95) is a classic study of Scottish country dancing: its history, famous figures and dances. The very different style of step-dancing has recently been rediscovered. *Traditional Step-Dancing In Scotland* by **J.F.** and **T.M. Flett** (S.C.P. pb, 1898218455, £12.99) is a heavily researched history of solo step-dancing, including the Highland Fling and sword dancing. Some of the dances are illustrated and fully explained. Non-traditional forms of dancing have also been popular in Scotland and *Oh, How We Danced!* by **Elizabeth Casciani** (Mercat Press pb, 1873644299, £9.99) reflects this, looking back at the story of ballroom dancing in Scotland with many amusing anecdotes.

Music

Scottish music is built around the song and the ballad and **The Greig-Duncan Folk Song Collection**, published by Mercat Press in seven hardback volumes, each costing £35, is the major collection of Scottish folk songs that aims to include all the ballads and folksongs of Scotland. The seven volumes, edited by Shuldham Shaw and E.B.Lyle, are :-

Vol.1 Nautical, Military & Historical Songs
0080257593 £35.00
Vol.2 Narrative Songs
0080284833 £35.00
Vol.3 Songs of the Countryside, of Home and Social Life
0080303919 £35.00
Vol.4 Songs of Courtship, Night Visiting Songs, Songs about Particular People
0080365736 £35.00
Vol.5 Songs of Love and Marriage. Part 1
1873644418 £35.00
Vol.6 Songs of Love and Marriage. Part 2
1873644426 £35.00
Vol.7 Songs of Love and Marriage. Part 3
1873644566 £35.00

Scotland's Music: A History of the Traditional and Classical Music of Scotland from Early Times to The Present Day, by John Purser (Mainstream hb 1851584269 £25.00) covers a wide range of times and musical traditions and can easily be described as one of the pre-eminent literary works on Scottish music. Ailie Munro's **The Democratic Muse: Folk Music Revival In Scotland** (S.C.P. pb 1898218102 £15.95) examines the ongoing attempts to rediscover the traditional folk music of Scotland and the music's recent revival, whether it be in festivals, ceilidhs, folk clubs, story-tellings or travelling people's culture. It looks to the Scottish emigrant populations of North America and sees how their native music survived. An Appendix contains four traditional songs with differing versions used by individual lead singers, along with their comments. The book is a revised and updated version of *The Folk Music Revival In Scotland* (1984) and provides an invaluable guide for students and enthusiasts of the subject. **Scottish Fiddle Music of the 18th Century** by David Johnson (Mercat Press pb 1873644663 £5.95) is a study of a hundred years of Scots fiddle music that includes edited texts of ninety pieces of music. A thorough history of the bagpipe from its origins right through to the present day is provided by Roderick Cannon's **The Highland Bagpipe and its Music** (John Donald pb 0859764168 £15.00). **Musick Fyne** by James D. Ross (Mercat Press hb 1873644175 £16.99) is an acclaimed study of music and culture in Renaissance Scotland that was short-listed for the 1994 Saltire Award. **Songs Of Scotland**, by Wilma Paterson & Alasdair Gray (Mainstream hb 1851587225 £25.00) is a superb modern collection of a hundred traditional Scottish songs complete with music, their history and illustrated by a series of Alasdair Gray's distinctive images. **Seventy Scottish Songs** (Dover pb 0486270297 £9.55) is a collection of famous and not so famous Scottish songs through the ages with full musical scores and words, selected and arranged by Helen Hopekirk. **A Little Scottish Songbook** (Appletree Press hb 0862815592 £4.99) provides the words and music to twenty six classic songs, illustrated by Clare Hewitt. **The Nineties Collection: New Scottish Tunes In The Traditional Style** (Canongate pb 0862415993 £12.99) is a collection of some of the best new traditional music selected by well-known fiddler and composer Ian Hardie. Finally John Ord's **Bothy Songs and Ballads of Aberdeen, Banff, and Moray, Angus and the Mearns** (John Donald pb 085976303X £11.95) is a reprint of the original 1930 book which will appeal to anyone interested in folk song and folk culture, as it is a collection of traditional songs as sung in the farm bothies of the North-East.

Natural History

ATKINSON, ROBERT
Island Going
Birlinn pb 1874744319 £9.99

In 1935 Robert Atkinson and John Ainslie set out on an ornithological search for the rare 'Leach's fork-tailed petrel', a search that was to last twelve years and take them round some of the most remote islands of Scotland. In this travelogue Atkinson details his ornithological adventures and much more: he describes the wildlife, the living conditions of the islanders, their traditions and histories. An all-encompassing vision of the Hebrides that was to inspire many later accounts.

AIRD, W.J. WITH MACDONALD P.
The Scenery Of Scotland: The Structure Beneath 3rd ed.
N.M.S. pb 0948636246 £3.99

A fine introduction to the geology of Scotland, which looks at the ways in which the landscape has been formed, with excellent aerial photographs and diagrams of the processes involved.

BAXTER, COLIN & GOODIER, RAWDON
The Cairngorms: The Nature of the Land
Colin Baxter pb 1900455722 £8.00

The Cairngorms are one of the few really wild areas left in Britain and the subject of many unresolved issues concerned with conservation, land use and development. This book delves deep into the interior of this region. The highly descriptive text by conservationist, mountaineer and biologist Rawdon Goodier is accompanied by Colin Baxter's distinctive photographs.

BAXTER, COLIN & THOMPSON, DES
Scotland: Land Of Mountains
Colin Baxter pb 1900455749 £15.00

This is a journey through the principal mountain regions of Scotland accompanied by photographs that capture the peaks' physical impressiveness. It provides a factual account of the history, ecology and land usage, stressing the need for major conservation efforts.

BOYD, J.M. & I.L.

The Hebrides: A Habitable Land
Birlinn pb 1874744556 £8.99
The Hebrides: A Natural Tapestry
Birlinn pb 1874744564 £9.99
The Hebrides: A Mosaic Of Islands
Birlinn pb 1874744572 £8.99

A trilogy that spans the human and natural history of the
Hebrides written by world renowned experts on wildlife and
nature. The books cover the geology, climate, plant and animal
habitats and communities and the nature reserves on Rum and
St Kilda. They combine accessibility with authoritative and
wide-ranging information on Scotland's natural history.

CAMPBELL, LAURIE & DENNIS, ROY

Golden Eagles
Colin Baxter pb 0948661404 £16.00

A collaborative work between a photographer and a writer
who between them have devoted many years to tracking and
observing these magnificent birds. This book is a unique
record of one of the world's most inspirational creatures.

CRAMB, AUSLAN

Fragile Land: The State of the Scottish Environment
Polygon pb 0748662286 £9.99

The importance of environmental issues in Scotland has never
been higher. Auslan Cramb, a leading environmental
spokesperson, overviews the current situation and argues that
the only hope for the future is a dramatic change in the way
society views green issues.

CRUMLEY, JIM

The Company of Swans
Harvill pb 1860464262 £5.95

This beautifully produced
book follows the struggles of
a pair of mute swans on a
remote area of a loch. It is
heavily invested with Jim
Crumley's personal
relationship with one swan
in particular and is hauntingly
illustrated with engravings by
Harry Brockway.

DUTTON, G.F.

Some Branch Against The Sky: The Practice and Principles of Marginal Gardening
David & Charles hb
07153064051 £6.99

The story of a unique nine acre garden in the Highlands which is part garden, part wilderness. The book examines the ways in which a gardener can tread the boundaries between cultivation and wilderness, and work with nature and climate rather than against them.

HUNTER, JAMES

On The Other Side of Sorrow: Nature and People in the Scottish Highlands
Mainstream hb 1851587659
£17.50

James Hunter takes issue with environmentalists and others who argue that the Highlands and Islands should be conserved and protected. He argues instead for a single strategy for cultural, social and ecological renewal, with a restoration of woodlands and people to the glens.

JILL, DUCHESS OF HAMILTON

Scottish Plants For Scottish Gardens
HMSO pb 0114958033 £12.95

A book that aims to open Scottish gardeners' eyes to the full range of native plants and their gardening possibilities. It includes a detailed checklist of native Scottish flora.

MACNALLY, LEA

Highland Year
Birlinn pb 1874744777 £9.99

This acclaimed account of the natural world of the Highlands covers many animals but particular attention is given to the 'monarch of the glen', the red deer. The author is a naturalist and former deer-stalker, and this edition of the book is enhanced by his own photographs.

MAGNUSSON, MAGNUS

Rum: Nature's Island
Luath Press pb 0946487324
£7.95

This history of Rum charts the island's story from the earliest times right up to its present day status as a National Nature Reserve.

MAGNUSSON, MAGNUS & WHITE, GRAHAM (Eds)

The Nature of Scotland: Landscape Wildlife and People
Canongate pb 0862416744
£14.99

A comprehensive and heavily illustrated single volume overview of Scotland's nature. Each chapter is written by an acknowledged expert and asks deep and searching questions about Scotland's environment and the threats to its survival.

MAXWELL, GAVIN (1914-1969)

Gavin Maxwell was an aristocrat who had many interests and talents. As well as being a writer he was an instructor for the SOE in World War II (despite being handicapped), a shark fisher, explorer and poet. At the time, his passion for wildlife and the environment was regarded as so extreme that he was considered eccentric. His first book, *Harpoon At A Venture* (1952), is a lively account of his doomed attempt to introduce shark fishing to Skye. This was followed by *A Reed Shaken By The Wind* (1957), an account of his travels among the Marsh Arabs of Southern Iraq. He is best remembered for *Ring Of Bright Water* (1960), the poignant tale of his relationship with an otter and the surrounding environment. A sequel, *The Rock Remains,* was released in 1963. A sometimes difficult man in his private life, he was a consummate artist of description, with an ability to set the feeling and atmosphere of a place with great skill.

Harpoon at a Venture
House Of Lochar pb 1899863281 £9.99
A Reed Shaken By The Wind
Eland pb 0907871372 £8.99
Ring of Bright Water
Penguin pb 0140039236 £6.99

SCOTT, MICHAEL
Collins Guide: Scottish Wild Flowers
HarperCollins pb 0002199823 £7.99

A copiously illustrated reference book with all the information you will need to recognise Scotland's countless wild flowers.

THOM, VALERIE
Collins Guide: Scottish Birds
HarperCollins pb 0002199831 £7.99

A valuable guide with colour illustrations and photographs which gives detailed information about the birds, their habitats and where they can be found - an ideal book for bird identification.

YOUNG, FAY & BURBIDGE, BRINSLEY
The Book of the Scottish Garden
Canongate pb 0862416698 £9.99

An extensive record of Scotland's gardens that uses the photographic collection compiled by Brinsley Burbidge for the Royal Botanic Gardens of Edinburgh, with text by Fay Young.

Photography

General Photography

Scotland embraced the new art of photography early in its history, thus many major historical photographers and photographs are Scottish. **Light From The Dark Room: A Celebration Of Scottish Photography** (N.G.S. pb 0903598582 £12.95) draws on images from the Scottish National Photographic Collection and several large Canadian collections. It displays the rich diversity of these photographs starting from the ground-breaking work of Hill and Adamson in the 1840s and moving right up to the present day to produce a fascinating and revealing guide to Scottish photography. **Scotland Of One Hundred Years Ago** (ed. Lamont-Brown, Sutton hb 0750914211 £18.99) is an interesting photographic history of Scotland during Queen Victoria's reign that portrays a country undergoing dramatic transformations in every walk of life. **Dear Happy Ghosts: Scenes From The Outram Picture Archive 1898-1990** (ed. William, Mainstream hb 1851583718 £14.95) is a collection of newspaper photographs of events, great and small. They are of particular fascination due to the noticeable changes in ordinary people's social and financial conditions and provide a glimpse into lives gone by. Contemporary Scottish photography is well represented in **New Scottish Photography** by Stevenson & Brittain (N.G.S. pb 0903598094 £12.95). The new wave of Scottish photographic artists have been using photography in many different ways, from traditional black & white to documentary imagery, installation and scuptural works which push back the boudaries of art. This book celebrates the rich variety of photographic works currently being produced in Scotland, setting them in context with the recent cultural renaissance. Stylishly laid out and heavily illustrated, the book also has an informative and pertinent text.

Individual Photographers

Thomas Begbie created a unique photographic record of the capital city in the 1850s. **Thomas Begbie's Edinburgh** (John Donald hb 0859763374 £32.00) gives the viewer a superb insight into mid-Victorian Edinburgh, from the crumbling closes and slums of the Old Town to the opulent splendour of the New. These historically priceless images are beautifully reproduced in a splendid book. Glasgow-born artist Calum Colvin first entered the art world in 1985. His photographs build on the memories, traces and debris of others, and he often defies the normal system of perspective by placing characters onto an already established set or scene. His work seen in **Calum Colvin: The Seven Deadly Sins And Four Other Things** (Portfolio pb 0952060817 £9.95) frequently represents the dilemmas of Scottish identity and exile. Over the last 30 years the internationally acclaimed artist and poet Ian Hamilton Finlay has created Little Sparta, a contemporary neo-classical garden. Robin Gillanders has been photographing there over the past four years. **Little Sparta: A Portrait Of A Garden** (N.G.S. 040359885X £35.00 hb) is an artistic response to Finlay's poetic garden. David Octavius Hill and Robert Adamson were pioneers of the new art of photography. When they took a series of photographs of the fishermen and women of the Firth of Forth at work and at rest, they almost single-handedly invented the art of social documentary. Some of their photographs are rightly regarded as masterpieces. **Hill & Adamson's The Fishermen and Women of the Firth of Forth** (N.G.S. pb 0903598159 £15.95) prints in sepia the sixty plates of the series (some of which have lain neglected as negatives for over 150 years) and reveals the beauty and character of this ground-breaking work. Also included in the book is a full introduction putting Hill and Adamson and their works in their historical context. **A Poem Of Remote Lives: Images Of Eriskay 1934**, by Michael W. Russell (Neil Wilson hb 1897784465 £20.00) is a photographic celebration of Eriskay and the story of the German photographer, Werner Kissling, who took the pictures. Kissling was also, in 1934, the first man to make a Gaelic film. His unique, evocative pictures show a lifestyle which seems to belong to the distant past but was in fact only sixty years ago. In his book Russell attempts to discover the full story about this enigmatic photographer. Possibly Scotland's best known photographer of the last fifty years was Oscar Marzaroli. **Glasgow's People 1956-1988** (Mainstream hb 1851585923 £14.99) is a collection of his influential work and features photographs of people living and working in Glasgow. **Shades of Scotland 1956-1988** (Mainstream hb 1851582134 £14.95) is a series of photographs taken by Marzaroli over the course of thirty years, covering the full spectrum of Scottish life and landscape, with words by James Grassie. **Shades of Grey** (Mainstream hb 1851580476 £14.99) also by Marzaroli has text by William McIlvanney. Richard Ovendon's **John Thomson, Photographer**

(N.L.S. hb 0114958835 £25.00) is a book which uncovers the work of Edinburgh born John Thomson, one of the 19th century's most influential photographers. He was instrumental in establishing photo-journalism and the use of photographs in illustrating books.

Landscape Photography

Scotland's landscape is renowned for its wide variety, breathtaking natural beauty and the many moods it displays over the seasons. The best known of contemporary landscape photographers is Colin Baxter. **Scotland** (Colin Baxter pb 1900455773 £9.00, also available in French, German, Italian and Japanese) is a collection of photographs featuring some of Colin Baxter's best work and shows his ability to capture the many aspects of the Scottish scenery. Jason Hawkes' excellent aerial photographs of Scotland in **Scotland From The Air** (Weidenfeld 0297834738 £19.99) studiously avoid cliches and offer instead a unique perspective of the Scottish landscape. Each image is skilfully expanded on by Giles Gordon's text. **Orkney: Pictures & Poems** (Colin Baxter pb 1900455714 £16.00) consists of forty eight George Mackay Brown poems inspired by the island, specially written to accompany evocative photographs of its landscape by Gunnie Moberg. The timeless grandeur of the Highlands is celebrated in **Highland Wilderness** (Constable hb 0094715602 £25.00), a beautifully realised book containing eighty magnificent full colour photographs by Colin Prior. The accompanying text, by Magnus Linklater, is very topical in its fiercely conservationist plea to preserve the Highland wilderness.

Other books of landscape photography can be found listed in the Travel section.

Georg and Johanna Kissling

Poetry

ANNAND, J.K.

Selected Poems 1925-1990
Mercat Press pb 1873644035
£7.99

This selection gathers works from all the stages of J.K. Annand's sixty year writing career, a wide diversity of works that range in tone and location from his wartime experiences at sea and bawdy verses of *Carmina Burana*, to the peace of the Border hills, children's poetry and translations of Bavarian folksongs.

BARBOUR, JOHN (1320–1396)

Barbour is commonly regarded as the Father of Scottish poetry and history. Little is known about his early life. However, what is certain is that he was the Archdeacon of Aberdeen from 1357 till his death. His epic poem *The Bruce* was written in the 1370s. It is a long, romanticised work about the life and actions of Robert The Bruce, full of chivalric themes which sees Bruce as the blueprint for the ideal monarch, but which none the less sticks closely to historical fact. The language of Barbour's time can be somewhat difficult for the modern reader, yet Barbour's work contains much that is well worth reading, including vivid descriptions of historical events. The Mercat Press edition is a modern English prose translation of this seminal work.

The Bruce (Ed. A.A.M. Duncan)
Canongate pb 0862416817 £8.99
The Bruce Translated by G. Eyre-Todd
Mercat Press pb 1873644582 £11.99

BATEMAN, MEG

Meg Bateman's work is both formal and emotional at the same time. She writes in Gaelic, her second language which she studied at university, partly due to the fact that she finds the culture so different from that of her upbringing and can express difficult events and emotions in some degree of secrecy, but mostly because her Gaelic studies had given her an idea of the kind of verse she herself wanted to write. The language is stripped down to the bare essentials, creating a delicate and often unsettling feeling. The Polygon book is a bilingual edition of Meg Bateman's first collection of poetry. Her work is precise and disciplined yet full of feeling. In these poems she communicates some of the most intimate aspects of her life: the birth of her child, family life, love and loss, and the fragility of human relationships.

Lightness & Other Poems: Aotromachd agus dain elie
Polygon pb 0748662278 £6.95

BLIND HARRY (c.1440–c.1492)

Although little is documented about this poet who wrote the epic *Wallace*, there are accounts of payments made to him by James IV between 1490 and 1492, and from his writing it looks likely that he lived in the lowlands. He was probably not blind from birth, as his descriptive work is vivid, particularly in relating battle scenes. The *Wallace* was written in 12 books and portrays a heroic figure of great integrity who struggled against the English. Although Wallace is presented as a larger-than-life character and his heroics much exaggerated, the poem still throws light on this leader, constitutes a potent declaration of national identity and is one of the most influential books ever published in Scotland. Hamilton's edition was first published in 1722, and this 1998 print is the first since 1859. It is well presented, with an introduction, annotations and illustrations.

Blind Harry's Wallace: William Hamilton of Gilbertfield
Introduced by E. King
Luath Press pb 0946487332 £7.50

BROWN, GEORGE MACKAY

> "Decay of language is always the symptom of a more serious sickness."
>
> George Mackay Brown

George Mackay Brown has been publishing verse since the fifties, all of it deeply influenced by the landscape, ways of life and folklore of his native Orkney. *Following a Lark* is a typical, recent collection of poems, many of which celebrate ancient northern ceremonies. They are rooted in his Orcadian life, strong in religious imagery and all containing a strong link to the wider world.

Following A Lark: Poems
John Murray pb 0719556201 £7.99
Selected Poems 1954-1992
John Murray pb 0719556244 £8.99
Water
North & South pb 1870314271 £3.95
The Wreck of the Archangel
John Murray pb 0719556155 £7.99

Bruce, George
Perspectives: Collected Poems 1970-1986
A.U.P. pb 0080350623 £6.99

Bruce's poetry is inspired by the rugged land- and seascapes of North East Scotland, and he was influenced by the work of Ezra Pound. Much of his work is concerned with the constancy of the land and the enduring qualities of its inhabitants. The ordered advance of history and the changeless nature of childhood are two of his other main themes, and these interests are often linked together within a single work.

Buchan, John
Collected Poems
S.C.P. pb 1898218471 £12.95

A single volume that contains all of Buchan's poetic works, some published for the first time.

Buchan, Peter
Collected Poems and Short Stories
Gordon Wright pb 0903065770 £16.95

An interest in the North-East fishing communities is the main source of inspiration in Peter Buchan's writing. These collected works particularly display his ability in character study.

BURNS, ROBERT (1759–1796)

Robert Burnes (his original family name) was born in Alloway near Ayr. The son of a poor farmer, he nevertheless received a literary education. He wrote his first song in 1774. All of his early works were lyrics to folk tunes, a form he was to return to in later life. In 1780 he joined a Masonic lodge, and this was to have a major influence on his life and career. When his father died in 1784 he changed the spelling of his name. After fathering several illegitimate children and struggling to make a success of being a farmer, he decided to emigrate to Jamaica and published his first collection of poems to raise the fare. However, after receiving favourable reviews and modest financial success he changed his plans and published a much larger collection of poetry in 1787, the 'Kilmarnock edition' of *Poems Chiefly In The Scottish Dialect*. He used the proceeds to pay off his brother's debts and take up the lease of a farm in Nithsdale. He moved to Dumfries and took a job in the excise service in 1789, holding this post until his death in 1796. *The Merry Muses Of Caledonia* was a work posthumously published - a collection of bawdy and *risqué* verse celebrating lust and love, featuring work by Burns and others. Immediately after his death myths of his womanising and drunkenness quickly grew. As well as writing around 650 poems and songs, he also wrote numerous letters on many subjects. His work, loved throughout the world, had a huge effect on the Romantic movement. His reputation as a poet was largely created by his early works. He is regarded as one of the world's finest poets, and over 2000 editions of Burns in fifty languages are available.

"Gie me ae spark o' Nature's fire,
That's a' the learning I desire;
Then, tho' I drudge thro' dub an' mire,
At pleugh or cart,
My Muse, tho hamely in attire,
May touch the heart."

Robert Burns, Epistle to J Lapraik

Burns Anthology (Collins Gem)
HarperCollins pb 0004705009
£3.99
Burns Encyclopaedia (Maurice Lindsay)
Hale pb 0709057199 £12.99
Burns Quotation Book
Hale hb 0709052871 £9.99
Burns Supper Companion (Hugh Douglas)
Alloway hb 0907526012 £5.95
A Choice of Burns's Poems And Songs (Introd. by Sydney Goodsir Smith)
Faber pb 0571068359 £7.99
Complete Letters
Alloway hb 0907526322 £29.50
Complete Works of Robert Burns (J.A. MacKay)
Alloway hb 0907526624 £24.95
The Jolly Beggars Or Love & Liberty: A Cantata
Luath Press hb 0946487022 £8.00
Poems and Songs 2nd ed.
OUP pb 0192811142 £11.99
Poems Chiefly In The Scottish Dialect
Famedarm pb 0905489071 £4.95
Poems In Scots and English
Everyman pb 0460877860 £2.99
Poetical Works
Chambers pb 0550210202 £7.99
Robert Burns (Ed. Peter Porter)
Aurum Press hb 1854102257 £5.95
Robert Burns Deluxe Boxed
Alloway hb 0907526683 29.50
Robert Burns For Beginners (Rennie McOwan)
St. Andrews Press pb 0715207156 £5.99
Selected Poems
Penguin pb 0140423826 £6.99

BURNSIDE, JOHN (b.1955)

Born in Dunfermline, John Burnside moved to England when he was only eleven. This experience of being uprooted from his native land and culture partially shaped the way he examines the world. His poems explore a variety of subjects: the world of nature, human emotions and thought, and spiritual matters - the soul, especially rebirth and renewal. He sees his poetry as an interweaving of all these themes and a response to the mysteries of the world. His 1992 collection *Feast Days* won the Geoffrey Faber Memorial Prize and he was shortlisted for the T.S. Eliot Prize for *The Myth of the Twin*.

The Myth of the Twin
Cape pb 022403894X £7.00
Normal Skin
Cape pb 0224042866 £7.00
Swimming In The Flood
Cape pb 0224041983 £7.00

Two Poems by John Burnside

Husbandry

Why children make pulp of slugs
with a sprinkling of salt
or hang a nest of fledglings on a gate
with stolen pins
is why I sometimes turn towards the dark
and leave you guessing,
only to know the butter and nickel taste
of cruelty;
   to watch, and show no sign
of having seen.
    Not
wickedness, that sometimes celebrates
a tightness in the mind;
but what I comprehend
of fear and love:
cradled remoteness, nurtured by stalled desire;
willed deprivation;
the silence I'm learning by heart.

Solstice

The shortest day.
We ought to stop the clocks
for hours, in the mid-afternoon:
snow on the gardens that never entirely settles;
birds in the smokebush
never completing their song.
Or say, between one heartbeat and the next,
we step outside ourselves and walk away:
a lifetime of birds' eggs and squills
in the empty mirror;
larch cones and burrwood
revealing the nowhere of home.

Butlin, Ron
Histories of Desire
Bloodaxe pb 1852243392 £6.95

A versatile and inventive poet
who explores those things
that are beyond our reach
or deeply hidden within us.
The poems develop from an
imaginative response to the
demands of life, love and
desire often with wit or parody.

Clanchy, Kate
Slattern
Chatto pb 0701163321 £6.99

Kate Clanchy's first full-length
collection of poetry is both
elegant and controlled.
There are poems about both
men and boys, thoughts on
time and memory set in class-
rooms and sports fields, as
well as haunting love poems,
written with Clanchy's strong,
intelligent and witty style.

Cockburn, Ken
Souvenirs and Homelands
S.C.P. pb 1898218935 £4.95

These poems are based on observations made by the poet while
passing through places such as Sutherland, Wales and Haiti.
Of key importance to many of these works are family life and
our relationship with the past. They are written in rap, haiku
and other forms. Cockburn's poems give formative impressions
of the places he passes through, however briefly glimpsed.

Conn, Stewart
In the Blood
Bloodaxe pb 1852243295 £6.95
In the Kibble Palace
Bloodaxe pb 1852240334 £5.95
The Luncheon of the Boating Party
Bloodaxe pb 185224142X £5.95

In his collection *In the Blood* Stewart Conn returns to his roots in
Ayrshire and the Upper Clyde, taking in history, social change
and shifts in identity. He also explores other places and inborn
preoccupations, pushing at the boundaries but always keeping in
touch with his Scottishness. These well crafted poems are notable
among other things for their rhythm and Conn's feeling for the
delicacy of life. The centrepiece of *The Luncheon of the Boating
Party* is a sequence of poems inspired by the famous Renoir
painting. Other poems are also set in southern France, Scotland
and further afield. They bear Conn's hallmark quality of skilful
evocation of character and place.

Cook, Margaret Fulton
Good Girls Don't Cry
Chapman pb 0906772753 £5.95

Margaret Fulton Cook's poetry compassionately and
courageously deals with fear, abuse and violence in graphic
detail. She has described her driving force as 'giving voice
to those who scream in silence.'

Craig, David
The Grasshopper's Burden
Arc pb 0946407681 £5.95

Born and educated in
Aberdeen, David Craig has
lived for many years in
Cumbria. This collection is
Craig's reaction to the slow
destruction of life on the
planet. The poems mix
environmental issues with a
love of nature, both relayed
in an unsentimental way.
Craig shows nature's
vulnerability to mechanisation
and civilisation and asks his
readers to share in his
contemplation of the natural
world's richness which he
sees as ominously threatened.

CRAWFORD, ROBERT

Much of Robert Crawford's earlier poetry relies on what he
terms 'Scottish resources' for its inspiration. His work is often
written in humorous language with the juxtaposition of
seemingly incongruous images. His first collections are
engaging, positive celebrations of Scotland and all things
Scottish, although he has never shied away from being critical.
He is a strong advocate of the idea that a small country need
not be insular. His more recent work has moved away from
these themes. *Masculinity* is a more personal work, looking for
a feasible charting of the male role in today's society and
examining his own experiences during childhood and as a
man, husband and father. Through his poetry and critical
work he has become a significant figure in the recent Scottish
literary resurgence.
Masculinity
Cape pb 0224043714 £7.00
Scottish Assembly
Chatto pb 0701135956 £5.99
Sharawaggi: Poems In Scots (with W.N.Herbert)
Polygon pb 0748660666 £6.95
Talkies
Chatto pb 0701139285 £5.99

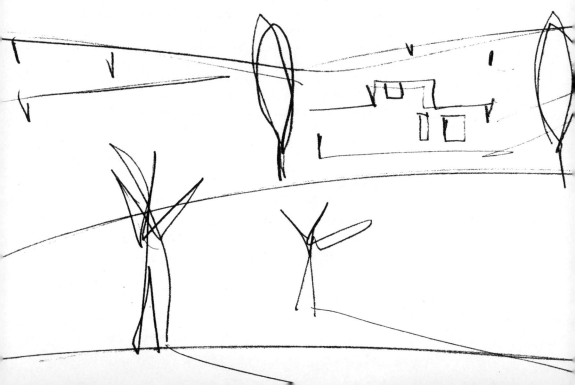

Crockatt, Ian
Flood Alert
Chapman pb 0906772796 £5.95

Ian Crockatt's varied poetic landscape has for the last two decades ranged over the wide domain of human concerns and emotions. His work is known for its emotional compactness and intensity.

CUTLER, IVOR

Ivor Cutler is a poet, singer and humorist whose unique brand of absurd poetry has gained him a huge cult following. His work often takes the form of surreal monologues recounting a mixture of reality and fantasy from his childhood, for example 'Life In A Scotch Sitting Room', which is filled with bizarre and humorous ideas: a grandmother recreates an image of the sea by pouring treacle from jug to jug, with children adding their contributions to the illusion. He has a keen sense of the ridiculous and there is depth behind the apparent triviality. All the books are illustrated by Cutler himself with the exception of *A Stuggy Pren*, which includes photographs by Katrina Lithgow of the poet at home. The latest work from this gifted eccentric, *Flat Man*, is published concurrently with a CD of the same name and shows that the man who played Buster Blood-vessel in *The Magical Mystery Tour* is still on top form.

Flat Man
Arc pb 1900072173 £4.00
Is That Your Flap, Jack?
Arc pb 0946407762 £4.00
Large Et Puffy
Arc pb 0902771701 £4.00
Nice Wee Present From Scotland
Arc pb 0902771736 £4.00
Private Habits
Arc pb 0902771892 £4.00
A Stuggy Pren
Arc pb 0946407940 £6.95
Wet Handle
Arc pb 1900072068 £4.00

DUFFY, CAROL ANNE

Born in Glasgow, Carol Anne Duffy's early years were spent in the Gorbals and Nitshill. In the early 1960s her family moved to Stafford and she spent many of her formative years feeling like an outsider and adapting in an attempt to fit in. The psychological needs of the individual are often examined in her work, which is frequently in the form of a powerful monologue and carefully balances elements of romance, social realism and acute psychological perception. She has described some of her concerns as identity, language and the effects of time on our lives. She won both the Whitbread and Forward prizes for *Mean Time* and has also written several plays.

Mean Time
Anvil Press pb 0856462470 £6.95
Selected Poems
Penguin pb 0140587357 £5.99
Selling Manhattan
Anvil Press pb 0856462950 £7.95
Standing Female Nude
Anvil Press pb 0856461504 £6.95

DUNBAR, WILLIAM
(c.1460–c.1520)

William Dunbar, a poet at the court of James IV, was perhaps the most important literary figure in Scotland at the end of the fifteenth century. His voice characterises that time and culture in distinctive fashion and the whole variety of themes, moods and styles he uses in his poems still speak to a modern audience of his world its life, loves and concerns. (See also under **Robert Henryson** for joint collection).

The Poems of William Dunbar
Mercat Press pb 0901824941 £4.99
Selected Poems
Longman pb 0582061873 £20.00

DUNN, DOUGLAS
(b.1942)

Born in Inchinnan, Renfrewshire, Dunn trained as a librarian and for a while worked in Hull University library. His early poetry shows an affinity with that of Philip Larkin and demonstrates an understanding of modern urban life, while also reflecting touches of contemporary American writing from his year in Ohio. Since the 1980s his work has developed more intimate as well as political themes, particularly a preoccupation with Scottish concerns. A winner of numerous literary prizes, he gained especial praise for *Elegies*, a collection of poems written after the death of his wife in 1981. In *Elegies* he draws on his artistic talent and harnesses it to poignantly and eloquently express his deep-felt grief. He has also published short stories and a translation of verse by Racine. He is known as a skilful worker who carefully uses internal rhymes and alliteration to create delicate effects.

Andromache
Faber pb 0571142494 £5.99
Dante's Drum Kit
Faber pb 0571170552 £6.99
Elegies
Faber pb 0571134696 £7.99
Northlight
Faber pb 0571152295 £4.99
Selected Poems, 1964-83
Faber pb 0571146201 £9.99

DUTTON, G.F.

G.F. Dutton is a writer and scientist who has written on various different subjects. The poetry in *The Concrete Garden*, his third collection, is clear, hard and striking and delights in the huge landscape of Scotland, whether it be the ocean or the greyness of high-rise blocks. He moves between feelings and lively perceptions of the landscape with cool, clear ease. All of his poetry collections have been critically acclaimed.

The Concrete Garden
Bloodaxe pb 1852241411 £5.95
Squaring the Waves
Bloodaxe pb 1852240075 £4.95

Fell, Alison
Dreams, Like Heretics
Serpent's Tail pb 185242561X £8.99

The poems in this collection are full of loss and yearning, relayed with both elegance and wit. Alison Fell moulds her images into metaphors of regeneration and longing. The sequence 'In Memoriam D.C.' movingly reveals memories of a now dead lover and the struggle to cope with grief.

Ferguson, Gillian
Air For Sleeping Fish
Bloodaxe pb 185224416X £6.95

Gillian Ferguson is a city dweller whose artistic imagery is drawn from her intense but fragmented contact with the world of nature. She makes symbolic use of flowers, imbuing them with personal meaning. This contact with the natural world is the inspiration of her powerful love poems, as well as those that draw on important scraps of memory or find mythical elements in everyday life.

Finlay, Ian Hamilton
The Dancers Inherit The Party and The Glasgow Beasts
Polygon pb 0748662073 £6.95

A complete collection of Ian Hamilton Finlay's early poetry in traditional verse form.

GARIOCH, ROBERT (1909–1981)

Robert Garioch was an intelligent and craftsmanlike poet who worked mainly in Scots. Some of his best known poems concern the city of his birth, Edinburgh. He was also noted for criticising double standards in public life, while taking care to defend the underdog. After his death, his *Complete Poetical Works* were published. *A Garioch Miscellany* is a complementary work, which for the most part contains his own letters and reviews. However it also includes reminiscences by Sorley Maclean (with whom Garioch shared his first published collection), Derek Bowman and Edwin Morgan. As an extra bonus the book contains a reprint of Garioch's play, *The Masque of Edinburgh*, set, unsurprisingly, in that city.

Complete Poetical Works
Macdonald hb 0904265935 £5.99
A Garioch Miscellany
Lines Review Editions pb 0863340571 £7.95

Garry, Flora
Collected Poems
Gordon Wright pb 0903065827 £7.95

Flora Garry started writing poetry in her native *braid* Buchan dialect, much of it inspired by her family and her upbringing. This is a complete collection of her works in both Scots and English, some of it previously unpublished, and including two prose pieces.

Gorman, Rody
Fax and Other Poems
Polygon pb 0748662162 £6.95

A collection of Rody Gorman's poems in Gaelic and English, characterised by their emotional power and sharp wit. Their subjects include everyday objects such as fax machines or walking boots.

GRAHAM, W.S.
(1918–1986)

Born in Greenock, Graham lived most of his adult life in Cornwall. His poetry is one of deep emotional resonance and staying power. His work is marked by his technical skill, constant refinement and deepening level of insight. His *Selected Poems* ranges across his entire career and includes the previously unpublished 'As Brilliance Fell'.
Aimed At Nobody
Faber pb 0571167454 £5.99
Collected Poems
Faber hb 0571114164 £25.00
Selected Poems
Faber pb 0571176593 £9.99

Gray, Alasdair
Old Negatives
Cape pb 0224026569 £5.95

Old Negatives shares some of the same subject matters (namely love, faith and language) as Gray's fictional work. The verses are stylishly and aptly complemented by his own illustrations.

Green, Stanley Roger
Waiting for the Mechanic
S.C.P. pb 1898218943 £4.95

Green's poems are shrewd philosophical comments based on careful observations of the natural world. His work is rich in evocation and ironic humour.

Greig, Andrew
The Order of the Day
Bloodaxe pb 1852241020 £5.95
Western Swing
Bloodaxe pb 185224268X £7.95

Western Swing is in feel a sequel to Greig's novel *Electric Brae* and his earlier poem 'Men On Ice'. It is an epic poem in which the narrator is driving across Rannoch Moor in search of Brock, Ken and Stella and a lost healing blade. His only company is in the form of a mysterious but jovial figure - the Heretical Buddha. The narrative takes us to various locations, from Glencoe to Katmandu, with the final stages taking place on a pier in Fife. In his works Greig likes to deal with high risk situations and the feelings they arouse. (See also under **Kathleen Jamie** for joint collection).

Hay, George Campbell
The Collected Poems and Songs of George Campbell Hay
EUP hb 0748610634 £95.00

The first complete edition of the works of George Campbell Hay who is one of the major figures in 20th century Gaelic poetry, also respected for his work in Scots and English.

Henderson, Hamish
Elegies for the Dead in Cyrenaica
Polygon pb 0904919145 £6.95

Henderson's collection of verse is concerned with the ordeals of the regular soldier and the pointlessness of war. It is a response to his experiences as an intelligence officer during World War II in North Africa.

HENRYSON, ROBERT (c.1420–1490)

Although connected to the group of poets known as the 'Scottish Chaucerians', this term only sums up part of Henryson's influences and poetry. Henryson was undoubtedly influenced by Chaucer, but he was by no means a mere imitator - a more accurate description of him is 'Makar' (a 'maker' or 'poet'). He was a well educated individual with knowledge of the latest intellectual thoughts and achievements of his time. From this solid grounding he wrote work in many different voices, from ballad tales to classical fables, using a wide range of imagery and subjects.

Poems And Fables
Mercat Press pb 0901824534 £5.99
Testament of Cresseid
Penguin pb 0140445072 £5.99

Henryson, Robert & Dunbar, William
Selected Poems
Penguin pb 014042248X £8.99

HERBERT, W.N.

Born in Dundee, it was during his stay as a student in Oxford that W.N. Herbert perceived the view of Scotland as 'not quite a country, possessing a language which is not really a language'. For him to use exclusively Scots or English was, he felt, in a sense to deny some feature of Scottish experience, so he uses both. In this way he can critically examine Scotland's present standing. *Cabaret McGonagall* is a collection which demonstrates Herbert's versatility. It is rich and challenging, including poems and ballads on, amongst others, a suicidal Pict, a mad Edinburgh surgeon and Morayshire's unsavoury Third Corbie. These vigorous poems adopt various voices and build into a richly satisfying piece of work. *The Testament of the Reverend Thomas Dick* is a poetic journey through time and space in which Herbert uses the visions of a 19th century Dundonian astronomer for inspiration, visions of a fantastic cosmos of angels and flying saucers. The poems are both lively and experimental, Herbert using the collision of myth and history, fact and fantasy, religion and science to great effect in poems that are witty, accessible and have a clear narrative.

Cabaret McGonagall
Bloodaxe pb 1852243538 £7.95
Dundee Doldrums: An Exorcism
Galliard pb 1872859089 £6.95
Forked Tongue
Bloodaxe pb 1852242671 £7.95
The Testament of the Reverend Thomas Dick
Arc pb 0946407924 £7.95

HOGG, JAMES (1770–1835)

Hogg's poetry is steeped in the Border Ballads tradition of his background. He was well versed in faery lore and legends as well as Bible stories from the Old Testament. He frequently drew on this background in his poems, as well as using standard ballad devices such as implicit belief in the supernatural, dreams and apparitions. He was also a renowned master of folk song writing, his best work initially being written for his own pleasure rather than a wider audience.
Selected Poems and Songs
S.A.P. hb 0707304717 £7.50

Hutchison, Alexander
Moon Calf
Galliard pb 1872859011 £9.95

Alexander Hutchison creates in his works his own original and occasionally provocative perspective. To do this he uses a wide tonal range, coupled with teasing wit and mystery. His work first began to appear in the early 70s, and its ingenuity, particularly evident in poems such as 'Mr. Scales Walks His Dog', almost demands the reader's delight.

JAMIE, KATHLEEN

A Flame In Your Heart
(with Andrew Greig)
Bloodaxe pb 1852240172 £5.95
The Queen of Sheba
Bloodaxe pb 1852242841 £6.95
The Way We Live
Bloodaxe pb 1852240342 £4.95

Jamie is a widely-travelled poet and writer who uses her travelling experiences to inform her work. Her poems are the places where she makes 'exchanges with the world'. She is reluctant to be categorised as a 'Scottish' or 'female' poet. Figures such as queens, princes and wandering monks often feature in her work, figures she views as forms of energy or aspects of the self. For her, poetry is another form of exploration. *The Queen of Sheba* is a highly acclaimed collection of work that was shortlisted for numerous awards and won several, including a Somerset Maugham Award. The poems are about Scotland and beyond, looking at life with a critical eye. In them Kathleen Jamie explores new combinations of culture and language. The subjects are various: the land, national identity, gender, sex and politics. The poems are dynamic and fearlessly self-aware, with sometimes a darker tone than in her earlier work.

KAY, JACKIE (b.1961)

Jackie Kay's first collection, *The Adoption Papers*, won an Eric Gregory Award, a Scottish Arts Council Award, a Forward Poetry Award and a Saltire Award and was also adapted for radio. It explores the emotional domain of adoption as seen from the perspective of three people: a black girl who is being adopted, her white adoptive mother and her natural mother. Her poetry is notable for its direct passionate quality, depth and sense of humour. It investigates many areas including blackness, Scottishness and gay sexuality. Her second collection explores the nature of love in various different relationships. The poems are set in the past as well as the present and include a wonderful sequence on Blues singer Bessie Smith.

The Adoption Papers
Bloodaxe pb 185224156X £5.95
Other Lovers
Bloodaxe pb 1852242531 £5.95

Kinloch, David
Paris Forfar
Polygon pb 0748661832 £6.95

David Kinloch's ambitious poetry has numerous voices, ranging from very serious to playful and bizarre. This collection displays many of them from the Reverend Robert Walker, immortalised in Raeburn's famous painting, once again skating on Duddingston Loch, to the collection's centrepiece, a sequence of poems which form an elegy for a gay man who has died of AIDS. The poems explore marginality, both sexual and linguistic, pointing to haunting links between the two.

KUPPNER, FRANK

Second Best Moments in Chinese History is a collection of 501 quatrains which has similar pre-occupations to Kuppner's first acclaimed collection (now out of print) *A Bad Day For The Sung Dynasty*, although its tone is different. Kuppner has a very distinctive voice, and the Zen-like quality of his work makes the reader feel as if they are entering his personal dream world. *Everything is Strange* contains two long poems, the title work and 'In a Persian Garden.'

Everything Is Strange
Carcanet pb 1857540719 £8.95
Second Best Moments In Chinese History
Carcanet pb 1857543106 £8.95

LEONARD, TOM

Born in Glasgow, Tom Leonard writes neat and skilfully composed poems in his native Glasgow dialect. He uses many local words and turns of phrase which can make his work seem at first daunting for the non-Glaswegian reader. However he circumvents this exclusivity by using natural speech rhythms which ensure that the meaning comes through when the poem is read aloud. Among his subject matters are the city of Glasgow and its people, and he writes about them in a strongly realistic and ironic voice, in which his sense of humour is always evident.

Intimate Voices
Galoping Dog pb 0099523612 £5.99

LINDSAY, MAURICE

Lindsay has been a major figure in Scottish literature, as poet, critic and journalist for more than fifty years. He is particularly known for his work on Burns, including the pioneering Burns Encyclopedia. *Collected Poems* show Lindsay's compassionate voice, seasoned with humour and satire. This major collection highlights his ability to find the wonder and mystery in everyday and mundane experiences of life. *Speaking Likenesses* is a retrospective collection of poetry by Lindsay that shows his poetic strengths of sharp detail and joyful lyricism over the last fifty years.

Collected Poems 1940-1990
Mercat Press pb 0080409105 £12.99
News of the World:
Last Poems
S.C.P. pb 1898218323 £4.95
On The Face Of It: Collected Poems Volume 2
Hale hb 0709051425 £9.99
Speaking Likenesses:
Postscript
S.C.P. pb 189821896X £5.95

LOCHHEAD, LIZ

Liz Lochhead is a poet who uses clear, uncomplicated language and the drama of domestic situations in her work. She is adept at creating striking scenes and characters that comment, among other subjects, on relationships, sexual politics and love in its many forms. Her work displays her ear for the subtleties of Scottish language and is often both lyrical and ironic, critically examining everyday life and the jaded world of consumerism. Her work in poetry and for the theatre shows a flawless sense of dramatic timing. Human relationships as seen from a woman's viewpoint are the key to Liz Lochhead's *Dreaming Frankenstein*, a complete collection of her poetry from 1967-1984. She uses her skills as a storyteller and careful observer to make immediate poems about pain, loss, acceptance and triumph.

Bagpipe Muzak
Penguin pb 0140120270 £6.99
Dreaming Frankenstein & Collected Poems
Polygon pb 0748661581 £6.95
True Confessions And New Cliches
Polygon pb 0748661565 £6.95

Lumsden, Roddy
Yeah Yeah Yeah
Bloodaxe pb 1852244038 £7.95

Roddy Lumsden's first collection is concerned with the twisting, ever changing nature of relationships. The poems cover a wide range of settings and situations, from revenge and phobias to weddings and bars, looking at lovers and losers. Although written in a formal style they are also lyrical, with a frenetic edge.

MACCAIG, NORMAN (1910–1996)

MacCaig is one of the most important Scottish poets of this century. Born in Edinburgh, he was educated at Edinburgh's Royal High School and studied Classics at Edinburgh University. He was a conscientious objector during World War II. From 1934 onwards he worked in education, first as a schoolteacher for forty years, then as a University lecturer. He was awarded the Queen's Medal for Poetry in 1986. His early collections, such as *Far Cry* and *The Inward Eye*, belong to the New Apocalypse movement which he had left by the time *Riding Lights* was published (1955). His subsequent poems display his love of the Scottish landscape, carefully evoked with descriptive prowess. Many of his works relate to everyday life while still having metaphysical concerns, and his deep love of nature and animals is frequently evident. His tone is often sly, wry and humorous. Much of his later work is marked by a strong and heartfelt desire to be open and honest. This candour is well demonstrated in the sequence of poems he wrote after the death of his friend A.R. Macleod ('Poems For Angus'). His work is hugely popular and widely acclaimed. *Selected Poems* is an excellent introduction to Norman MacCaig's work that moves effortlessly from poems about the city to love poems and those celebrating the beauty of the Highland landscape. This selection includes some of his best works from over the last forty years. *Three Scottish Poets* is a collection selected by Roderick Watson of some of the best work from three of Scotland's finest poets, now in its third reprint and including some previously unpublished work. *Norman McCaig : A Celebration* is an anthology specially written for Norman MacCaig's 85th birthday. It includes pieces by over ninety writers, including Ted Hughes, Seamus Heaney, Janice Galloway and A.L. Kennedy.

Collected Poems
Chatto & Windus pb
0701160101 £9.99
Norman MacCaig:
A Celebration
Chapman pb 0906772745 £8.00
Selected Poems. (Ed. D. Dunn)
Chatto & Windus pb
0701166398 £8.99
Three Scottish Poets: Norman MacCaig, Edwin Morgan & Liz Lochhead.
Canongate pb 0862414008 £4.99

Norman MacCaig

MACDIARMID, HUGH (1892–1978)

Born Christopher Murray Grieve in Langholm, Dumfriesshire, the son of a postman, he gained much of his radicalism from his father's political views. After his father's death in 1911 he turned to journalism, becoming the editor reporter for the *Montrose Review* in 1921. His first book, *Annals of the Five Senses*, appeared in 1923 and was dedicated to John Buchan who later provided the preface to MacDiarmid's first collection of poems, *Sangschaw*. *A Drunk Man Looks At The Thistle*, his greatest work, was released in 1926. MacDiarmid's poem is one of the recognised masterpieces of Scottish literature. 2685 lines long and written between 1925 and 1926, the poem revolves around a drunk man lying in front of a giant thistle which seems to be in a state of metamorphosis. The images the man sees and the interpretations he puts on them reflect the state of mankind and Scotland, for example bagpipe music, a brain laid bare and a copy of the man himself. Eventually the images become the *Yggdrasil* (the Scandinavian tree of life) and the poem considers a final riddle. The poem overall is an examination of man's genesis and place in eternity. Built around the same structure as 'Tam O'Shanter' and covering some of the same themes as 'The Wasteland', this thoroughly modernist work is one of the finest pieces of poetry ever produced in Scotland. MacDiarmid continued to write and publish numerous poems and articles, moving to Shetland in 1933. Despite his poverty he produced three books during this time: *Scottish Scene*, in conjunction with Lewis Grassic Gibbon; *At The Sign of the Thistle*, a collection of essays; and *Stony Limits*, a collection of poetry. MacDiarmid published numerous works over the years, around thirty of them being major books. He died in Biggar in 1978 and was buried in Langholm where his memorial now stands. MacDiarmid's poems have a huge range of styles, moods and interests. He wrote poems of political protest and profound meditation. Some of his work, especially the later pieces, can appear daunting, but within the 1500 pages of his complete poems there lies the work of a great poet who has much to say both about Scottishness and the universal human condition.

Complete Poems 1
Carcanet hb 185754014X
£30.00
Complete Poems 2
Carcanet hb 185754062X
£30.00
A Drunk Man Looks At The Thistle
S.A.P. pb 0707305411 £4.95
Selected Poems
Penguin pb 0140187545 £8.99
Selected Poetry
Carcanet hb 0856359866
£18.95

Hugh MacDiarmid

MACLEAN, SORLEY
(SOMHAIRLE MACGILLEAIN) (1911–1996)

MacDonald, Donald J.
Chi Mi: The Poetry of Donald John MacDonald
Birlinn pb 1874744858 £12.99

The first complete book of Donald John MacDonald's poetry to be published. He is now regarded as one of the greatest Gaelic poets of the 20th century and his work is presented here in Gaelic, with accompanying English translations and notes by Bill Innes.

Mackie, Alastair
Ingaitherins: Selected Poems
A.U.P. pb 0080350712 £6.99

Mackie's poems are notable among other things for their linguistic variations coupled with sardonic wit. Written in the Scots of his childhood, they bear repeated reading well and simmer with intellectual activity.

Born on the island of Raasay, Sorley Maclean was educated in Portree, Skye and at Edinburgh University where he gained a first class Honours degree in English. After graduating he started to write poetry and became a close friend of Hugh MacDiarmid. He embarked on a career as a teacher, which was interrupted by World War II during which he was seriously injured at the Battle of El Alamein. On returning from the war he recommenced teaching, retiring in 1972. In 1990 he received the Queen's Gold Medal for Poetry. Maclean's work was to have a major influence on Scottish Gaelic poetry. His first poems were published in 1940, but it wasn't until his 1943 collection (*Dain do Eimhir agus Dain Eile*) that he was recognised as a significant talent. At the heart of this series of elegies and love poems is a sequence of love poems addressed to Eimhir, a beautiful heroine of the early Irish sagas. Other works were to have strong political sentiments. In 'Gaoir na h-Eorpa' MacLean expresses his personal despair at the Fascist victory in Spain. Much of his work links love and political commitment, and reveals his despair at the futility of war. His work has been translated and issued in bilingual editions throughout the world. His unique voice, radically different use of language, subject matter and imagery, place Maclean's poems at the very pinnacle of 20th century Scottish Gaelic poetry.
From Wood To Ridge: Collected Poems (McVitie's Prize Winner)
Vintage pb 0099887207 £8.99

MacNeacail, Aonghas

Aonghas MacNeacail is fast becoming one of Scotland's best known poets and one of the most individual voices in Gaelic poetry. *A Proper Schooling* is his third collection, which won the 1997 Stakis Scottish Book of the Year prize. The work covers a wide range of emotional tones but all are linked by MacNeacail's sense of struggle. This is a bilingual edition.
A Proper Schooling And Other Poems
Oideachadh Ceart agus dain eile (Stakis Prize Winner)
Polygon pb 0748662189 £6.95
Rock And Water
Polygon pb 0748660658 £6.95

MacNeil, Kevin
Love and Zen in the Outer Hebrides
Canongate pb 0862418127 £6.99

This is the first collection of poetry from a talented and original new voice in Scottish poetry. MacNeil's influences range widely from the cultures of the Hebrides, Scotland, Europe and America to Eastern religious thought, especially Zen Buddhism, combining these influences in a dynamic fashion and creating poetry that is both very modern and Scottish and very much his own.

Mary Queen of Scots
Bittersweet Within My Heart
Pavilion pb 1857936612 £4.99

Mary Queen of Scots' collection of poetry is one of the few first-hand works that survives, giving a unique insight into this famous historical figure.

MacPherson, James

Ossian was a legendary 3rd century Gaelic warrior poet. MacPherson's 'translations' of Ossian's poems created a real uproar in the late 18th century when they were first published. They were a *cause celèbre* in Scotland and greeted with praise by some Edinburgh literati who saw in them a Scottish epic cycle to rival those of Ancient Greece or Rome. However, further afield reaction to the poems was less warm. Indeed in London and Dublin they were declared to be fraudulent and created by MacPherson himself. This edition includes all his Ossianic poems and gives a thorough explanation of the genesis of the work and the impact it had on Romantic culture throughout Europe.
The Poems of Ossian and Related Works (Ed. Howard Gaskill)
EUP pb 0748607072 1£6.95

James MacPherson

McSeveney, Angela
Coming Out With It
Polygon pb 0748661379 £6.95

Angela McSeveney writes intimate poetry in a straightforward fashion. Her subject matters are wide but tend to have their origins in everyday life. Her work can be described variously as insightful, honest and funny.

Martin, Angus
The Song of the Quern
S.C.P. pb 1898218927 £4.95

Angus Martin's substantial themes come from the heritage of his native Kintyre: fishing, farming and genealogy as well as his friends and family are all sources of inspiration for this award-winning poet.

Mary Queen of Scots

MORGAN, EDWIN

Born in Glasgow and a graduate of Glasgow University, Morgan served with the Royal Army Medical Corps in the Middle East during World War II. His first collection, *The Vision of Cathkin Braes*, gave an indication of his future poetic themes which include first and foremost Glasgow, and also film, science fiction and the Middle East. Never afraid to experiment, he has written poems in the 'concrete' style. He has described his poetry as 'an instrument of exploration, like a spaceship'. Some of his poems use scientific and technological vocabulary. Examples of this approach can be found in *Virtual & Other Realities*. Morgan displays his versatility and passion for language in this collection, which includes one of his cinematic poems, 'A Voyage', charting a sperm's journey from ejaculation to fertilisation, linking this primal risk to the heroism and risks involved in space exploration, one of his recurrent themes. Known as an acute commentator on the Scottish experience, his work often has a great sense of fun, while also being surreal and slightly disturbing. He is an accomplished linguist, and has translated the work of many Russian and European poets, as well as Edmond Rostand's play *Cyrano de Bergerac*.

Collected Poems
Carcanet pb 185754188X £14.95
Collected Translations
Carcanet pb 1857542533 £14.95
Hold Hands Among the Atoms
Mariscat pb 0946588147 £4.95
Selected Poems
Carcanet pb 0856355968 £5.95
Sonnets From Scotland
Mariscat pb 0946588066 £3.75
Sweeping Out The Dark
Carcanet pb 1857540727 £8.95
Virtual and Other Realities
Carcanet pb 1857543475 £6.95

Meade, Gordon
Scrimshaw Sailor
Chapman pb 0906772737 £6.50

Meade's poetry has its heart in the Fife coastline. He uses powerful descriptions of the maritime world, encouraging contemplation and a new understanding of that world through his work.

MUIR, EDWIN (1887 - 1959)

Edwin Muir's childhood was spent on Orkney, but at the age of fourteen he and his family moved to Glasgow, where both his parents and two of his brothers died in a relatively short period of time. This overwhelming tragedy was to influence his work, and the theme of banishment from paradise crops up time and again. After undergoing psycho-analysis in London his interest in the importance and meaning of dreams became apparent in his work. His style is traditional in form and technique, and he uses symbolic imagery in his personal vision of the Fall from Eden. A longing for the past innocence of childhood, along with an awareness of the dangers this longing entails, and his desire to transcend the restrictions of time are all common themes. His work shows a hatred of injustice and tyranny in its many forms. He decided to write exclusively in English, and his denial of the power of Scots in literary terms and as a way of gaining Scottish literature an international standing led to a rift between himself and his close friend Hugh MacDiarmid. He was also a translator of modern European literature, notably the work of Kafka.

Collected Poems
Faber pb 0571132162 £12.99
The Complete Poems of Edwin Muir
ASLS hb 0948877138 £50.00

Neill, William
Selected Poems 1969-1992
Canongate hb 0862414768 £5.99

William Neill is a versatile poet who writes in English, Scots and Gaelic. He can express serious passions and concerns, or he can be witty and humorous. His work often contains a strong feeling for the land and he is unafraid to tackle larger national issues. This is a collection of his finest work between 1969 and 1992.

O'Rourke, Daniel
The Waistband And Other Poems
Polygon pb 0748662324 £7.95

Edwin Morgan described these poems as 'strong, vivid and pointed . . . a spirited and accomplished collection.' Some of O'Rourke's poems are reflective works, frequently about his personal feelings on subjects such as childhood, his parents, or grief. Others are more upbeat and thematically linked to cities and city life.

Paisley, Janet
Alien Crop
Chapman pb 0906772656 £5.95

Janet Paisley's poetry is formed by her own distinctive character. In this sequence she confronts painful, intimate experiences and emotions with care and humour, speaking largely about a woman's personal experience and the joys and sufferings of ordinary people.

PATERSON, DON
(b.1963)

Born in Dundee, Don Paterson is also a jazz musician, although he sees no connection between his music and his poetry. His poems are often tightly packed with unusual vocabulary and he mixes in various disparate elements in roughly equal measure. These include scenes from the Scottish working class experience, philosophical reflections, imaginative journeys and elements of the surreal. His work can be playful in an intellectual fashion and teases the reader's expectations. He is regarded as one of the most innovative and acute poets around. His work has won both the T.S. Eliot and Forward Prizes. His second collection, *God's Gift to Women*, was recently published. Trains, drink, sex and death are the constant obsessions to be found in this collection, which builds on the award-winning voice found in *Nil Nil*. Paterson is a poet who creates striking poetic stances with his taste for the macabre and his love of extravagant jokes.

God's Gift To Women
Faber pb 057117762X £6.99
Nil Nil
Faber pb 0571168086 £6.99

Road

by Don Paterson

(after Antonio Machado)
Traveller, your footprints are
the only path, the only track;
wayfarer, there is no way,
there is no map or Northern star,
just a blank page and a starless dark;
and should you turn round to admire
the distance that you've made today
the road will billow into dust.
No way on and no way back,
there is no way, my comrade: trust
your own quick step, the end's delay,
the vanished trail of your own wake,
wayfarer, sea-walker, Christ.

Pow, Tom
Red Letter Day
Bloodaxe pb 1852243686 £7.95

Tom Pow revels in language, using lyricism and eloquent phrasing to achieve a subtle yet powerful effect. These poems mix global events with touches of intimacy and personal experience. He is skilled in describing the land in various countries and settings, and his work promotes humanity and balance in the face of a chaotic external world.

Ransford, Tessa

Tessa Ransford's poetry has religion as its central theme. Her first works were marked by their religious intensity and since then her work has found a more gentle tone, *Dancing Innocence* showing particular poetic artistry.
Dancing Innocence
Macdonald pb 0863340636 £6.95

Reid, Alastair
Oases: Poems And Prose
Canongate hb 0862417171 £9.99
Weathering: Poems And Translations
Canongate pb 0862410843 £4.95

Oases is a celebration of this restless Scot who has travelled the world and written nearly twenty books of poetry and prose. It draws on the best of his writing over the years. His ability to turn any subject into his own is extraordinary. As a poet he loves exploring nature, but many of his works also show a deep concern for humanity. *Weathering* is an earlier collection of his best poetry.

Riach, Alan
First and Last Songs
Chapman pb 0906772710 £8.50

This collection of personal poems is rooted in memory, friendship, love and family. Riach's poetry is rich in colour and reveals his wry sense of humour.

Robertson, James
Sound Shadow
B & W pb 1873631499 £7.95

This first collection of poetry was completed while Robertson was Writer in Residence at Hugh MacDiarmid's Brownsbank Cottage near Biggar. The poems are warm and sympathetic meditations on time and memory, sprinkled with social comment and humour.

Robertson, Jenny
Loss and Language
Chapman pb 0906772621 £6.50

In this collection which moves in location from Ardnamurchan and Orkney to Poland and Russia, Jenny Robertson explores the borders which separate and define us, with particular reference to women's experiences of loss, restoration and language.

Robertson, Robin
A Painted Field
Picador pb 0330350595 £6.99

A Painted Field was shortlisted for the 1997 Forward Prize for Best First Collection. Robertson's work is full of his own distinctive dark yet lush tones. Poems such as his version of Ovid, 'The Flaying Of Marsyas', are noticeable for their intimacy and examination of desire and memory, whether on the personal or national level. The collection's focal point is a sequence called 'Camera Obscura', which counterpoints a contemporary narrative of Edinburgh with an imagined diary by Victorian photographer David Octavius Hill. The sequence portrays a life in crisis and the last flowering of the Scottish Enlightenment. Robertson's impressive range and original voice mark him out as one of the more powerful new Scottish poets.

Rush, Christopher
A Resurrection of a Kind
Mercat Press pb 0080304001 £6.00

A collection of Rush's poems in Scots and English.

SCOTT, ALEXANDER
(1920–1989)

Scott wrote equally clearly in English and his own native Scots. His poetry is memorable for its range and its striking, colourful language that has a dramatic grandeur to it. He was a severe judge of the idiosyncrasies of his fellow Scotsmen. His work had several strands, and as well as commenting on Scotland he reached a level of universal inclusiveness with his droll sonnets which included 'Marilyn Monroe Still, 1968' and 'To Mourn Jayne Mansfield'. He also wrote some plays and a biography of William Soutar. He was a founder member of the Association for Scottish Literary Studies and a tireless promoter of Scottish literature. His *Collected Poems* is a good reflection of the interests, styles and subject matter of his poetry over the course of his entire career.

The Collected Poems of Alexander Scott
Mercat Press pb 1873644280 £9.99

Scott, Sir Walter
Selected Poems
Carcanet pb 0856359580 £8.95

During his lifetime Scott was renowned as a collector, editor and writer of epic ballads. His own work is distinguished for its descriptive passages and themes of romance and Scottish history. The most famous of his own ballads is probably 'The Lady Of The Lake', set in the Trossachs and telling of three men's love for the daughter of outlawed Lord James Douglas.

Smith, Alexander
A Summer in Skye
Birlinn pb 1874744386 £8.99

In 1864 poet and essayist Alexander Smith spent six weeks on Skye. This book is a magnificent prose poem which celebrates his time there, and Smith's many connections with the island, both emotional and spiritual.

"When the Access card is lost, there shall be sorrow in the glen . . . The man who sings through the nose will signal the downfall of the Mod . . . The end of the world is near when the MacBrayne's ship will be on time..."
Iain Crichton Smith, Thoughts of Murdo

SMITH, IAIN CRICHTON

Born and raised on the Isle of Lewis, Iain Crichton Smith was educated at Nicholson Institute, Stornoway and Aberdeen University. He worked for many years as a teacher while pursuing his career as a writer. He was brought up to speak both Gaelic and English. His poetic output has been prolific, drawing considerable praise, and his bilingual inheritance has been at its core. The tensions apparent in his linguistic background mean that he occasionally remakes his Gaelic work in English. He is a poet who is known for using numerous different voices over the course of time. His work has several recurring themes: the hard life of rural communities, religion, especially his dislike of the Free Church, our impotence in the face of death and despair, the lost world of childhood and his anger at the recession of Gaelic culture. His work is heavily centred on his native culture and he shows a perceptive eye for the grandeur of the Scottish landscape. He uses traditional rhythmic structure which has become freer over the years and he also has a strong sense of harmony. These factors allow him to successfully pull together contrasting images.

Collected Poems
Carcanet pb 1857542452 £9.95
Ends And Beginnings
Carcanet pb 185754093X £8.95
The Human Face
Carcanet pb 1857542517 £7.95
A Life
Carcanet pb 0856356441 £6.95
Selected Poems
Carcanet pb 0856355976 £6.95

SMITH, SYDNEY GOODSIR

(1915–1975)

Sydney Goodsir Smith was a major poet in the second generation of the Scottish Renaissance. Although born in New Zealand he moved to Edinburgh as a young man and his first poems were written in Scots, their themes being love, freedom and nationalism. In these early works he often used language gathered from the Middle Scots makars. One of his later well-known works is a long poem about Edinburgh in the tradition of Robert Fergusson, 'Kynd Kittock's Land'. Later works reveal his gift for comic poetry and demonstrate his ability to show the ridiculous, often at his own expense.

Collected Poems
Calder hb 0714535044 £12.99
Stevenson, Robert Louis

Stevenson's achievements as a poet have been largely neglected, yet he produced work in a wide range of styles from folk ballads to witty conversational pieces. He was fascinated by a large variety of verse techniques and these collections use known and previously unpublished work to show the full extent of his poetic achievement.
Robert Louis Stevenson (Ed. J. Calder)
Everyman pb 0460878093 £2.00
Selected Poems (Ed. Angus Calder)
Penguin pb 0140435484 £6.99

THOMSON, JAMES
(1834–1882)

Born in Glasgow, his family moved to London when he was eight. He was educated at the Royal Military Asylum in Chelsea and married Matilda Weller, the daughter of a sergeant. This union was to have a profound emotional effect on his life, especially after her death in 1853, when he became prone to bouts of depression and turned to heavy drinking, from which he would eventually die. His major work is *The City of Dreadful Night*, a long, compelling, bleak work in which man's isolation in the universe is symbolised by the modern city. Thomson's world in the poem is a universe without God, full of horror and anguish in which men, haunted by hallucinations, have to live in the knowledge that life is without reason. Thomson's free-flowing rhythms and use of plain vocabulary further strengthen this powerful work.

The City of Dreadful Night
Canongate pb 0862414490
£4.99

Tennant, William
The Comic Poems of William Tennant
S.A.P. hb 0707305691 £15.00

A prolific 19th century poet whose comic works were highly popular during his life, but who has been overlooked until recently.

THOMSON, DERICK (RUARAIDH MACTHOMAIS)

Born in Stornoway in 1921, Derick Thomson is a strong advocate of Gaelic culture who writes principally in Gaelic and usually translates his own work into English, releasing it in a bilingual edition. His poetry is rooted in his sense of duality at being a Gael in an English-speaking world. His other main and connected themes are island life at the time of his childhood, his affection for this past and his sense of alienation.

Creachadh na Clarsaich:
MacDonald hb 0904265579
£10.00
Collected Poems 1940-1980 Meall Garbh/Rugged Mountain
Gairm hb 1871901375 £7.50

WHITE, KENNETH

Born in Glasgow, White studied at the University there, and after travelling widely settled in France where he took up citizenship in 1979. Better known abroad, his work is highly acclaimed, especially in France where he has received some of its most prestigious literary awards and is regarded as a founding father of the post-modernist movement. Much of his work has been inspired by his travels, and his Zen-influenced philosophy coupled with his astute powers of observation create works of an intense, expressive nature written in a crisp, literary style. In recent years his work has found a new Scottish audience.

The Bird Path: Collected Longer Poems
Mainstream hb 1851582452
£12.95
Handbook for the Diamond Country
Mainstream hb 1851582843
£12.95

Poetry Anthologies

There are several interesting general anthologies of Scottish poetry available. **The Oxford Book of Scottish Verse** (ed MacQueen & Scott OUP pb 09282600X £10.99) spans seven centuries of Scottish poetry and verse and contains over three hundred works, including all the major poets, with a full range of pieces from each period of time. Emphasis has been placed on verse written in Scots, and the poetry of the 15th and 16th centuries is covered in particular detail. **The Penguin Book of Scottish Verse** (Ed. Scott Penguin pb 0140585281 £8.99) is an erudite anthology covering more than six hundred years of Scottish poetry. It contains work by a vast and diverse range of writers from Robert Burns to Edwin Muir. All the major poets are well represented, but Scott also includes some less well known regional poets. He provides biographies of individual poets as well as a glossary of unusual words. **The Poetry of Scotland: Gaelic, Scots And English 1380-1980** (ed. Watson EUP pb 0748606076 £19.95) is a collection of the best of Scottish poets which includes a full introduction, short biographies on each writer, notes on the poems and modern English translations alongside the Gaelic poems. **The Scottish Collection** (HarperCollins pb 0004721667 £4.99) is an illustrated volume of Scottish verse presented in a pocket gift book format. **The Faber Book of Twentieth Century Scottish Poetry** (Dunn, Douglas (Ed) Faber pb 0571154328 £14.99) provides an authoritative overview of Scottish poetry this century, and covers poetry in Scots, English and Gaelic. **Dream State: The New Scottish Poets** (ed. O'Rourke Polygon pb 0748661697 £10.95) is a ground-breaking collection of new Scottish poets and represents some of the best new poetic talent in Scotland. Twenty five poets writing in English, Scots and Gaelic are included, among them Robert Crawford, W.N. Herbert, Kathleen Jamie and John Burnside, and each poet is given an opportunity to talk about themselves and their work in a short introduction. **Ten Northeast Poets** (ed. Wheeler Mercat Press pb 0080324312 £5.99) is an anthology which includes the work of poets such as Violet Jacob and John C. Milne along with less well-known poets, and brings to light the poetic heritage of the North East. One of the more unusual collections of Scottish poetry is **The Bannatyne Manuscript** (Ed. Denton Fox & William A. Ringler National Library of Scotland. hb 0859675408 £150.00), subtitled 'Ane most godlie, mirrie and lustie Rapsodie maide be sundrie learned Scots poets and written be George Bannatyne in the tyme of his youth.' When Edinburgh was hit by the plague in 1568, George Bannatyne (1545 -1608), like many of his fellow citizens, fled the city. He retired to his father's estate in Forfarshire and started compiling the work of the makars, the Scots poets of the 15th and 16th century. The resulting work was the *Bannatyne Manuscript* presented here in a facsimile edition with annotations.

Particular anthologies cover particular themes, particular regions of the country or particular groups of poets. **An Anthology of Scottish Women Poets** (ed. Kerrigan EUP pb 0748602437 £17.50) brings together over one hundred women poets in a wide-ranging collection. It includes poets writing in many styles and traditions from the Middle Ages to the present day. **In Flanders Fields: Scottish Poetry and Prose of the First World War** (ed. Trevor Royle Mainstream pb 1851583033 £9.99) covers Scotland's contribution to First World War literature. A wide range of writers and poets are featured including John Buchan, Violet Jacob, Hugh MacDiarmid and Naomi Mitchison. **Scottish Love Poems** (ed. Antonia Fraser Canongate pb 0862415837 £6.99) is a very personal selection of Scottish love poetry that reminds the reader of the wealth of love poetry in Scotland from the past and the present. The ballad tradition has existed for centuries in Scotland, particularly in the North-East and the Borders. **Scottish Ballads** (ed. Lyle Canongate pb 0862414776 £5.99) is an exceptional collection that celebrates the many fine works in this genre and contains over eighty of the best ballads. **Our Destiny: A Treasury Of Travellers' Verse** (ed. McPhee S.C.P. pb 189821882X £7.99) is a collection of poetry in Scots, English and Cant about the culture and heritage of travellers as seen from the viewpoint of the younger generation. **Land Out There** (eds. Bruce and Rennie Mercat Press pb 0080409075 £12.99) is an unusual anthology, of both prose and poetry, that focuses on the Scottish land, from the descriptive geology of Scotland as told by Hugh Miller, to contributions by visitors to Scotland such as Hans Andersen, and including pieces by Sorley Maclean, Nan Shepherd and Norman MacCaig. The collection covers all the major aspects of the Scottish landscape and its influence on people. **Under Cover** (ed. Nicholson & Ogden-Smith Mainstream 1851585486 £6.99) consists of poetry and short stories by fifty of Scotland's finest writers that explore themes of homelessness, unemployment, isolation and despair, but nonetheless manage to retain a sense of triumph in the face of adversity. The anthology was published to mark the 25th anniversary of Shelter. **The Ice Horses: The Second Shore Poets Anthology** (eds. Ian McDonough & Stewart Conn S.C.P. pb 1898218854 £5.95) contains work from the poets who have featured at the Shore Poets readings in Edinburgh. They include some of Scotland's finest contemporary poets in their ranks, among them Tom Pow, Valerie Gillies and Iain Crichton Smith. **Mungo's Tongues** (ed. Hamish Whyte Mainstream pb 185158580X £9.99) is a collection of poems from Glaswegian poets, some of the works dating back three hundred years, that chart the ever changing face and mood of the city, supplemented by drawings, photographs and prints from the Mitchell Library. **North-East Song and Story: An Anthology of Narrative Verse and Song from NE Scotland** (ed. Wilson S.C.P. pb 1898218811 £9.99) features the work of many writers from the area who have been unjustly neglected but who nevertheless made a significant contribution to Scottish literature.

The Gaelic and Celtic traditions of song, poetry and prayer are very strong in Scotland. In the last century efforts were made to preserve these before they were lost forever. Alexander Carmichael was a Victorian civil servant who did much to note down the oral traditions of the Gaels and collected the writings in *Carmina Gadelica*, a poignant and moving religious work. The six volumes of the *Carmina Gadelica* are a remarkable record of the Gaelic oral tradition, of poems, blessings, prayers, curses and spells. These are woven through with traces of Celtic Christianity. **Carmina Gadelica** (ed. Carmichael Floris Books pb 0863155200 £14.99) is a selection from the Gaelic originals, handed down for generations, and these English translations recapture much of their dignity and spirit. This edition contains many of the original notes. **New Moon of The Seasons: Prayers from the Highlands and Islands** (Floris Books pb 0863155138 £4.99) and **The Sun Dances: Prayers and Blessings From the Gaelic** (Floris Books pb 0863155030 £4.99) contain selected extracts from *Carmina Gadelica*. **Carmichael's Book** (ed. Finlay Morning Star hb 0952766906 £10.00) is an anthology of poems in Gaelic and English, celebrating Carmichael's life and work. Contributors include Sorley MacLean, Iain Crichton Smith, Meg Bateman, Ian Hamilton Finlay, Valerie Gillies and Ian Stephen. **St Kilda Waulking Song (**Morning Star pb 0952766920 £10.00) is a collaboration between the Dundee based artist Will Maclean and the poet Valerie Gillies, with a commentary by William Gillies. It includes the original text of the *St Kilda Waulking Song* collected by Carmichael from Euphemia MacCrimmon in the 1800s, and a new translation of the song by Valerie Gillies. **Iona: The Earliest Poetry of a Celtic Monastery** (ed. Clancy & Markus EUP pb 0748605312 £12.95) is poetry from one of the birthplaces of Celtic Christianity. **Gair Nan Clarsach/The Harp's Cry: An Anthology Of 17th Century Gaelic Poetry** (O Baoill Birlinn pb 1874744130 £10.99) presents forty three selected poems from a turbulent period in Scottish history. The aim is to illustrate the full range of verse and song from this time. English translations are provided by poet Meg Bateman. Several anthologies celebrate the continuing triumphs of poetry in Gaelic. **An Tuil/The Flood: An Anthology of 20th Century Scottish Gaelic Verse** (ed. Black Polygon pb 0748662197 £12.99) provides a comprehensive study of Scottish Gaelic poetry this century and features the work of over fifty poets. **A Celtic Resurgence. Writing The Wind: The New Celtic Poetry** (ed. Crowe Birlinn pb 1883197120 £14.99) is a collection of contemporary Celtic language poets that features celebrated names such as Sorley Maclean, Aonghas MacNeacail and Iain Crichton Smith as well as more than fifty new poets. All the poems have English translations. **Modern Scottish Gaelic Poems/Nua-Bhardachd Ghaidhlig** (ed. Macaulay Canongate pb 0862414946 £4.99) is an important bilingual anthology that features some of the very best modern Gaelic poets including Sorley Maclean, George Campbell Hay, Derick Thomson, Iain Crichton Smith and also Donald Macaulay, who provides an introduction to the anthology. **In the Face Of Eternity/An Aghaidh Na Siorraidheachd: Eight Gaelic Poets** (ed. Whyte Polygon pb 0748660917 £9.95) shows how the new generation of Gaelic poets has responded to their poetic inheritance. It includes some of the leading lights of Scottish Gaelic poetry such as Aonghas MacNeacail, Meg Bateman, Mairi Montgomery and Christopher Whyte. **Moch Is Anmoch** (House Of Lochar pb 1899863311 £6.99) is a collection of original Gaelic poetry and song by former Mod medallist Donald McNeill and other Colonsay bards, with translations and notes by Alastair Scouller. **A Little Book of Celtic Verse** (Appletree Press hb 0862816033 £4.99) is a pocket-sized collection, with illustrations.

Politics & Social Studies

Callander, Robin
How Scotland Is Owned
Canongate pb 0862417724
£9.99

A fascinating companion volume to Andy Wightman's *Who Owns Scotland*, which shows the full absurdity of the laws governing land ownership in Scotland. An issue of major importance to many Scots, even more so now that a Scottish Parliament is imminent.

Clements, Alan et al
Restless Nation
Mainstream hb 1851588841
£14.99

A pictorial history of Scottish politics since the war, a half-century that has proved to be one of the most politically turbulent Scotland has experienced since the Jacobite Rebellion. The informative text explores the ever more separate world of Scottish politics and how Scotland's relationship with the rest of Britain has become one of the key issues in the Westminster Parliament. One of the co-writers is television journalist and *Newsnight* presenter Kirsty Wark.

Dunnett, Ninian
Out On The Edge
Canongate pb 0862417775
£7.99

This book is an up-to-date assessment of how Scots feel about their country and themselves. It is constructed from numerous interviews with Scots during the 90s. The interviews range widely in subject and the book also has humour, folklore and song woven into the text to create a rounder view. The book succeeds in its aim of reaching the heart of the Scottish experience.

Finlay, Richard J.
Independent and Free
John Donald pb 0859763994
£15.00

A significant study of the origins of the Scottish National Party and the political reasons it came into existence, covering the years 1918 to 1945.

Gray, Alasdair
**Why Scots Should Rule
Scotland, 1997**
Canongate pb 086241671X
£4.99

Alasdair Gray passionately
argues the case for Scottish
independence in this book
which puts forward a welter
of social, cultural and
geographical factors in its
favour. It makes for a
powerful political read.

Harvie, Christopher
**Scotland and Nationalism:
Scottish Society and Politics
1707-1994**
Routledge pb 0415090415
£14.99

Harvie's provocative and
imaginative work analyses
Scottish politics and society
over almost three centuries,
providing many interesting
insights into this complex
subject. In this updated
edition he draws on the rich
vein of research produced by
Scottish historians and writers
in the 1980s.

*McCrone, David, Morris,
A. & Kiely, R.*
**Scotland the Brand: The
Making of Scottish Heritage**
EUP pb 0748606157 £12.95

Scotland is well known for its
romantic tartan, whisky and
shortbread image, but is this
image a positive thing that
attracts tourists or a result of
negative stereotyping? This
book explores the images
that the heritage industry
creates around Scotland
and asks how they affect the
way in which Scotland
defines itself.

Marr, Andrew
The Battle for Scotland
Penguin pb 0140246398 £6.99

Until Labour's 1997 victory
and the 'Yes Yes' devolution
vote, Scotland had been
wrestling with its identity and
minority status for a long
time, particularly during the
recent years of Conservative
dominance at Westminster. A
hindrance in the struggle has
been that many Scots (and
certainly most people outside
Scotland) know surprisingly
little about Scottish political
history. Andrew Marr provides
an excellent and lively
account of Scotland's
distinctive political past
from Victorian times to the
present, with a new afterword
assessing recent important
events.

Paterson, Lindsay
The Autonomy of Modern Scotland
EUP pb 0748605258 £12.95

This book examines the actual degree of autonomy that Scotland has and compares it to other small countries in Europe and federal States in North America, coming to the conclusion that Scotland has as much independence as most. It also analyses the frequently changing nature of this independence, viewing the forthcoming Parliament as a part of this process, and more the latest compromise between nationalist assertion and unionist caution than a real step towards independence.

Neat, Timothy
The Summer Walkers
Canongate pb 0862415764 £14.99

A contemporary 'group self-portrait' of the horse-dealers, tinkers, hawkers and pearl fishers of the North-West Highlands, that also illuminates their secret language (the Beialrearich), their ethnic origins and their crafts.

Wightman, Andy
Who Owns Scotland?
Canongate pb 0862415853 £14.99

A vital and in-depth guide to the current pattern of land ownership in Scotland, tracing how this deplorable situation has its roots in Scotland's history. A provocative and timely work.

Wright, Kenyon
The People Say Yes
Argyll pb 1874640920 £7.99

Kenyon Wright chaired the cross-party Constitutional Convention on a Scottish Parliament. In *The People Say Yes* he charts the story of the making of Scotland's parliament, from the dark Thatcherite days of the 80s, when it seemed a very distant dream, to the present.

Reference

A number of general reference works are essential additions to any Scottish library. **A Directory of Scotland's Organisations**, compiled by Baird & Whittles (Whittles pb 1870325273 £35.00), is a highly useful reference work that lists over 2000 organisational bodies including major institutions of state, professional associations and charities, covering the entire range of Scottish professional and social life. **The World Directory of Scottish Associations** by Michael Brander (Neil Wilson pb 1897784279 £14.99) is similarly useful. **Scottish Dates**, by Osborne & Armstrong (Birlinn pb 1874744408 £6.99) lists important historical dates chronologically. Each event is analysed in three different ways: the event itself, how it was viewed at the time, and the wider historical perspective. In effect the book is a highly useful short history of Scotland. **Scotland: The Facts** by Michael Turnbull (Neil Wilson pb 1897784619 £7.99) is an up-to-date Scottish statistics book covering just about everything you wanted to know about Scotland, from the heaviest rainfall to the smallest butterfly, and all points in between. David Daiches's **The New Companion to Scottish Culture** (Polygon pb 0748661484 £10.00) covers all significant elements of Scottish culture, old and new, from eating habits and football to street games and artistic movements, with over 400 articles and 3,500 index entries. **Dictionary of Scottish Quotations** (ed. Angela Cran & James Robertson Mainstream hb 1851588124 £ £20.00) is a standard quotations dictionary. With over 4000 entries this collection represents a unique view of Scotland's culture and people. English, Scots and Gaelic are all represented and every major subject from football to religion is covered. It is an erudite yet accessible selection of words of wit and wisdom by Scots or about Scotland, suitable for all kinds of readers. J.D. Sutherland's **A Little Book of Scottish Quotations** (Appletree hb 0862816785 £4.99) is a splendid small collection of quotations on Scotland and the Scots. **Scottish Proverbs** by Colin Walker (Birlinn pb 1874744300 £5.99) contains numerous contemporary and historic proverbs, listed A-Z and is ideal as a gift book or reference guide. An unusual and interesting reference work is **The Name's The Same: Scottish Placenames Worldwide** by Stuart Conroy (Argyll hb 1874640378 £9.99) Conroy gives the stories behind some 700 Scottish placenames that have been adopted in some of the world's far-flung places, tales that bear witness to a mass migration. Mike Darton's **Dictionary of Placenames In Scotland** (Dobby pb 1858820111 £9.99) and David Dorward's **Scotland's Place Names** (Mercat Press pb 1873644507 £9.99) both give the stories behind thousands of place names in the country.

Gaelic & Scots Languages

Gaelic literature is a rich and rewarding field that could easily occupy an entire guide to itself. Unfortunately space considerations mean that with the exception of bilingual or translated works, mostly in the Fiction and Poetry sections, there are no Gaelic works in this Guide other than reference books. For readers interested in pursuing Gaelic books further, any branch of Waterstone's will be able to help. Alternatively the Gaelic Books Council print a classified catalogue of Gaelic and Gaelic-related books in print, costing £3.00. They can be contacted at: The Gaelic Books Council, 22 Mansfield Street, Glasgow G11 5QP. Tel: 0141 337 6211 E-mail: fios@gaelicbooks.demon.co.uk

There is a range of Gaelic language learning books available designed to take the student from learner level to near-fluency. A pack, **Scottish Gaelic In Three Months**, consisting of two cassettes and a book is published by Hugo (pb 0852852355 £19.95). The book is also available on its own (Hugo pb 0852852347 £4.95). A complete language course **Speaking Our Language** is produced by the publishers Canan. (**Speaking Our Language: Series 1: Study Pack 1** 189787300X £7.95 **Study Pack 2** 1897873018 £7.95 **Series 2** 1897873034 £14.95 **Series 3** 1897873093 £14.95 **Series 4** 1897873190 £14.95.)

Teach Yourself Gaelic (Hodder & Stoughton 034055925X £16.99) is a book and cassette which provide a complete course in both spoken and written Gaelic, ideal for beginners or those needing to refresh their skills. It is easy to work through, fun to use and gives clear instructions at each stage along with exercises to help you put your learning into practice. The book includes a guide to pronunciation, grammar summary and a Gaelic-English vocabulary. The cassette, recorded by native Gaelic speakers, links in with the book's exercises and adds some new ones. **Learn Scottish Gaelic: A Language Learning Sticker Book 1 At Home/A-Staigh** (Marshall pb 1840280735 £3.99) and **Book 2 At The Market/Anns Na Buthan** (Marshall pb 1840280743 £3.99) are two fun learning books which each use thirty five stickers to help children between the ages of five and seven learn 160 basic Gaelic words. Each image, when correctly attached to the background, gives an easy-to-follow guide to the pronunciation of that word. Edward Dwelly's **Illustrated Gaelic-English Dictionary** (Birlinn hb 1874744432 £14.99) was first published between 1901 and 1911 and has become recognised as the standard work for native speakers and learners alike. The Berlinn edition is an enhanced and enlarged reproduction of the original containing every Gaelic word in all previously published dictionaries along with many never printed before, and includes a concise Gaelic grammar. Gairm publish an **English-Gaelic Key To Dwelly** (Gairm pb 0901771473 £2.00). Malcolm Maclennan's **Gaelic Dictionary: Gaelic-English/ English-Gaelic** (Acair pb 0861521714 £11.99) is the only comprehensive, one volume English-Gaelic, Gaelic English dictionary, originally published in the 1920s and still standard for learners today. It is less detailed than Dwelly but easier to use. Derick S. Thomson's **The New English-Gaelic Dictionary** (Gairm pb 1871901324 £7.50) is intended for both learners and native speakers. This very practical dictionary features many words and their Gaelic equivalents not listed elsewhere, and makes clear the different meanings of individual English words. It includes many helpful phrases and sentences to demonstrate correct usage, as well as descriptions of part of speech. **Gaelic Proverbs** (ed. Alexander Nicolson Birlinn pb 1874744149 £9.99) is a new edition of the long out-of-print classic 1881 anthology of proverbs and phrases. The spelling has been modernised and the index revised but the bulk of the book is unchanged, including Nicolson's own English translations along with the Gaelic. It is still the largest and best known book on the subject. **A Little Book of Gaelic Proverbs** (Appletree Press hb 0862815967 £4.99) is a pocket-book full of proverbs, presented in Gaelic and English. Finally, and most unusually, **The Gaelic Minister's Cat** (Mercat Press pb 1873644337 £4.99) is a version of the Scottish alphabet game which will impart some words of Gaelic to even the least skilled linguist.

The Scots language is covered by a number of basic reference works. Chambers publish two invaluable books, the **Concise Scots Dictionary** (Chambers hb 0550118500 £19.99) and the **Scots Thesaurus** (Chambers hb 0550118527 £19.99). The mysteries of the modern Scots language are unravelled in an ideal beginner's book, Collins Pocket Scots Dictionary (HarperCollins pb 0004707168 £4.99) while, at the other end of the scale, **The Edinburgh History of the Scots Language**, edited by Charles Jones (EUP hb 0748607544 £150.00) is the first full record of the development of the Scots language, including several essays by some of the world's foremost scholars on the subject. Douglas Kynoch has been a prolific recorder of the traditional Doric dialect version of spoken Scots and Scottish Cultural Press have published several useful works by him. **A Doric Dictionary: Doric-English, English-Doric** (S.C.P. pb 1898218803 £5.99) and **Teach Yourself Doric: A Course for Beginners** (S.C.P. pb

1898218145 £4.95) are both basic books. **Doric Proverbs and Sayings** (S.C.P. pb 1840170077 £5.95) is a collection of over 1200 proverbs and sayings from the North-East of Scotland that cover a wide range of topics and sentiments. **Doric For Swots** (S.C.P. pb 1840170166 £4.99) is a book for the more advanced students of the ancient tongue. Canongate publish **A Dash O'Doric** (pb 0862415616 £5.99) and **Anither Dash O'Doric** (pb 086241637X £5.99) Both books take an informative and humorous look at the dialect and wit of the North-East.

From further North John J. Graham's **Shetland Dictionary** (Shetland Times pb 090066293X £9.95) is the latest edition of this dictionary relating Shetland words to their English equivalents.

Investigation into family history is beoming more and more popular and there are plenty of books to help those of Scottish descent discover their roots. **Tracing Your Scottish Ancestors: A Guide to Ancestry Research in the Scottish Record Office** (HMSO pb 0114958653 £9.99) is an essential illustrated reference guide for anyone using the records held in the Scottish Record Office to trace their ancestors. Kathleen Cory's **Tracing Your Scottish Ancestry** 2nd ed. (Polygon pb 0748662154 £7.95) is packed full of information on heraldry, tartans, surnames and resource centres vital in any genealogical search. It also gives tips on basic research techniques. Joan Ferguson's **Scottish Family Histories** (National Library of Scotland hb 0902220683 £14.95) is a reference book ideal for anyone tracing their family line, listing all the known works on Scottish families - books, pamphlets, manuscripts and periodical articles. It lists 3,200 entries with the relevant sources under each family name, and details of which Scottish libraries hold the works. Holton & Winch's **My Ain Folk: An Easy Guide To Scottish Family History** (Tuckwell Press pb 1862320241 £5.99) is a beginner's guide to genealogy that shows you how to trace your family roots using the latest technology as well as all the more traditional methods. George Black's **The Surnames of Scotland** (Birlinn hb 1874744831 £ £20.00) is a classic genealogical guide to over eight thousand Scottish family names that gives the names' origins, meanings and history, and includes notes on the development of names and their place in Scottish history. Two other, more compact books on names are available, both compiled by Donald Whyte. **Scottish Surnames** (Birlinn pb 1874744394 £7.99) has more than two hundred and eighty of the most popular surnames packed into an easy-to-use reference that gives the full historical and geographical origins of the names listed. **Scottish Forenames** (Birlinn pb 1874744726 £6.99) is a companion volume to *Scottish Surnames* in the same format, and includes examples from throughout Scottish history. Much Scottish history is built around the clan and the tartan has become of importance to many of Scots descent. **The Scottish Clan and Family Encyclopaedia** by George Way Of Plean & Romilly Squire (HarperCollins hb 0004705475 £30.00) is a major reference work that gives the history, tartans and mottos of Scotland's many clans. **The Collins Guide to Scots Kith And Kin** (HarperCollins pb 0004356659 £4.99) is a less extensive guide to the clans and surnames of Scotland. Collins also publish two pocket reference titles in this area, **Clans And Tartans** (HarperCollins pb 0004708105 £6.99) and **Scottish Surnames** (HarperCollins pb 0004704630 £5.99). Further books on the subject are Hugh Cheape's **Tartan** (National Museum of Scotland pb094863670X £5.99), an authoritative history of tartan from its medieval origins to its uses as an integral part of clan identity, Roddy Martine's **Scottish Clan and Family Names: Their Arms, Origins and Tartans** (Mainstream pb 1851584188 £9.99) and **Clans and Tartans** (Appletree Press hb 0862815479 £4.99), a compact book in full colour that covers the history and tales surrounding some of Scotland's most famous clans and their tartans.

Philosophy & Religion

Philosophy

See also Scottish Enlightenment in the History section

Beveridge, C. Tumbull, R.
Scotland After Enlightenment
Polygon pb 0748662235 £12.99
A study of the effects of the
Enlightenment, paying
particular attention to the
education system, the
advance of modern
philosophy, Jacobitism and
images of the Scottish city.

Broadie, Alexander
Tradition of Scottish
Philosophy
Polygon pb 0748660291 £9.95

HUME, DAVID (1711–1776)

The son of a Berwickshire landowner, David Hume was born in
Edinburgh. He began studying Law at Edinburgh University but
moved on to Philosophy, his real interest. Because of his lack of
business acumen his father permitted him to pursue his philosophical interests. He lived in France during the mid-1730s,
and while there wrote his *Treatise On Human Nature*. On returning
to Scotland in 1739 he stayed at the family estate in Berwickshire where he wrote *Essays, Moral and Political*. Much
misunderstood during his own lifetime, his perceived dislike of
the church deprived him of two important academic positions:
the Chair of Moral Philosophy in Edinburgh, and the Chair of
Logic at Glasgow which was taken up instead by Adam Smith.
From 1745-46 he was tutor to the mentally deranged Marquis
of Annandale. Hume's exceptional *Dialogues Concerning Natural
Religion,* written in 1750, were wisely published posthumously.
During most of the 1750s he lived in Edinburgh and became
librarian at the Faculty of Advocates. He went on to take up
several important diplomatic posts, becoming secretary to the
British Ambassador in Paris from 1763~65 and subsequently
Secretary of State to the Northern Department in London. He
retired in 1768 to live in Edinburgh once again, until his death
from cancer in August 1776. A crucial figure in the Scottish
Enlightenment, he extended the empiricist views of John Locke
and was an important influence on Immanuel Kant. He is
regarded as one of the world's most outstanding philosophers
and his work as the cornerstone of philosophy in the 18th
century, and still highly influential on empiricists to this day.

Dialogues Concerning Natural
Religion And The Natural
History Of Religion
OUP pb 0192829327 £5.99
Enquiries Concerning
HumanUnderstanding And
Concerning The Principles Of
Morals 3rd ed.
OUP pb 019824536X £8.50

Selected Essays
OUP pb 0192830724 £5.99
Treatise of Human Nature
2nd ed.
OUP pb 0198245882 £8.99
Well Temper'd Eloquence
(Ed. IA Merikoski)
Tuckwell Press pb 187048245X
£14.99

SMITH, ADAM (1723–1790)

Adain Smith, another major Enlightenment figure, was born in Kirkcaldy, Fife. He was educated at Glasgow University, studying philosophy and mathematics, and spent a short period of time at Oxford. On his return to Scotland in 1746 he moved to Edinburgh and made a living lecturing on a variety of subjects. In 1751 he took up the Chair of Logic at Glasgow University, and soon also became Professor of Moral Philosophy there. He left Scotland in 1764 to tutor the third Duke of Buccleuch in France and Switzerland, returning two years later. He spent the next ten years in Kirkcaldy, where he wrote *An Inquiry Into The Nature And Causes Of The Wealth Of The Nations*. Eventually he moved back to Edinburgh where he remained till his death. Adam Smith's theory of economics stood on the basic premise that free-market practice should be unimpeded by government interference. This simple idea was to be the fundamental basis of modern world economics and has heavily influenced the concept of capitalism, not just in his own and Victorian times but also in the present day.

An Inquiry Into The Nature And Causes Of The Wealth Of The Nations
OUP pb 0192817965 £6.99
The Wealth Of The Nations Books I-III
Penguin pb 0140432086 £6.99

Religion

Bamford, C. & Parker Marsh, W.
Celtic Christianity: Ecology & Holiness
Floris Books pb 0863155146 £6.99

The early Christian Celts saw strong links between nature and divinity. This anthology is based around stories, verses, prayers and sayings that illustrate these links. Some of the selections are attributed to ancient sages such as St. Cuthbert and St. Patrick, others are anonymous. What they all show is that the early Celtic Church had a deep-seated understanding of nature, an understanding that some present Christian movements are now trying to recover.

Brown, Callum G.
Religion And Society in Scotland Since 1707
EUP pb 0748608869 £14.95

A provocative and topical work that examines the role the Kirk has played in forming our national identity. It charts the rise and recent fall of the importance of religion in Scottish history.

Knight, Christopher & Lomas, Robert
The Hiram Key: Pharaohs, Freemasons and the Discovery of the Secret Scrolls of Christ
Arrow pb 0099699419 £6.99
Rosslyn Chapel in the village of Roslin near Edinburgh is a building rich in history. It dates from the 15th century and is covered in Celtic, Masonic and Knights Templar symbols which the authors of this book believe point to the resting place of the secret teachings of Christ, teachings they believe are at the heart of secret Masonic rituals.

Lorimer, William
The New Testament In Scots
Penguin pb 0140075712 £16.99
This version of the New Testament was translated into Scots by the scholar and linguist William Lorimer during the last ten years of his life. The language is rugged, well-chosen and illuminating. The books can be recommended to believers and non-believers alike. All lovers of the Scots tongue should own it and either dip into it or read the Gospels in particular from start to finish.

Low, Mary
Celtic Christianity and Nature: Early Irish and Hebridean Traditions
EUP pb 0748607722 £12.95
Celtic Christianity is often said to have had the love of nature at its core. Mary Low's erudite and accessible work looks at how native beliefs about nature were altered by early mediaeval Christians of the Hebrides and Ireland.

MacDonald, Iain (Ed)
St. Columba
Floris Books pb 0863151434 £2.50
St Magnus
Floris Books pb 0863151647 £2.50
St Margaret
Floris Books pb 0863151655 £2.50
St. Mungo
Floris Books pb 0863151663 £2.50
St. Ninian
Floris Books pb 0863151671 £2.50
Short studies of saints associated with Scotland, all compiled from original sources.

Stuart, Jamie
The Scots Gospel
St Andrews Press pb 0715206737 £4.95
Pocket-sized stories from the New Testament in modern scots. A companion volume to his hugely popular *Glasgow Gospels* and *Auld Testament Tales.*

Wallace, martin
A Little Book of Celtic Saints
Appletree press hb 0862814561 £4.99
The life and times of the saints in a pocket-sized and illustrated edition.

Sport

Books Chiefly Concerned With Scottish Football
by Jason Ormiston, Waterstone's, 13-14, Princes Street, Edinburgh

Many believe that the breakaway Scottish Premiership will see the further impoverishment of the majority in the Scottish game. With this backdrop, club histories are a reminder of what we might lose if wealth in the game is concentrated in too few hands.

A book like *Black Diamonds and the Blue Brazil* by **Ron Ferguson** (Famedram pb, 0905489535, £5.95), a social history of the club and town of Cowdenbeath, glories in past industrial strength and football success, the relationship between the two being obvious. Who could ever think that football would be so important? As a barometer of human emotion, football is exemplary. These social histories record extremes of happiness and pain on the terraces and outside the factory gates. The history of football is a history of industry. This is also clear in the oral history *Oh Hampden in the Sun*, by **Peter Burns** and **Pat Woods** (Mainstream pb, 1851589112, £9.99) a record of people's memories of Celtic's 1957 League Cup victory over Rangers by 7 goals to 1. It is a populist social history of fifties' working class culture.

The three comprehensive volumes of *Rejected FC of Scotland*, by **Dave Twydell**, (Yore Pub., Vol.1 pb, 0951332198, £12.95; Vol.2 pbd, 1874427305, £12.95; Vol.3 pbd, 1874427178, £13.95) are a stark reminder of what can be lost when clubs lapse or have been kicked out of the Scottish leagues. These volumes catalogue in detail the demise of the many clubs that have withered away. Who is next to fade from the pools coupon?

With the league breakaway in mind, but before it became a reality, **David Bennie's** *A Season in Hell* (Mainstream hb, 185158904X, £14.99) is a ground by ground deconstruction of league football and a *fin-de-siècle* account of the decomposing Scottish game. It is a funny nostalgic account not to be confused with Gibbon's *Decline and Fall of the Roman Empire*.

The only books worth Scottish football's while are those that highlight the importance of football to ordinary people. Football in Scotland has managed to avoid its own commodification largely because it is not very good. Yet ever since Graeme Souness strode manfully amongst us there has been an articulation of the polarised nature of football (the haves and the have nots), expressed in many different ways. From **Irvine Welsh's** interest in Hibernian in *Marabou Stork Nightmares* (Vintage pb, 009943511X, £5.99) to **Walter Smith's** ghost-written autobiography *Mr. Smith* (Mainstream hb, 1851586687, £12.99), there has been much to enlighten, and unfortunately, obscure the true nature of Scottish football.

This is all a rather bleak picture. I suspect much of what we recognise as Scottish football will remain intact through a combination of bloody minded determination, the kind that saw us keep Brazil to 4-1 in 1982, and good humour. Indeed, Scottish football would be truly awful without its humour. Take a flick through *Scottish Football Quotations*, edited by **Kenny MacDonald** (Mainstream pb, 1851586431, £6.99) and you will understand what I mean. For example,

" *I knew my days were numbered when I was warming up behind the goal at Parkhead one day and one of our fans shouted, 'Kinnaird we like the Poll Tax more than we like you'.* "

Scottish football may not be first class, but its humour could gag for any World XI. The sadly departed *The Absolute Game* (TAG), Scotland's former premier football fanzine, was a very funny publication that kept us arrogant whilst our football made us humble. It is in this vein that *Hampden Babylon: Sex And Scandal In Scottish Football* by **Stuart Cosgrove** (Canongate pb, 086241296X, £4.99) was written. The Thatcher generation was delighted to realise just how much sex and scandal there was in Scottish football (the back pages of the Scotsman always dealt with more serious matters). A generation of terrace satirists have stood erect, freed by the coruscating attitude that inspired *TAG, Hampden Babylon,* and *Scottish Football Quotations.* Long may it continue.

Football

The Scottish Football League Review (ed. W.C. Cotton Programme Pubs pb 0953152812 £6.95) is an invaluable reference work - the 1997-98 edition came out in November last year. Next year's edition will be out at the same time this year. In **Billy Bremner's Scottish Football Heroes** (Breedon Books hb1859830773 £14.99) one of Scotland's football greats selects his own list of football legends. **Scottish Football Quotations** (ed. Kenny MacDonald Mainstream pb 1851586431 £6.99) is not just a book about Scottish football, but also about the Scottish male, Scottish culture and all the contradictions that lie within each of these. Its finest quality is the way it highlights the sometime absurdities that have created football culture. One need only mention 1978, for example, for the Scottish male and the devolutionist to turn sullen, the debacle being neatly summed up by the manager of Peru, "I want to congratulate Scotland for the team they presented to us." From its origins as a one-off radio comedy special, *Only An Excuse?* has become the single most important reason Scottish football can never take itself too seriously again. The book **Only An Excuse?** by Philip Differ (Mainstream pb 1851586997 £7.99) contains some of the best comic lines from this radio, TV and stage phenomenon. Quirky football books are few and far between but **In Ma' Head, Son: The Footballer's Mind Revealed** by Pat Nevin & George Sik (Headline pb 0747257256 £6.99) is one of the few, and it is no surprise that Pat Nevin is involved. Nevin, football's professor, allows Sik, psychiatry's uncompromising centre-back, to analyse one of the game's more sensitive players. This book is a unique footballing publication. Indeed where else would you find this remark? "The people I was associating with were more musicians, actors, dancers - even road-sweepers, although my road sweeping mate Willie was a Wagnerian, Proustian aesthete." Pretentious? Nevin? Nah, just misunderstood. Even more serious is Bill Murray's **The Old Firm: Sectarianism, Sport and Society In Scotland** (John Donald pb 0859761215 £11.95). This is a hard-hitting exploration of the relationship between Scotland's largest two teams, compulsive and controversial in its analysis of events historical and contemporary. **The Old Firm In The New Age** (Mainstream hb 1851589848 £14.99) is another book by the same author. Celtic and Rangers have undergone a major revolution since 1986. Sparked by the spending spree initiated by Rangers' Graeme Souness, the changes at Rangers came thick and fast, including the signing of Maurice Johnstone, a Catholic, in 1989. While Rangers embraced this revolution it took a virtual civil war at Celtic's Parkhead to force change. Bill Murray goes on to assess whether 'business based on bigotry' has left the Old Firm teams for good. Most serious of all, one might argue, is a book which examines Argentina '78. The tragi-comedy of Argentina 1978 has had a lasting impact on the Scottish national psyche. With a build-up unparalleled in Scottish sport, the reality was one of the all-time lows in Scottish football. The full facts of the shambles that was Argentina '78 are painfully re-examined in Mike Wilson's **Don't Cry For Me Argentina: Scotland's 1978 World Cup Adventure** (Mainstream pb 1851588957 £9.99), which has accounts from all the key figures involved in the debacle.

Unsurprisingly more books have been written about Celtic and Rangers than any other club side. **Voices Of The Old Firm** by Stephen Walsh (Mainstream hb1851587136 £14.99) is the history of Rangers and Celtic as told by players, managers and supporters. John Quinn's **Jungle Tales** (Mainstream hb 1851586733 £9.99) is an exercise in pure nostalgia for Celtic fans. It contains stories from the Jungle, a now demolished part of the Parkhead ground. The dramas and events that were witnessed by the supporters of this area of the ground are lovingly retold here, often in the fans' own words. In **Not Playing For Celtic: Another Paradise Lost** (Mainstream hb 1851587578 £12.99) by David Bennie life is seen through the eyes of an ardent and loyal Celtic fan. Humorous, entertaining and covering just about every major Scottish issue, the book is coloured throughout by Bennie's life-long love affair with Celtic. Other clubs, even the smallest, do, however, produce their literature. Robert Reid's **Red And Yellow Forever** (GD Records pb 0952715619 £8.99) is a *real* fan's eye view of the much joked-about Partick Thistle who are as much victims of the Old Firm dominance as anyone else, perhaps even more so given their proximity. However, Robert Reid tells us in vivid detail why he has had so much fun following Thistle for a lifetime, and why the pain of some fairly terrible times has still been worth it. His style is engaging and, for an official history, not in the slightest bit sycophantic. As oil came on-stream in Aberdeen the fortunes of its football club improved, especially in Europe. This peaked with Aberdeen's victory in the 1983 Cup Winners Cup. Clive Leatherdale uses a tabloid style, best suited to his matter-of-fact book **Aberdeen - The European Era** (Desert Island hb 1874267112 £16.99) Glorying in statistics, interesting ones at that, the book's editorial comment takes a positive spin on most issues yet maintains an independent streak fuelled by informed hindsight. This is pure footballing history. It contains excellent graphics and is a nicely produced book which justifies its price. Dunfermline Athletic get their moment of glory in John Lloyd's **Simply the Best** (John Donald pb 0859764486 £8.50), a celebration of the players, games and events that have formed this club's history. Written from an insider's viewpoint, the book contains many interesting anecdotes and behind-the-scenes facts. Hibs are thoroughly memorialised in two books. Alan Lugton's **The Making of Hibernian 1893-1914** (John Donald hb 0859764842 £14.95) is the second volume of what promises to be a monumental history of the club that took nearly 30 years to research. (The first volume is sadly unavailable.) It's quite extraordinarily extensive and exhaustive in its coverage of players, managers and matches. **Hibernian: The Easter Road Story** (John Donald pb 0859764265 £8.50) brings up to date John Mackay's previous histories of Hibs, focusing in detail on the last ten years in this remarkably thorough look at the team. During the '50s Conn, Bauld and Wardhaugh were three Hearts players who scored nearly 1000 first team goals between them. **The Terrible Trio** by Brian Scott (John Donald pb 0859763064 £2.50) is the story of the men who made Hearts the dominant team of that decade.

Indeed it is individuals that make up the game in Scotland and there are plenty of biographies available of the great names in the sport. Bill Shankly is a football legend, born and brought up in Glenbuck, an Ayrshire coaltown. He went on from these humble beginnings to become one of football's greatest heroes, leading Liverpool to three championships, two FA Cups and the UEFA Cup. **Shanks** by Dave Bowler (Orion pb 0752802461 £5.99) is the authorised biography of the man. **Dalglish: My Autobiography** (Hodder & Stoughton pb 0340660120 £6.99) is a remarkably frank and candid autobiography from another of Scotland's football legends. He's also the subject of the first of two books by renowned football writer Stephen Kelly, **Dalglish** (Headline pb 0747241244 £5.99). **Fergie: The Biography Of Alex Ferguson** (Headline hb 0747219184 £16.99) provides a deep and insightful biography of the famous manager. **Jock Stein: A Scot's Life** (Argyll pb 1874640130 £6.99) is an-easy-to-read biography which is part of the Scots Legends series. It follows Stein's beginnings from a humble miner to becoming one of the most successful Scots football managers ever. Author Glenn Telfer looks at the connection between his working class background and his desire to succeed, and views him as a major cultural figure with significance beyond the confines of the football world. Andy Goram, Rangers' and Scotland's flamboyant, eccentric and frequently controversial goalkeeper, has seen his share of negative publicity. In **Andy Goram: My Life** (Virgin pb 0753502135 £5.99), co-written with Ken Gallacher, he tells his side of the story: the drinking, the bust-up with Rangers manager Walter Smith, and his decision to walk out on his country before a vital qualifying match. Finally Craig Brown, the Scottish football team's highly regarded manager, has been in his post since 1993, and remarkably he is Scotland's first manager to take the national squad to the European Championship and the World Cup finals in succession. **Craig Brown: The Autobiography** (Virgin hb 1852277564 £15.99), written with Bernard Bale, charts his career in football from his time as a player for Dundee to his highly successful reign as Scotland's manager. He uses the book as a platform to answer the critics who have dogged him throughout his time as a manager.

"To the Scots, football's a lovely, incurable disease."
Tommy Docherty

Rugby

Douglas, Derek
The Thistle: A Chronicle of Scottish Rugby
Mainstream hb 1851587373 £15.99

Derek Douglas charts the highs and lows of Scottish rugby from its establishment as a major sport during the Victorian era to the recent turmoil the game has experienced. He revisits some of the exceptional games and tells of the great players of the past. The book is completed with the use of some great photographs.

Hastings, Scott & Douglas, Derek
Great Scott!
Mainstream hb 1851588930 £14.99

The autobiography of Scotland's most capped rugby player covers all his major rugby achievements and has some quite controversial things to say about the modern professional game.

Golf

Ballingall, Peter
The DK Pocket Guide to Golf Practice Drills
Dorling Kindersley 0751302457 £9.99

If you wish to improve your handicap, no matter how skilled a golfer you are, this book will be of help. It gives lots of vital tips for posture and swing in a handy size for fitting into the pocket.

Campbell, Malcolm
The DK Pocket Guide to Golf Etiquette
Dorling Kindersley 0751303941 £9.99

The rules and etiquette of golf, written and unwritten, are renowned for their quirkiness. This guide comes in a pocket-sized edition and is designed to prevent any arguments, injury or offence on the golf course.

> **"Golf is an indispensable adjunct to high civilisation."**
> Andrew Carnegie

Campbell, Malcolm
Ultimate Golf Techniques
Dorling Kindersley hb
0751302570 £20.00

A lush, well laid out and comprehensive guide to golf techniques that analyses the skills of some of the world's greatest golfers. Containing over 500 tips, it is ideal for practical instruction and developing your game.

Donegan, Lawrence
Four-Iron In The Soul
Viking hb 0670871141 £15.99

A classic book for all armchair sports enthusiasts. Lawrence Donegan always wanted to be a major golfer but was prevented by what he describes as 'a lack of talent'. So he did the next best thing and became a caddy to a professional player. The book is about their adventures together on the golf circuit, a marvellous combination of travelogue and sports book hilariously written.

Geddes, Olive M.
A Swing Through Time: Golf In Scotland, 1457-1743
N.L.S. pb 0114942099 £6.95

This work sheds light on the great controversy surrounding the origins of golf through careful research of early documents, looking at early images of people playing the game (was the picture of St Cuthbert the first?), the involvement of monarchs (was Mary Queen Of Scots seen playing golf not long after her husband's murder?), and covering all historical aspects of this globally popular sport.

Hamilton, David
The Scottish Golf Guide
Canongate pb 0862415314 £5.99

Scotland has more golf courses per head of population than any other country, and David Hamilton's guide details every one of them.

Jarrett, Tom
St. Andrews Golf Links: The First 600 Years
Mainstream hb 1851586652 £14.99

This official work tells the 600 year history of the Home of Golf, St. Andrews. Jarrett studies the game's evolution and the major influence of the Royal and Ancient Golf Club. He tells of some of golf's most dramatic moments and the many golfing greats who have played the game there. A major book on golf's most important location.

McGuire, Brenda & John
Golf at the Water's Edge:
Scotland's Seaside Links
Abbeville Press hb 0789203235
£10.00

Golf was born in Scotland
and therefore many of the
world's oldest courses are
located here. This book is an
anecdotal history and tour of
Scotland's seaside courses,
including the legendary St.
Andrews course. Details on
each course are accompanied
by watercolour illustrations
by John McGuire, and there
is full information for golfers
who may wish to do this tour
themselves.

Mackenzie, Richard
A Wee Nip at the 19th Hole
HarperCollins hb 0002188473
£12.99

A very different golf history
that celebrates the many
colourful characters, including Old Tom Morris,
'Stumpie Eye' and 'Trap
Door', who have been St
Andrews caddies down
through the ages.

Mair, Norman
Muirfield: Home of the
Honourable Company
(1744-1994)
Mainstream hb 1851586172
£20.00

Although the question of
which is the oldest golf club
is hotly debated, the oldest
surviving records belong to
the Honourable Company
of Edinburgh Golfers whose
1744 minute book contains
the original Rules of Golf.
In 1891 the Honourable
Company transferred to
Muirfield. This stylish book
is a celebration of this great
course and the historic club
who play there.

Fishing

Coutts, James
Fishing Scotland: A Guide To Game Fishing: Argyll, The Isles, Loch Lomond, Stirling & The Trossachs
Fishing Scotland pb
1900417049 £4.99
Invernessshire, The Isle Of Skye, Moray & Nairn
1900417030 £4.99
Ross And Cromarty, Sutherland & Caithness
1900417057 £4.99

A series of guides to the waters of Scotland, full of useful information and invaluable for game fishers.

Garner, Lewis
The Best Fishing In Scotland
Dobby hb 1858820057 £14.99

A game fisher's guide which itemises where to fish, the best times, flies and the most effective fishing tactics and techniques. There are full details of each loch, river and pool and their surrounding area, including information on suitable nearby accommodation. Some of the less accessible and less expensive waters are also covered.

Headley, Stan
Trout & Salmon Flies of Scotland
Merlin Unwin hb 1873674260 £20.00

An illustrated guide to the best contemporary fishing flies for Scottish waters, which includes valuable contributions from regional experts on the dressing of flies, along with numerous local tips.

Sandison, Bruce
Trout & Salmon Rivers and Lochs of Scotland
Merlin Unwin hb 1873674317 £19.99

A single volume that catalogues all the rivers and lochs in Scotland. Four years in the making, Bruce Sandison's book tells trout and salmon anglers everything they need to know about fishable waters, from details about location and boat hire to fishing permission addresses and permit costs.

Walking & Climbing

Munros and others

If you're interested in the recently re-classified Munros the SMC Hillwalkers' **Guide Vol.1: Munros 2nd ed.** (S.M.C. pbd 0907521312 £14.95) is the best guide available, regarded as the climbers' bible to these hills. The second volume, **Corbetts & Other Scottish Hills** (S.M.C. hb 0907521517 £16.95) is similarly invaluable. The recent creation of eight new Munros and the deletion of some has brought about the production of a new set of Munros tables. This new edition, **Munros Tables 1997 Edition** (S.M.C. hb 0907521533 £15.95), includes full details of all the Munros, as well as lists of the Corbetts, Donalds and Grahams. It is fully up-to-date in all aspects of the information provided. **The Munro Almanac** (Neil Wilson hb 1897784392 £7.99) and **The Corbett Almanac** (Neil Wilson hb 1897784724 £7.99), both by Cameron McNeish, are best-selling guides which contain all the latest information, as well as details of the new classifications. **The First Fifty: Munro-Bagging Without A Beard** (Corgi pb 0552139378 £9.99) demonstrates a refreshingly different approach to walking the Munros. In this exceptionally funny book TV presenter Muriel Gray debunks many of the myths surrounding hill-walking and explains in her uniquely humorous style the joys of hill walking: the solitude, wildlife and sense of achievement. She proves once and for all that you don't have to be a muscle-bound hunk with a beard to enjoy Scotland's wilderness. **The Last Hundred: Munros, Beards and a Dog** (Mainstream hb 1851586075 £14.99), by Hamish Brown, is a lively and amusing collection of reminiscences of climbing the Munros over a long period of time in different seasons and in the company of different types of climber. **The Munros In Winter: 277 Summits In 83 Days** (David & Charles pb 0715306898 £9.99) is Martin Moran's gripping story of his record-breaking completion of all the Munros in harsh winter conditions. Andrew Dempster's **The Grahams: A Guide To Scotland's 2,000ft Peaks** (Mainstream ppc 1851588477 £14.99) is a guide to all 224 Grahams, Scotland's mountains between 2,000 and 2,500ft, with illustrations throughout.

General Walking and Climbing

Brown, Dave & Mitchell, Ian
Mountain Days & Bothy Nights
Luath Press pb 0946487154
£7.50

Tales from and about
Scotland's bothies are the
subject of this stalwart of the
mountaineering fraternity.
Bothies were traditionally the
old cottages and huts used as
seasonal dwellings for
farmers, and now used by
hillwalkers and climbers for
shelter. Over the years these
shelters have given rise to a
rich oral culture, some of
which is relayed in this
volume.

Brown, Hamish
**The Fife Coast: From the Forth
Bridges to Leuchars by the
Castle Coast and the East Neuk**
Mainstream hb 1851586083
£12.99

A book of walks that has been
carefully divided into sections
to allow its use as a town
guide, a complete route
overview or as a guide to
sampling the delights of any
particular area along the way.

Burton, Anthony
The Caledonian Canal
Aurum Press pb 185410554X
£9.99

This is a guide for walkers,
cyclists and boaters to one
of the greatest achievements
of the canal building age.
It includes maps, navigation
information and full details
of public transport, boat hire,
accommodation and tourist
organisations.

Chalmers, John
**One Hundred Hill Walks
Around Glasgow 3rd ed.**
Mainstream pb 1851585362
£6.99

**Chalmers, John & Storey,
Derek**
**One Hundred Hill Walks
Around Edinburgh 2nd ed.**
Mainstream pb 1851585370
£6.99

These guides include maps
for each walk, Ordnance
Survey references, parking
details, short cuts, hints on
clothing and definitive
indexes.

Connon, Heather & Roper, Paul
The Highland Highway
Mainstream ppc 1851587918
£9.99

The Highland Highway is a
105 mile long high-level
route from Loch Lomond to
Fort William that covers some
of Scotland's most dramatic
scenery. This volume includes
route descriptions, sketch
maps and highlights to
encounter along the way.

Craig, David
Native Stones
Pimlico pb 071267361X £10.00

While Craig's book is focused on climbing, by examining his motives, reasons and justifications it becomes much more: a book about life that covers a multitude of subjects from parenthood and childhood to literature, fear and ambition. Much acclaimed, it has an appeal far beyond the climbing fraternity, and Craig's ability to communicate life's varied aspects with both passion and clarity grips the reader's imagination.

Crockett, Ken
Ben Nevis
S.M.C. hb 0907521169 £14.95

A useful climbing guide to Scotland's and Britain's highest mountain.

Greig, Andrew
Summit Fever
Canongate pb 0862417422 £9.99

A dramatic and personal account of a novice climber's first full-blown Himalayan expedition.

Marsh, Terry
On Foot In Southern Scotland: 40 Walks in the Southern Uplands
David & Charles pb 0715305468 £9.99

Terry Marsh uses his extensive experience of the footpaths that cross southern Scotland to bring together this selection of 40 walks.

McNeish, Cameron
The Best Hillwalking In Scotland
Neil Wilson pb 1897784732 £10.99

Cameron McNeish is regarded as one of Scotland's most experienced hillwalkers. In this well illustrated guide, complete with maps and full details of local accommodation, he takes us round his favourite hill walks in Scotland. These range from the Trossachs and Glencoe to around Badenoch and Ullapool. McNeish's experience as a walker gives the reader a real appreciation of these remote routes.

McNeish, Cameron & Else, Richard
Wilderness Walks
BBC hb 0563371765 £17.99

An illustrated guide book for walkers or armchair travellers that features twelve of the most spectacular walks in Scotland.

POUCHER, W.A.

During his life W.A. Poucher became famous as a climber and mountain photographer. His books give detailed information on walking and climbing, and this, together with the many photographs taken by the author himself, has ensured their enduring popularity. *The Best Of Poucher's Scotland* contains his hundred best loved photographs, complete with his own detailed captions. Carefully selected by his son, the photographs are a visual testament to the incomparable beauty of the wild places of Scotland.

The Magic of Skye 3rd ed.
Constable pvc 0094695709 £10.95
The Scottish Peaks 8th ed.
Constable pvc 0094758506 £10.99
The Best of Poucher's Scotland
Constable pvc 0094755701 £12.99

STORER, RALPH

Ralph Storer's books provide excellent guides to a large variety of routes for walkers, climbers and mountain bikers. For example, in *100 Best Routes on Scottish Mountains* the routes are graded as to their difficulty, and much helpful back-up information is given. Lesser known hill tracks and peaks are included, all the walks are circular and no rock climbing is necessary.

100 Best Routes on Scottish Mountains
Warner pb 0751518905 £6.99
50 Classic Routes on Scottish Mountains
David& Charles hb 0715305565 £14.99
50 Best Routes on Scottish Mountains
David & Charles hb 0715302590 £14.99
50 More Routes on Scottish Mountains
David& Charles hb 0715302604 £14.99
50 Best Routes on Skye and Raasay
David & Charles hb 0715303953 £14.99
Exploring Scottish Hill Tracks: For Walkers and Mountain Bikers
David & Charles pb 0715302574 £11.99

WAINWRIGHT, A.

Wainwright In Scotland
0718134095 £13.99 Mermaid Bks pb

Using his highly popular anecdotal style Wainwright documents a journey around some of Scotland's most impressive landscapes, including Sutherland, the Argyll coast and the Cairngorms. As he describes his travels he draws on almost half a century of annual journeys to Scotland, thus creating a very distinctive picture of the glens and ever-changing seascapes.

Boxing

Burrowes, John
Benny: The Benny Lynch Story
Mainstream pb 1851584234
£6.99

A biography of Scotland's greatest boxer who died in tragic circumstances in 1946. His background in the Gorbals is vividly remembered here, and the book also serves as a slice of real social history from Scotland in the 1930s.

Healy, Thomas
A Hurting Business
Picador pb 0330351680 £6.99

Healy's unsettling book details his early days growing up in the Gorbals of Glasgow. It was during this time that he began to associate the lives of great boxers with his own. He could see that his alcoholism and the obstacles and hardships of his world mirrored the lives of many boxers, and here he tells both his own story and that of some boxing champions.

Cycling

Collins Pocket Reference:
Cycling In Scotland
HarperCollins 000471010X
£9.99
spiral bound

Henniker, Harry
101 Bike Routes In Scotland
Mainstream hb 1851587853
£9.99

A cycling guide that covers the whole of Scotland and features a wide variety of routes for all types of cyclists.

101 Mountain Bike Routes
In Scotland
Mainstream ppc 1851589368
£14.99

Diving

MacDonald, Rod
Dive Scapa Flow 3rd ed.
Mainstream ppc 185158983X
£14.99

A practical and comprehensive guide to diving the spectacular wrecks of the scuttled World War I German fleet, sunk in Scapa Flow.
Dive: Scotland's Greatest
Wrecks
Mainstream hb 185158532X
£12.99

Miscellaneous

Parke, Hilary
Ski & Snowboard: Scotland
(1998 ed.)
Luath Press pb 0946487359
£6.99

An informative guide to the slopes of Scotland, giving the skier or snowboarder invaluable advice on a wide range of topics. This is an updated edition of the *Scottish Skiing Handbook, 1989.*

Reid, Jamie
A Licence to Print Money
Mainstream pb 1851588167
£8.99

Jamie Reid examines the history and the facts of the huge industry that is gambling in its many forms, be it on dogs, horses or roulette wheels. He talks about the rich cast of characters who have been at the centre of the bookmaking and betting worlds, and examines the industry as it is today.

Robertson, George
Tennis In Scotland
S.L.T.A. hb 095257540X £20.00

George Robertson's book celebrates the Scottish Lawn Tennis Association's centenary. It is a fascinating account of the sport's history in Scotland over the last 100 years, concentrating on the various items of interest and areas of change in which the Association has been involved over this period of time

Stark, Ian
The Stark Approach:
Reflections on Horses, Training and Eventing
Mainstream hb 1840180609
£15.99

Ian Stark is a leading figure in the equestrian world, twice winner of the Badminton Horse Trials and with an Olympic medal to his name. This volume takes a behind-the-scenes look at his life and gives much practical information on his training methods.

Transport

Donald, Stuart
In The Wake of The Vital Spark: Para Handy's Scotland
Neil Wilson hb 1897784554
£9.99

A look into the real world of the Clyde puffers and the people who manned them, the world that was to inspire Neil Munro's short stories.

MacDonald, Dan
The Clyde Puffer
House Of Lochar hb
1899863125 £8.95

A fascination with the world of the Clyde puffer is conveyed in Dan MacDonald's book containing 52 photographs, most of which are his own.

Paterson, Len
The Light In The Glens: The Rise and Fall of the Puffer Trade
House Of Lochar hb
1899863141 £16.99

A heavily illustrated history of the puffer from its origins as a horse-drawn canal scow to its role as the main supplier of goods to the Highlands and Islands. Paterson gives details of everyday life on board, as well as a historical overview of the puffers' importance.

Rixson, Denis
The West Highland Galley
Birlinn hb 1874744866 £20.00

Denis Rixson assesses the role of the traditional Highland galleys or birlinns (a Gaelic adaptation of a Norse design) which were of crucial importance to the Highland economy for almost a millenium.

Ferguson, David M.
Shipwrecks of North East Scotland
Mercat Press pb 1873644140
£8.99

An account of maritime disasters around the North East coast of Scotland ranging in time from the earliest times to the present day, covering Napoleonic warships, smuggling craft and all points in between.

History of Railways of Scottish Highlands
House of Lochar pb

Thomas, John
Vol.1: The West Highland Railway
1899863214 £10.99

Vallance, H.A.
Vol.2: The Highland Railway
1899863079 £9.95

Vallance, H.A.
Vol.3: The Great North of Scotland Railway
0946537607 £7.99

Thomas, John
Vol.4: The Callander & Oban Railway
0946537615 £7.99

Thomas, John
Vol.5: The Skye Railway
0946537623 £7.99

Prebble, John
The High Girders: The Story of the Tay Bridge Disaster
Penguin pb 0140045902 £7.99

Prebble tells the complete story of the Tay Bridge from its inception and construction to its brief moments of glory followed by the disaster and all its repercussions.

Swinfen, David
The Fall of the Tay Bridge
Mercat Press pb 1873644345 £9.99

The carefully researched story of the Tay Bridge disaster which cost the lives of 75 people one night in 1879.

Whyte, Iain Boyd & Baxter, Colin
Benjamin Baker: Forth Bridge
Colin Baxter hb 3930698188 £29.00

The Forth Bridge was one of the greatest engineering achievements of the Victorian age. Iain Boyd Whyte details the many reasons why this historic structure exudes functional elegance while Colin Baxter's colour photographs illustrate its scale, power and geometry.

Kennedy, Duncan
The Birth and Death of a Highland Railway: The Ballachulish Line
House Of Lochar pb 1899863117 £10.95

The story of the famous and much missed Ballachulish Line from its construction at the start of this century to its closure in 1966.

McKinstry, S.
Sure As The Sunrise: A History of Albion Motors
John Donald hb 0859764605 £20.00

A history of Scotland's oldest continuously operating motor company.

Travel & General Interest

Scotland Touring Guides

There are many excellent guide books which cover Scotland as a whole. Among the best are some of the familiar names. The *Blue Guide: Scotland* by John Tomes (11th ed., Blue Guides pb, 0713644621, 15.99), as well as giving detailed descriptions of Edinburgh and Glasgow suggests touring routes for the whole of Scotland. It includes maps, details of leisure activities and is particularly strong on the history, art and architecture of the country, providing a wealth of background information. Historical sites are also well covered in *Cadogan Guides: Scotland* (Cadogan Bks, 0947754636, £13.99) by R. Miers. This guide describes the best spots for walking, climbing, sailing, golfing or enjoying the scenery. It includes information on accommodation and places to eat, along with full travel details. A star ratings system is used in the *Michelin Green Guide To Scotland* (Michelin pb, 206157503X, £8.99) to alert visitors to the must-see sights in their area. As well as giving details of these sights, the guide provides background and practical information. The purchase of a separate map is necessary with the Michelin guide. Fodor's *Scotland 1998* (Fodor pb, 067903532X, £14.99), as well as containing maps and city and countryside touring advice, is full of helpful tips and recommendations on sights, sports and shopping, not to mention accommodation and eating places. All the reviews come from residents of the areas covered. *Frommer's Scotland* (3rd ed., Frommer pb, 0028608739, £12.99) covers similar ground to those above. It also contains a golf guide, details of where to shop at the source for woollens and tartans, and includes both city and regional maps. Written with its trademark vigour *The Rough Guide to Scotland* (2nd ed., Rough Guides pb, 1858283027, £9.99) seeks out the latest attractions in Edinburgh and Glasgow, gives practical advice on outdoor activities throughout Scotland and recommendations on accommodation, food and drink. There is plenty of background information on a variety of topics, and over thirty maps. Further invaluable information is provided by the **Scottish Tourist Board's** *Touring Guide to Scotland* (HarperCollins pb, 000448679X, £4.99), *Collins Touring Guide: Scotland* and the more compact *Collins Pocket Reference: Scotland* (HarperCollins pb, 0004708709, £5.99) all with excellent travel information.

Some guides take a particular angle on the subject. *Scotland The Best* by **Peter Irvine** (HarperCollins hb, 0004721500, £12.99, pb 0004721519, £9.99) is the premier guide to the very best Scotland has to offer from hill walks and ceilidhs to seafood and beaches. Taking an environmentally friendly approach is **Jackie Redding's** *Scotland the Green* (Findhorn Press pb, 189917141X £4.50) which emphasises places serving vegetarian or vegan food or with other strong environmental connections. For anyone alarmed by the costs of entertainment, help is at hand in **Anna Fenge's** *Scotland on a Shoestring* (Mainstream pb, 1851589376, £6.99) which concentrates on the things you can do for very little or that are free. Finally, for those interested in Scotland's many historical sites and buildings, the following three books are among the many useful guides on offer. **David Clark's** *Battlefield Walks: Scotland* (Sutton pb, 0750902612, £9.99) gives details of twelve circular walks around major battlefield sites from Bannockburn to the Second World War airfield at RAF East Fortune. The walks are intended for the everyday walker as well as the more experienced, and include full back-up details. Information about every authentic Scottish castle is included in *The Castles of Scotland* (Constable pb, 0094734305, £12.95) by **Maurice Lindsay**, a highly authoritative and well illustrated guide that has become a standard work for tourists and enthusiasts alike. Focusing on Scotland's historic towns, in *Mercat Cross And Tolbooth: Understanding Scotland's Old Burghs* (John Donald pb, 0859761967, £7.50) **Craig Mair** shows how to recognise the many historical features of the Scottish burghs that can still be seen today.

For information on the various different types of accommodation available, the following **Scottish Tourist Board** publications contain details provided by the hotels, B & Bs and campsites themselves:
Where To Stay: Bed & Breakfast '98
0854195203 £5.99
Where To Stay: Caravan & Camping '98
0854195211 £3.99
Where To Stay: Hotels & Guest Houses '98
085419519X £8.99
Where To Stay: Self Catering '98
085419522X £5.99

The *Discovering* series paperbacks published by John Donald are comprehensive guides written by recognised authorities on the areas covered. Each volume has a highly readable style and is filled with interesting facts and anecdotes about people, places, and events connected with its region. The books will be of great value to both visitors and natives, as well as providing useful information for local historians.

Smith, Robert
Discovering Aberdeenshire 2nd ed.
0859764915 £8.95

Orr, W.
Discovering Argyll, Mull and Iona
0859762696 £8.95

Gemmell, Alastair
Discovering Arran
0859762904 £8.95

Strawhorn, J.
Discovering Ayrshire
0859761991 £8.95

Willis, D.
Discovering The Black Isle
0859762637 £8.95

Spence, Alan
Discovering The Borders 1
0859763609 £8.95
Discovering The Borders 2
0859763773 £8.95

Whyte, I. & K.
Discovering East Lothian
085976222X £8.95

Lamont-Brown, R.
Discovering Fife
0859762041 £8.95

Macleod, I.
Discovering Galloway
0859761142 £8.95

MacLean, L.
Discovering Inverness-shire
0859762289 £7.50

Grant, J.S.
Discovering Lewis and Harris
0859761851 £8.95

Simpson, Eric
Discovering Moray, Banff and Nairn 2nd ed.
0859764923 £8.95

Thompson, F.
Discovering Speyside
0859762300 £7.50

Hendrie, W.F.
Discovering West Lothian
0859761622 £8.95

Edinburgh

Scotland's capital is a favourite destination for tourists visiting the country, and thanks to the wealth of historical sites, attractive parks and architecture, the world-renowned Festival and countless other events and activities on offer, it does not disappoint. There is an equal abundance of guides to the city, of which the following is a selection of the best:

Part of a highly respected series of guides, *Edinburgh The Best!* by **Peter Irvine** (HarperCollins plc, 0004721527, £5.99) casts its eye over the Scottish capital, picking out the very finest it has to offer overall. The broader-based *Handbook To Edinburgh* (Mercat Press pb, 1873644736, £9.99), is a complete guide that covers a wide range of topics including literature, folklore, history and shopping. For a comprehensive reference book on the capital look no further than *The Edinburgh Encyclopaedia* (Mainstream hb, 1851587624, £20.00). Edited by **Sandy Mullay**, it covers the Old and New Towns as well as many of the outlying villages, with detailed information in an A to Z arrangement. If you really want to know about a city, ask someone who lives there. The *Time Out Guide To Edinburgh* (Penguin pb, 0140266844, £9.99) is compiled by residents of the city and provides detailed 'insider' information on, for example, tourist attractions, clubs, pubs and markets. Focusing on Edinburgh's central area, **Iseabail Macleod's** *Edinburgh Pocket Guide* (Colin Baxter flx, 1900455013 £5.00), is a compact guide illustrated with Colin Baxter photographs. Many items of interest are highlighted and the guide (which is available in several languages) comes complete with maps and a detailed information directory. The 'Insight Compact Guide' *Edinburgh* (A.P.A pb, 9624213569, £3.99) is another small-format book that covers the capital's major points of interest. Meanwhile visitors (or natives) with very young children will appreciate the invaluable *Edinburgh For The Under Fives: A Handbook For Parents* (6th ed., Edinburgh. For Under fives pb, 0951239759, £4.95). This guide is compiled by local members of the **National Childbirth Trust** and contains details of fun activities for pre-school children, as well as useful information such as toddler-friendly eating-places and changing facilities.

The 'Athens of the North' is a very attractive city, and lends itself extremely well to the art of photography. *Edinburgh Through The Lens* by **Ian Torrance** (John Donald hb, 0859763226, £14.95) reflects this, and is an excellent photographic gift book evoking the many different moods and atmospheres of the Scottish capital. **Colin Baxter** has also produced a distinctive photographic portrait of the city in *Edinburgh* (Colin Baxter pb, 094866133X, £9.00), available in French, German and Italian as well as English.

Edinburgh's historical heritage is a natural source of fascination for tourists, and there are plenty of helpful books on the subject. *The Place Names Of Edinburgh: Their Origins And History* by **Stuart Harris** (Gordon Wright hb, 0903065835, £45.00) is a monumental reference book that covers the history and derivation of all the street, close and place names in Edinburgh, thus providing much information about the city's past. **Alastair Hardie** concentrates on Edinburgh's most famous street in *Close Encounters In The Royal Mile* (John Donald pb, 0859764141, £4.50), an excellent guide to the 83 closes off the Royal Mile that points out many features of interest. The history of one of the best-known buildings in the Royal Mile is detailed in **D. Smith's** *John Knox House: Gateway To Edinburgh's Old Town* (John Donald pb, 0859764370, £6.50). One of the most important medieval buildings in Scotland, for centuries it was at the heart of Edinburgh's commercial, cultural and religious developments. Two books which double as historical and walking guides cover the Old and New Towns respectively. *Walks In Edinburgh's Old Town* by **Michael and Elspeth Wills** (Mercat Press pb, 1873644698, £5.99) is a pocket-sized guide to the closes of the historic heart of the city, complete with easy-to-read maps, while **David Dick's** *Capital Walks In Edinburgh: The New Town* (Neil Wilson pb, 1897784201 £5.99) provides historical information on over fifty places or items of interest along three walking routes in the classically designed New Town.

An unusual glimpse into Edinburgh's past is found in *Edinburgh à la Carte: A History of Food in Edinburgh* by **Michael Turnbull** with **Paul Rogerson** (S.C.P. pb, 1898218870, £6.95). The city's mixed culinary past and present is described, from the son of the 2nd Duke of Queensbury roasting his kitchen boy on a spit and the apparent popularity of ground 'Murdered Man's Head', to the internationally famous restaurants of the present day which offer decidedly more palatable dishes. Still on the subject of food and drink, Maureen Horrox looks further afield in *The Teapot Trail: A Taste of Edinburgh and Tayside* (pb, 1873293739, £2.25), providing a nostalgic guide to the finest tea houses in Scotland which includes summaries of opening hours and highlights from the menu with a very personal appeal.

Last but by no means least, one of Edinburgh's fine green spaces is explored in *A Guide To Holyrood Park* by **Gordon Wright** et al (Gordon Wright pb, 0903065576, £2.95), which gives details of the Royal Park's geology, wildlife and history.

Glasgow

The vibrant city of Glasgow is known for its own proudly distinctive character, complete with an irreverent sense of humour and unique dialect, the Glasgow Patter. In recent years the city has been enjoying a widespread cultural renaissance that has attracted an increasing amount of visitors.

As he did for Edinburgh, **Peter Irvine** provides a thorough guide to Glasgow's top attractions in *Glasgow The Best!* (HarperCollins plc, 0004721535, £5.99), alerting visitors to those places and events not to be missed. *The Glasgow Encyclopaedia* by **Joe Fisher** (Mainstream hb, 1851582126, £20.00) is a single volume historical guide to the city, which charts its rise from one of the first industrial centres in the world to becoming the second city of the Empire in Victorian times, its later industrial decline and its more recent artistic renaissance that has attracted so much attention. Likewise, *The People's Palace Book Of Glasgow* by **Liz Carnegie** et al (Mainstream pb, 1840180684, £9.99) takes a historical approach. 1997 is the centenary of Glasgow's pioneering Social History Museum. This celebratory and lavishly illustrated book examines the city's history using the museum's large collection of artefacts. It includes sections on comics such as Rab C. Nesbitt, Billy Connolly and Stanley Baxter, tales from the city during World War II, and looks at the darker side of Glasgow, giving a rounded picture of the city's many faces. Away from the city centre, the two-volume *Villages Of Glasgow* by **A. Smart** is packed with fascinating information on Glasgow's outlying villages. Vol.1 (John Donald pb, 0859762327, £9.95) covers those to the north of the Clyde, while Vol. 2 (John Donald pb, 0859763919, £9.95) looks at those to the south. As for food and drink in the city, **David Phillips'** *Eating Out In Glasgow* (Argyll pb, 187464053X, £3.99) is an independently compiled guide that lists the many pubs, cafes, restaurants and wine bars in Glasgow, giving advice on service, prices, quality and atmosphere, while *The Glasgow Pub Companion* by **Rudolph Kenna** (Neil Wilson pb, 1897784481, £7.99) gives the lowdown on around 200 pubs, covering the old, the traditional and the new.

Highlands & Islands

The Highlands and Islands contain some of the most ruggedly beautiful landscapes in the world. They are very popular tourist areas with much to offer visitors in terms of outdoor pursuits, including excellent opportunities for sailing, climbing, fishing, shooting and walking. There are also the multi-faceted delights of visiting the many historical sites which range across the millenia, not to mention the joys of golf and whisky distilleries. The islands all have their own character and particular charms. All in all the Highlands and Islands have something for everyone.

In *The Scottish Highlands* (Mainstream hb, 1851581499, £17.99) **Dorothy** and **Alastair Dunnett** give their personal view of the area and include a selection of David Paterson's beautiful photographs. The scenic splendour of these regions is also evident in **A. and P. MacDonald's** *The Highlands And Islands of Scotland* (Weidenfeld & Nicolson pb, 0297832131, £7.99), a lush photographic history book that reveals the Highlands' social and historical significance. **Jim Crumley's** accounts of his journeys through his native Scotland have given him a justified reputation as one of Scotland's finest travel writers. He commits what he sees to the page in an eloquent and easily accessible fashion. His books on the Highlands include *Among Mountains* (Mainstream hb, 1851585443, £14.99), *Gulfs of Blue Air: A Highland Journey* (Mainstream hb, 1851588892, £15.99) and *The Heart of the Cairngorms* (Colin Baxter pb, 1900455277, £9.00). In the latter the author argues the case for conservation of the wilderness that is the Cairngorms in an impassioned exploration of the mountain heartland of Scotland. One of the Highland's most infamous place-names, the events at Glencoe put it at the heart of Highland history, but even without its bloody past Glencoe would be a famous area of wilderness due to its landscape of dramatic peaks. In *Glencoe: Monarch Of Glens* (Colin Baxter pb, 1900455730, £8.00), **Jim Crumley** examines Glencoe's mountaineering inheritance as well as its history and current issues surrounding its use. This large format book is illustrated by images from the camera of **Colin Baxter**.

The Scottish Islands by **Hamish Haswell-Smith** (Canongate hb, 0862415799, £25.00) is a gazeteer that covers every one of Scotland's islands. Beautifully produced, it contains information on all aspects of the islands, from hotels and how to reach them to historical and natural backgrounds - a book that is ideal for use when touring or just for browsing through. *Scottish Island Hopping* by **Maclean** et al (Polygon pb, 0748661646, £8.50) is a friendly guide full of useful inside knowledge from seasoned travellers who have an intimate uderstanding of the islands. The guide contains maps, details of places to stay, items of interest and potted histories of each island.

Among the islands, the Hebrides are particularly alluring with a strongly romantic image. *Hebridean Odyssey: Songs, Poems, Prose And Images* edited by **M. Sinclair** (Polygon pb, 0748661972, £12.99) provides a unique celebration of the cultural inheritance of these islands and a way of life that has almost gone. Using material mainly from the islanders themselves, this evocatively illustrated anthology builds into a beautiful representation of the Hebrides and their inhabitants. Focusing on particular islands, David & Charles publish the acclaimed Pevensey Island Guides. Each guide includes detailed and informative text and excellent photographs in a clear arrangement. The Western Isles covered are *The Isle of Arran* by **Robert McLellan** (pb, 0907115918, £7.99), *Islay* by **Norman Newton** (pb, 090711590X, £7.99) and *Mull & Iona* by **P.A. MacNab** (pb, 0907115926, £7.99). They are also available in hardback at £10.99 each.

Staying with Mull and Iona, another **Jim Crumley** book, *The Heart of Mull* (Colin Baxter pb, 1900455056, £9.00) is a lyrical exploration of the landscape and wildlife of one of the most beautiful Hebridean islands, while **E. Mairi MacArthur** has written two books about Iona. Iona is one of the Scottish islands that have been inhabited since prehistoric times. It is famous as the island from which St. Columba and his followers spread the Christian teachings. In *Iona: Island Guide* (Colin Baxter hb, 1900455110, £13.00) the author uses her own knowledge of Iona to produce a comprehensive guide to this beautiful island steeped in religious history. The book is illustrated with both photographs and drawings. *Columba's Island: Iona from Prehistory to Present* (EUP pb, 0748607374, £12.95) looks at Iona throughout the ages from several viewpoints: spiritual, social and historical, from the time of Iron Age inhabitants to the present day community.

Skye and St. Kilda are also among the better known western islands. *Skye: The Complete Visitors Guide* (2nd ed., Thistle Press pb, 0952095017, £7.95) is a wide-ranging touring guide that also contains details of over twenty classic walks on the island. It is informative on Skye's history and archaeology, as well as covering accommodation, visitor attractions and outdoor activities including fishing. **Derek Cooper** gives a detailed picture of the island as it once was and as it is today in *Skye* (Birlinn pb, 1874744378, £8.99), which is part gazetteer, part anthology, part guide and suitable for both armchair travellers and visitors. *Skye: The Island* by **James Hunter** (Mainstream hb, 1851588272, £12.99) includes photographs by Cailean Maclean, and gives a portrait of Skye that is passionate and moving without ever becoming sentimental or romanticised. The equally scenic St. Kilda is Scotland's first World Heritage site. **David Quine's** *St Kilda: Island Guide* (Colin Baxter hb, 0948661585, £15.00) is a comprehensive exploration of the island, covering in detail its history, geography and wildlife. It is well illustrated with photographs and drawings, and includes 16 maps. Also published by Colin Baxter is *St Kilda: A Portrait of Britain's Remotest Island Landscape* (hb, 0948661038, £16.00) in which **Colin Baxter** and **Jim Crumley** present a personal view in words and pictures of this intriguing island, rich in wildlife and with a previous long history of human habitation. **Charles Maclean** looks back at the period of man's habitation of the island in the richly illustrated *St Kilda* (Canongate pb, 0862413885, £5.99). This is a classic piece of social history, charting the island's society from nearly one thousand years ago to the present day. It examines the islanders' increasing contact with the mainland during the 19th century which eventually brought their society to an end in the 1930s, when the islanders could no longer support themselves and were evacuated at their own request. The destruction of St. Kilda's society reflects a process observable throughout the world, and its story is told here with skill and compassion.

The island of Mingulay, like St. Kilda, lost its inhabitants early on in this century. At one point in time this beautiful, rugged island was home to over 160 people, but in 1912 the lack of a proper landing place, the neglect caused by absentee landlords and the insufficient fertile land led to a voluntary and inevitable evacuation. The story of these events took years to research and is told by **Ben Buxton** in *Mingulay* (Birlinn pb, 1874744246, £10.99) in a poignant and moving way.

The islands of Orkney and Shetland are distinct from each other, yet share some common factors, notably the rival influences brought to bear on them by Scotland and Scandinavia. In his major ethnological work *The Northern Isles: Orkney And Shetland* (Tuckwell Press pb, 1862320586, £20.00) **Alexander Fenton** recreates the physical environment of past inhabitants of these islands, examining their everyday lives and thus giving the reader a key to understanding the character of these remote places. The Pevensey Island Guides *Orkney* (David & Charles pb, 0907115934, £7.99) and *Shetland* (David & Charles pb, 0907115888, £7.99) by **Patrick Bailey** and **Norman Newton** respectively, provide excellent guides to the islands in the same attractive format as the Hebridean island guides. One of Orkney's most famous sons was **George Mackay Brown**, whose writing is inextricably linked to the life of the island, past and present. In *Portrait of Orkney* (John Murray pb, 0719545390, £6.95) he gives a personal account of this island and its history, looking at the Orkney people's way of life and the landscape around them. The text is illustrated with photographs by Gunnie Moberg and drawings by Erlend Brown. As an unusual photographic record of the islands, **Norman Hudson** has compiled two volumes, both published by The Shetland Times: *Souvenir Postcards from Orkney* (pb, 1898852006, £16.95) and *Souvenir Postcards from Shetland* (pb, 0900662824, £14.95). During Victorian times and just after, collecting photographic postcards of scenic areas of Britain was all the rage. The postcards now constitute a unique photographic history of the area in question. These two volumes, each showing 200 early postcards, are part of that legacy.

The Borders

The Borders Region with its small towns and villages surrounded by hills has plenty to attract visitors: from Roman remains and medieval abbeys to outdoor activities such as fishing and walking, not to mention the often picturesque towns themselves. *The Borders Book* by **Donald Omand** (Birlinn pb, 1874744734 £9.99) provides a definitive history of the region from its geological and prehistoric foundations to the Roman invasion, the later feuds and fighting with England and right up to the present day. The book includes sections on the Borders dialects, customs and the all-important game of rugby. Former Liberal Party leader **Sir David Steel** and his wife **Judy** take us on a lavishly illustrated tour of the region in *Border Country* (Birlinn pb, 1874744491 £12.99). The Steels have lived in the Borders for many years, Sir David having been an MP there for over thirty years, and their intimate knowledge and love of the area gives us a unique insight into the customs, legends, traditions and historical heritage of this beautiful region of Scotland.

Aberdeen

Smith, Robert
The Granite City: A History of Aberdeen
John Donald hb 0859762777 £13.95

Aberdeen began as a town of 'ten crooked streets' and eventually expanded to become the oil capital of Europe. Aberdonian Robert Smith studies the changes the city has undergone over the years, looking at both its culture and its people.

Dundee

Crumley, Jim
The Road and the Miles: A Homage to Dundee
Mainstream hb 185158787X
£14.99

Nature writer Jim Crumley is a Dundonian, and this book is his tribute to the 'City of Discovery'. He examines post-war Dundee through a mixture of autobiography, fiction and poetry, with his thoughts on the city's streets and people. The book includes such themes as the unique McGonagall and Dundonians' passion for football, as well as Crumley's discovery of his own moving family history.

Inverness

Newton, N.S.
The Life and Times of Inverness
John Donald pb 0859764427
£9.95

Inverness has a long and colourful history, described here from prehistoric times right through to the present day. The author looks at the effect on the city and its people of such events as Cromwell's occupation, Culloden, cholera epidemics, religious disagreements, the Victorian age and the two World Wars. Included are details of local personalities, Inverness's fortunes in sport and trade, as well as schools and churches. A comprehensive guide to this Highland city.

Perth

Graham-Campbell, D.
Perth: The Fair City
John Donald pb 085976382
£9.95

This history of Perth looks back at its medieval origins and traces its story up to the present day. It includes entertaining and touching tales about the city, along with details of walks that can be made round medieval and Georgian Perth.

Kay, Billy (Ed)
Dundee Book: An Anthology of Living in the City
Manistream hb 1851587950
£14.99

Dundee is experiencing a renewed upturn in its fortunes, a welcome contrast to the days when reliance on one industry caused its downfall from being Scotland's second wealthiest city. This illustrated anthology explores the distinctive character of the city and its people throughout its eventful history. It covers ordinary Dundonians, famous Dundonians such as Liz McColgan and unusual visitors such as Daniel Defoe and Mary Shelley.

Stirling

Mair, Craig
Stirling: The Royal Burgh
John Donald pb 0859764206
£9.95

The Gateway to the Highlands has a rich and varied history that includes being the location for seven major battles, and also, in Holy Rude Church, for the christening and crowning of kings and queens. This chronicle of Stirling features the people and events that have been part of its remarkable history.

Needless to say, there are countless numbers of guide books to every part of Scotland, and it would be impossible to list them all here. Hopefully, this selection will have given an idea of the variety of books available and will encourage would-be travellers to browse the relevant section in their bookshops, where they will find many other equally fine guides along with those described above.

Travel Literature

Buchanan, Rev. John L.
Travels In The Western Isles From 1782 To 1790
Maclean Press pb 1899272046
£8.50

A reprint of the Rev. Buchanan's long out-of-print account of his time in the Western Hebrides as a Missionary Minister, which gives the modern reader unique insight into many aspects of 18th century island life.

Burrell, Sir William
Sir William Burrell's Northern Tour, 1758
(Ed. John G. Dunbar)
Tuckwell Press pb 1898410984
£14.99

Sir William Burrell was an English lawyer and Member of Parliament. His account of his wide-ranging journey through areas not normally visited by travellers at this time is an important historical document in many ways. His meticulous style and his love of art and antiques as well as agriculture, trade and industry, make him an interesting commentator on post-1745 Rebellion Scotland.

Zaluski, I. & P.
The Scottish Autumn of Frederick Chopin
John Donald pb 0859763897
£8.50

A lively and involving account of Chopin's travels round Scotland in 1848, including extracts from the composer's letters.

Cobbett, William
Cobbett's Tour In Scotland
(Ed. D. Green)
Mercat Press pb 0080303846
£8.95

Cobbett was one of the most widely read publicists of his time. In his *Tour In Scotland*, a section of his *Rural Rides*, he builds a still recognisable picture of the areas he visited. Primarily a major political journalist, he gives an invaluable detailed account of the political state of Scotland on the brink of Reform.

Cassells, Ian
A Light Walk
Whittles pb 1870325516 £11.95

In 1986 lighthouse man Ian Cassells carried out a sponsored walk covering all the then manned lighthouses on the Scottish mainland. The journey took him to some of the most remote and ruggedly beautiful parts of Scotland. This book recounts a journey of over 1,000 miles, visiting lighthouses comprising a large variety of styles and from different eras, with the author providing humorous anecdotes and historical details along the way.

Delaney, Frank
A Walk To The Western Isles: After Boswell And Johnson
HarperCollins pb 0586211322
£8.99

Following in the footsteps of Samuel Johnson and James Boswell's famous trip to the Highlands and inner Hebrides in 1773, Frank Delaney finds that many of the places where they stayed still remain and are remarkably unchanged. As he travels he draws ever closer to 'literature's most famous double act', seeing them through new eyes. As well as providing us with a modern recreation of their journey, Delaney re-invigorates our perception of Boswell and Johnson

Dunnett, Sir Alistair
The Canoe Boys: From The
Clyde Past The Cuillins
Neil Wilson pb 1897784422
£7.99

The adventures of Sir Alistair
Dunnett and Seumas Adam
as they travelled up the West
Coast of Scotland in canoes
in the early 1930s.

Gordon, Seton

When Seton Gordon
travelled the Hebrides and
the Western and Central
Highlands in the early 1930s
he wrote his much heralded
accounts of his journeys.
Using highly descriptive
narrative passages mixed in
with geographical and
historical details, he imbues
every page with the haunting
beauty of the landscape.
Hebridean Memories
Neil Wilson pb 1897784430
£7.99
Highways And Byways in the
West Highlands
Birlinn pb 1874744327 £9.99
Highways And Byways in the
Central Highlands
Birlinn pb 1874744335 £9.99

Gunn, Neil
Off In A Boat
House Of Lochar pb
1899863257 £9.99

This book is much more than
a record of Gunn's 1930s'
holiday in a boat, rather it is
an account of the time when
he resigned his civil service
job, sold his house and decided to write full time. During
this watershed in Gunn's life
and career he was also discovering the lure of the ocean,
the beauty of the islands and
further immersing himself in
the legends and traditions of
the Highlands. All these
strands are woven together
here into a coherent and
revealing whole.

Hedderwick, Mairi

Mairi Hedderwick, author of
the *Katie Morag* children's
books, has had a connection
with the Hebrides since
childhood, and had long
harboured the desire to
travel to every Hebridean
island. *Eye on the Hebrides* is
a gorgeously illustrated
account of her personal
voyage. It includes delicate
sketches of people and landscapes, and captures in words
and pictures the essence of
these islands. *Highland Journey*
recreates the sketching tour
of Scotland undertaken by
Victorian artist J.T. Reid. Her
own elegant watercolours
coupled with Reid's fine
engravings create a lush
impression of the Highland
landscape.
Eye on the Hebrides
Canongate pb 0862413486
£9.99
Highland Journey
Canongate pb 0862414504
£14.99

Hewitson, Jim
Clinging To The Edge: Journals From An Orkney Island
Mainstream hb 1851588213
£14.99

Journalist Jim Hewitson came across the island of Papa Westray in the early 1980s. *Clinging To The Edge* is a collection of eight years' worth of essays, articles and diary jottings about this fascinating island, battered by contemporary economics and Atlantic storms.

Hogg, James
A Tour Of The Highlands In 1803
Mercat Press pb 0901824801
£5.99

A facsimile of the 1888 edition of Hogg's journeys in the Highlands written in the form of letters addressed to Sir Walter Scott.

Johnson, Samuel & James Boswell

In 1773 Boswell finally persuaded Dr. Johnson to undertake a tour of Scotland and the Hebrides. Both published best-selling accounts of their famous journey which was to cement their friendship. They remain two of the finest pieces of travel writing ever published.

Journey To The Hebrides: A Journey to the Western Islands of Scotland and The Journal of a Tour to the Hebrides
Canongate pb 0862415888
£5.99
A Journey to the Western Isles of Scotland and the Journal of a Tour of the Hebrides
Penguin pb 0140432213 £6.99

Maclean, Rory
The Oatmeal Ark: From The Western Isles to a Promised Sea
Flamingo pb 000637977X £7.99

An inventive and clever travel book by the author of *Stalin's Nose*. *The Oatmeal Ark* is the story of Rory Maclean's recreation of his great-grandfather's journey from Scotland to Nova Scotia. Woven into the text is the voice of his great-grandfather's ghost. A voyage through memory and history as much as over land and sea.

Robinson, Neil
To The Ends Of The Earth: Norman McLeod and the Highlanders' Migration To Nova Scotia and New Zealand
Birlinn pb 1869502655 £14.99

This is the remarkable saga of Norman McLeod, a Highland preacher who sailed to Nova Scotia with over 800 of his followers in 1817 to create a new life. After 35 hard years there the Rev. McLeod (then in his 70s) gathered his people together and sailed to New Zealand where they settled permanently. An engrossing true-life adventure story that is beautifully relayed.

Martin, Martin
A Description Of the Western Islands of Scotland Circa 1695
Birlinn pb 187474419X £8.99

A compilation volume of the three earliest accounts of the Hebrides, including Martin Martin's *A Voyage To St. Kilda* and Sir Donald Munro's *A Description Of The Western Islands Of Scotland* (1549). These accounts cast light on a time in history before the Jacobite rebellions, when the old Highland social structures were still in place. Martin Martin's classic work is almost unique in being written by a Hebridean native rather than a visitor to the islands.

Muir, Alexander
From Aberdeen To Ottawa In 1845: The Diary Of Alexander Muir (Ed. G. Mackenzie)
Mercat Press pb 0080379834
£5.99

This book is the jounal of Alexander Muir who in 1845 set off from Aberdeen to visit relatives in Canada. It gives a historical account of crossing the Atlantic under sail and of Muir's travels within Canada by steam ship, canoe and on foot. He describes the established Canadian cities and newly formed farms and pays special attention to the contribution that Scottish settlers had made in the development of this nation.

Muir, Edwin
Scottish Journey: A Modern Classic
Mainstream pb 1851588418
£6.99

A wonderfully written travel book that takes Edwin Muir over the whole length and breadth of Scotland in his quest for the real nature of Scottish identity.

Muir, John (1838–1914)

Muir's reputation as one of the founding fathers of the modern environmental movement is rapidly expanding. Born in Scotland he emigrated to the United States and was instrumental in setting up that country's first national parks. In most interpretations of his life it is often overlooked that he was also a magnificent mountaineer who pioneered many new techniques and ideas. *Amongst the Mountains* focuses on this aspect of Muir's life and includes a lot of material that has previously been unavailable in the UK. *The Wilderness Journeys* is a collection of some of John Muir's finest writing that further illuminates his love of the wilderness. It includes the never previously published 'Stickeen'.
Amongst The Mountains (Ed G. White)
Canongate pb 0862417856
£5.99
The Eight Wilderness Discovery Books
Diadem hb 0906371341 £20.00
The Wilderness Journeys
Canongate pb 0862415861
£8.99

Pennant, Thomas
A Tour Of Scotland In 1769
Mercat Press pb 0950588490
£5.99

When Thomas Pennant started his tour in 1769 Scotland was regarded as *terra incognita* for the southerner. This valuable picture of the Highlands in the wake of the Government's strict policy of proscription of dress, ornament and weapon is a candid and revealing one, containing detailed observations of games, dress and characters, not to mention Scotland's natural scenery. The account includes illustrations by Moses Griffith.

"In God's wilderness lies the hope of the world - the great, fresh, unblighted, unredeemed wilderness. The galling harness of civilisation drops off, and the wounds heal ere we are aware."
John Muir

Prebble, John
John Prebble's Scotland
Penguin pb 0140082395 £12.50

An intimate journey through memory and landscape that spans from the Borders to the Highlands and Islands, simultaneously affectionate, contentious and expansive.

Bunyan, I. et al
No Ordinary Journey: John Rae, Arctic Explorer, 1813-1893
N.M.S. pb 0948636386 £4.99

A look at this courageous and controversial Orcadian explorer who travelled over 13,000 miles of the Canadian Arctic using native survival techniques.

Stevenson, Robert Louis

Stenvenson's travel writings vary widely from a journey on a sail-powered canoe, travelling on foot in rural France with a pack-donkey, to living in a deserted silver mine in America, yet they all share his enthusiasm for life and adventure. Both the volumes listed below include notes and critical apparatus. The Oxford edition also prints such rarely seen pieces as 'Memories of Fontainebleau' and 'Swiss Notes'.

Travels With A Donkey, An Inland Voyage and The Silverado Squatters
Everyman pb 0460872788 £2.99
Travels With A Donkey In The Cevennes And Selected Travel Writings
Oxford UP pb 0192826298 £4.99

Thomson, David
The People of the Sea
Canongate pb 0862415500 £4.99

This book recounts a series of journeys in search of the man-seal legends of the Celts, legends that view man and nature as inextricably linked. The record of these travels is told by David Thomson in a voice that is clear and haunting.

Weir, Tom
**Weir's World:
An Autobiography Of Sorts**
Canongate pb 0862415489 £9.99

This seasoned traveller talks about his past and his love of the Scottish landscape and wildlife in an unusual and charming autobiography.

Wordsworth, Dorothy
A Tour Of Scotland In 1803
Mercat Press pb 0901824291 £5.99

In 1803 Dorothy Wordsworth, accompanied by her brother William and his friend Coleridge, set out on a six week tour of Scotland. In those days a journey to Scotland was an exotic and adventurous voyage, at a time when very few tourists visited. Dorothy's keen observations and feel for poetic imagery record Scotland at a unique point in time. The journal contains her personal reflections on her experiences in Scotland.

INDEX BY AUTHOR

Waterstone's Branches

ABERDEEN
236 Union St
Tel: 01224 571655

ABERYSTWYTH
Arts Centre
University of Wales
Tel: 01970 623251

AMSTERDAM
Kalverstraat 152
Amsterdam
The Netherlands
Tel: 00 312 0 638 3821

ASTON UNIVERSITY
12 Gosta Gree
Aston Triangle
Tel: 0121 359 3242

ALTRINCHAM
24 George Street
(from Winter 1998)

AYLESBURY
31-32 Friars Square
Tel: 01296 423153

BASINGSTOKE
2 Castle Square
(from Winter 1998)

BATH
4–5 Milsom St
Tel: 01225 448515

University of Bath
Claverton Down
Tel: 01225 465565

BEDFORD
11-13 Silver Street
Tel: 01234 272432

Cranfield University
Bookshop
College Road
Wharley End
Tel: 01234 754280

BELFAST
Queen's Building
8 Royal Avenue
Tel: 01232 247355

BIRKENHEAD
188/192 Grange Rd
Tel: 0151 650 2400

BIRMINGHAM
24–26 High Street
Tel: 0121 633 4353
Fax: 0121 633 4300

Young Waterstone's
Tel: 0121 616 1557

Birmingham
University
Ring Road North
Edgbaston
Tel: 0121 472 3034

BLACKPOOL
4, The Tower
Shopping Centre
Bank Hey Street
Tel: 01253 296136

BOLTON
32–36 Deansgate
Tel: 01204 522588

BOURNEMOUTH
14/16 The Arcade
Tel: 01202 299449

Bournemouth
University
Talbot Campus
Fern Barrow
Poole
Tel: 01202 595528

BRADFORD
University of Bradford,
Great Horton Rd
Tel: 01274 727885

Management
Centre Bookshop,
Emm Lane
Tel: 01274 481404

The Wool Exchange
Tel: 01274 723127

BRUNEL UNIVERSITY
Cleveland Road
Uxbridge
Tel: 01895 257991

BRIGHTON
55–56 North St
Tel: 01273 327867

71-74 North Street
Tel: 01273 206017

BRISTOL
Computer Centre
University of Bristol
Tyndall Avenue
Tel: 0117 925 4297

27–29 College Green
Tel: 0117 925 0511

University of Bristol
Tyndall Avenue
Tel: 0117 925 4297

Cribbs Causeway
33 Lower Mall
Tel: 0117 950 9813

The Galleries
Broadmead
Tel: 0117 925 2274

BROMLEY
20–22 Market Sq
Tel: 0181 464 6562

BRUSSELS
Boulevard Adolphe
Max 71-75
B1000 Brussels
Belgium
Tel: 00 322 219 2708

BURY
4 Union Arcade
Tel: 0161 764 2642

CAMBRIDGE
6 Bridge St
Tel: 01223 300123
Fax: 01223 301539

CANTERBURY
20 St Margaret's St
Tel: 01227 456343

CARDIFF
2a The Hayes
Tel: 01222 665606

CARMARTHEN
Trinity College
Tel: 01267 238100

CHELMSFORD
The Meadows Centre
High Street
(from Winter 1998)

CHELTENHAM
88–90 The Promenade
Tel: 01242 512722

CHESTER
43–45 Bridge St Row
Tel: 01244 328040

CHICHESTER
The Dolphin and
Anchor
West Street
(from Winter 1998)

COLCHESTER
16 Culver Precinct
Tel: 01206 767623

University of Essex
Wivenhoe Park
Tel: 01206 864773

CORK
69 Patrick St
Tel: 00 353 21 276522

Boole Library
University College
Tel: 00 353 21 276575

COVENTRY
22 Cathedral Lanes
Broadgate
Tel:01203 227151

Coventry University
26 Earl Street
Tel: 01203 229092

Coventry University
Bookshop
Earl Street
Tel: 01203 230880

CRAWLEY
83-84 County Mall
Tel: 01293 533471

CROYDON
1063 Whitgift Centre
Tel: 0181 686 7032

DERBY
78–80 St Peter's St
Tel: 01332 296997

University of Derby
Keddleston Road
Tel: 01332 331719

Chevin Avenue
Mickelover
Tel: 01332 511462

DORKING
54–60 South St
Tel: 01306 886884

DUBLIN
7 Dawson St
Tel: 00 353 1 679 1260

The Jervis Centre
Tel: 00 353 1 878 1311

DUNDEE
35 Commercial St
Tel: 01382 200322

DURHAM
69 Saddler St
Tel: 0191 383 1488

University Bookshop
55-57 Saddler Street
Tel: 0191 384 2095

EASTBOURNE
120 Terminus Rd
Tel: 01323 735676

EDINBURGH
128 Princes St
Tel: 0131 226 2666

13–14 Princes St
Tel: 0131 556 3034/5

83 George St
Tel: 0131 225 3436

EGHAM
Royal Holloway
College
Egham Hill
Tel: 01784 471272

EPSOM
113 High St
Tel: 01372 741713

EXETER
48–49 High St
Tel: 01392 218392

5 Isambard Parade
St. Davids Station
Tel: 01392 273433
Tel: 01392 491250

FOLKESTONE
1–2 Guildhall St
Tel: 01303 221 979

GATESHEAD
17 The Parade
Metro Centre
Tel: 0191 493 2715

GATWICK
North Terminal Air-
side
Gatwick Airport
Tel: 01293 507112

GLASGOW
153–157
Sauchiehall St
Tel: 0141 332 9105

GUILDFORD
35–39 North St
Tel: 01483 302919

HANLEY
Stoke-On-Trent
The Tontines Centre
Parliament Row
Tel: 01782 204582

HATFIELD
University of
Hertfordshire
College Lane
Tel: 01707 284940

HEREFORD
18–20 Commercial St
Tel: 01432 275100

University of
Hertfordshire
Mangrove Road
Tel: 01707 285505

HUDDERSFIELD UNIVERSITY
Queensgate
Tel: 01484 472200

HULL
University of Hull
Tel: 01482 444190

The Grand Buildings,
Jameson St
Tel: 01482 580234

ILFORD
158-160 High Road
Tel: 0181 478 8428

INVERNESS
50–52 High St
Tel: 01463 717474

IPSWICH
15–19 Buttermarket
Tel: 01473 289044

KEELE
University of Keele
Tel: 01782 627001

KETTERING
72–76 High St
Tel: 01536 481575

KING'S LYNN
76–77 High St
Tel: 01553 769934

KINGSTON-UPON-THAMES
23–25 Thames St
Tel: 0181 5471221

LANCASTER
2–8 King St
Tel: 01524 32581

Lancaster University
Bookshop
Bailrigg
Tel: 01524 32581

LEAMINGTON SPA
1 Priorsgate
Warwick St
Tel: 01926 883804

LEEDS
36–38 Albion St
Tel: 0113 242 0839

93–97 Albion St
Tel: 0113 244 4588

6 Gledhow Wing
St. James Hospital
Beckett Street
Tel: 0113 243 3144

LEICESTER
21/23 High St
Tel: 0116 251 6838

LIVERPOOL
52 Bold St
Tel: 0151 709 0866

LUTON
University of Luton
Park Square
Tel: 01582 402704

LONDON

CAMDEN, NW1
128 Camden High St
Tel: 0171 284 4948

BUSINESS BOOK-SHOP
72 Park Road NW1
Tel: 0171 723 3902

CHARING CROSS RD, WC2
121 Charing
Cross Rd
Tel: 0171 434 4291

CHARING CROSS AND WESTMINSTER MEDICAL SCHOOL
The Library
Reynold's Building
St Dunstan's Road W6
Tel: 0171 589 3563

CHEAPSIDE, EC2
145–147 Cheapside
Tel: 0171 726 6077

CHISWICK, W4
220-226 Chiswick
High Road
Tel: 0181 995 3559

THE CITY, EC3
1 Whittington Ave
Leadenhall Market
Tel: 0171 220 7882

CITY UNIVERSITY
Northampton Square
EC1
Tel: 0171 608 0706

COVENT GARDEN, WC2
9 Garrick St
Tel: 0171 836 6757

EALING
64 Ealing Broadway
Centre
Tel: 0181 840 5905

EARL'S COURT, SW5
266 Earl's Court Rd
Tel: 0171 370 1616

ECONOMIST BOOK-STORE, WC2
Clare Market
Portugal Street
Tel: 0171 405 5531

GOLDSMITHS', SE14
Goldsmiths' College,
New Cross
Tel: 0181 469 0262

HAMPSTEAD, NW3
68 Hampstead
High St
Tel: 0171 794 1098

HARRODS, SW1
87 Brompton Rd
Tel: 0171 730 1234

IMPERIAL COLLEGE, SW7
Imperial College Rd
Tel: 0171 589 3563

IMPERIAL COLLEGE SCHOOL OF MEDICINE
Charing Cross
Campus
Reynolds Building
St Dunstan's Rd
Tel: 0181 748 9768

Hammersmith
Campus
Commonwealth
Building
Du Cane Road
Tel: 0181 742 9600

ISLINGTON, N1
11 Islington Green
Tel: 0171 704 2280

KENSINGTON, W8
193 Kensington
High St
Tel: 0171 937 8432

KING'S COLLEGE
Macadam House
Surrey Street
Tel: 0171 836 0205

KING'S ROAD, SW3
150-152 King's Road
Tel: 0171 351 2023

KINGSTON UNIVERSITY
2 Brook Street
Tel: 0181 547 1221

LONDON GUILDHALL UNIVERSITY
Calcutta House
Old Castle Street E1
Tel: 0171 247 0727

NOTTING HILL, W11
39 Notting Hill Gate
Tel: 0171 229 9444

OLD BROMPTON RD, SW7
99 Old Brompton Rd
Tel: 0171 581 8522

QUEEN MARY & WESTFIELD, E1
329 Mile End Road
Tel: 0181 980 2554

THAMES VALLEY UNIVERSITY
St. Mary's Road
& Westel House
Ealing,
Tel: 0181 840 6205

TRAFALGAR SQUARE, WC2
The Grand Building
Tel: 0171 839 4411

WIMBLEDON, SW19
12 Wimbledon Bridge
Tel: 0181 543 9899

MAIDSTONE
19 Earl St
Tel: 01622 681112

MACCLESFIELD
47 Mill St
Tel: 01625 424212

MAILING SERVICE
Tel: 01225 448595
Fax: 01225 444732

MANCHESTER
91 Deansgate
Tel: 0161 832 1992

MANCHESTER AIRPORT
Terminal 1 Airside
Tel: 0161 489 3405

MERRY HILL
95/96 Merry Hill
Shopping Centre
Brierley Hill
Tel: 01384 751551

MIDDLESBROUGH
9 Newton Mall
Cleveland Centre
Tel: 01642 242682

University of Teesside
Middlesbrough
Tel: 01642 242017

NEWBURY
64 Northbrook St
Tel: 01635 569998

MILTON KEYNES
51-63 Silbury Arcade
Tel: 01908 696260

NEWCASTLE
104 Grey St
Tel: 0191 261 6140

NORTHAMPTON
19 Abington St
Tel: 01604 634854

NORWICH
21–24 Royal Arcade
Tel: 01603 632426

University of East
Anglia
Tel: 01603 453625

NOTTINGHAM
1–5 Bridlesmith Gate
Tel: 0115 9484499

OXFORD
William Baker House
Broad Street
Tel: 01865 790212

PERTH
St John's Centre
Tel: 01738 630013

PETERBOROUGH
6 Queensgate
Tel: 01733 313476

PLYMOUTH
65/69 New
George St
Tel: 01752 256699

PRESTON
3–5 Fishergate
Tel: 01772 555766

READING
89a Broad St
Tel: 01189 581270

Reading University
Whiteknights
(PO Box 241)
Tel: 01189 8748

RICHMOND-UPON-THAMES
2–6 Hill St
Tel: 0181 332 1600

SALISBURY
7/9 High St
Tel: 01722 415596

SCARBOROUGH
97-98 Westborough
(from Winter 1998)

SHEFFIELD
24 Orchard Sq
Tel: 0114 272 8971

Meadowhall Centre
26 The Arcade
Tel: 0114 256 8495

SHREWSBURY
18–19 High St
Tel: 01743 248112

SOLIHULL
67-71 High Street
Tel: 0121 711 2454

SOUTHAMPTON
69 Above Bar
Tel: 01703 633130

Southampton Medical
School, Southampton
General Hospital
Tel: 01703 780602

University of
Southampton
Highfield
Tel: 01703 558267

SOUTHEND-ON-SEA
49–55 High St
Tel: 01702 437480

SOUTHPORT
367 Lord St
Tel: 01704 501088

ST. ALBANS
8/10 Catherine Street
Tel: 01727 868866

STIRLING
Thistle Marches
Tel: 01786 478756

STOCKPORT
103 Princes St
Tel: 0161 477 3755

STOKE
Staffordshire
University Bookshop
Station Road
Tel: 01782 746318

STRATFORD-UPON-AVON
18 The High St
Tel: 01789 414418

SUTTON
71-81 High St
Tel: 0181 770 0404

SWANSEA
17 Oxford St
Tel: 01792 463567

Taliesin Arts Centre
University of Wales
Singleton Park
Tel: 01792 281460

SWINDON
27 Regent St
Tel: 01793 488838

TAUNTON
County Hotel
East St
Tel: 01823 333113

TUNBRIDGE WELLS
32/40 Calverley Rd
Tel: 01892 535446

ULSTER
Central Buildings
University of Ulster
Cromore Rd
Coleraine
Tel: 01265 324 735

WATFORD
174–176 The
Harlequin Centre,
High St
Tel: 01923 218197

Wall Hall Campus
Aldenham
Tel: 01707 285745

WINCHESTER
1/2 Kings Walk
Tel: 01962 866206

The Brooks
Middle Brook Street
Tel: 01962 866206
(from Winter 1998)

WOLVERHAMPTON
13-15 Victoria Street
Tel: 01902 427219

University of
Wolverhampton
Wulfruna Street
Tel: 01902 322435

Dudley Campus
Castle View
Tel: 01902 323374

Shropshire Campus
Priors Lee
Telford
Tel: 01902 323815

WORCESTER
95 High St
Tel: 01905 723397

WREXHAM
9/11 Regent Street
(from Winter 1998)

YORK
28–29 High Ousegat
Tel: 01904 628740

You may find several of the above branches trading as Dillons.
These branches will be converting to Waterstone's in the near future.